People, Food, and Science

Patricia Cote

Ginn and Company

A XEROX COMPANY

Illustrations by Mel Klapholz
Color designs by John Martucci

Preface

People, Food, and Science and its accompanying manual, *Students'*
Activities and Experiments, offer students who have already had a
beginning foods course or a beginning home economics program
excellent opportunity to further their knowledge of food and to
broaden their understanding of some of the many problems associated
with food and its use. This is also an exciting and challenging text in
advanced food study for students in semester food courses. The
book's major purpose is to develop greater understanding of some
of the main concepts related to man's need for food and his efforts
to satisfy this need. The text explores the nature and composition
of food, the importance of food in the human body, and the management of food resources. The accompanying manual, *Students' Activities and Experiments,* closely follows the text and provides more
opportunities for individual study.

In organization, the text has three major parts. Each part is
planned to stimulate the student's interest and curiosity concerning
the "whys" as well as the "hows" in the study of foods. Colorful
illustrations used throughout explain, motivate, and give further
emphasis to the concepts developed in each chapter. For easy reference, the major concepts presented in each chapter appear in the
upper-left corner of the chapter opening page. Within the various
chapters, supporting concepts are italicized, providing a means for
students to locate them readily. The Appendix includes additional
reference tables to supplement those found within the text itself.

Part I cites man's growing interest in understanding food and its
relationship to his own body. This section of the text reviews some
of the historical events which led to the extensive research in food
and nutrition today. Some of the food habits of people living in
various parts of the world are discussed, with special attention to the
promotion of more understanding of the role of food and food
nutrients on an international basis.

Two maps illustrate the relationship of food supply to nutritional
status. A third map indicates the locations of the major immigrant
groups in the United States up to 1920, and a fourth contrasts the
transportation routes of Marco Polo's time with those of the present.

The last two maps serve to develop further understanding of why certain food preferences are centered in various regions of the United States and why it is now possible to secure foods from many different countries.

Following a brief study of plant and animal cell structures and their relationship to food, Part II concentrates on some of the scientific principles involved in food—its production, storage, preparation, and use. These principles are well illustrated by examples and illustrations. New knowledge is presented together with the more traditional theories and concepts. Furthermore, these concepts are considered on a thought-provoking theoretical plane and then brought to an exciting practical level through suggested laboratory experiences and other study activities.

Part III returns to the concepts presented in the first two sections in the text. Here scientific principles are applied in a practical way to problems of food purchase, storage, and preparation. Because many of the foods and customs of the United States have been introduced from other countries, special attention is given to international food customs and dishes. Since the preparation of international foods is stressed, thereby expanding the students' awareness of foods of different origins, students are encouraged to try new foods from other countries and are challenged to apply their recent knowledge of food and nutrition. Suggested recipes and menus are included together with ideas for ways to control the time required for preparation and to improve practices of management. Since many recipes require herb seasoning, a unique, informative herb chart is included for easy reference.

At the conclusion of each chapter, the major ideas are summarized in broad statements to aid the student in focusing on the main concepts just studied. Comprehensive questions are drawn from each chapter to further clarify the concepts presented. At the end of each chapter are bibliographies for the students' use in making further study of the specific topic discussed in the individual chapter.

Accompanying the text, *People, Food, and Science,* is a manual, *Students' Activities and Experiments,* which provides a series of activities and experiments. The main purpose of this manual is to provide a wide variety of opportunities for students to engage in laboratory work and study which will deepen their knowledge and understanding of the concepts presented in the text. Numerous possibilities are offered for both individual work and group activity. Students are asked to formulate their own conclusions and generalizations on the basis of facts learned from the text, observation, study, and discussion. In the latter part of the manual are additional recipes of foreign origin.

The Teachers' Manual has specific suggestions for the teacher to help her in using the text and its accompanying manual in the classroom. There are suggestions for introducing and developing each chapter, audiovisual materials, and supplementary references.

The author acknowledges with real pleasure her deep appreciation to Dr. Catherine Personius, Former Head, Department of Food and Nutrition, Cornell University, for her invaluable assistance and guidance in the preparation of Part II of the text and students' manual. Appreciation is also expressed to William Cote for his encouragement and advice and to all other persons who reviewed the manuscript and contributed their most helpful suggestions.

Patricia Cote

Contents

Part I The Significance of Food

Part II The Nature of Food

Part III The Management of Food Resources

Appendix

Index

Part I The Significance of Food

1 FOOD FOR SURVIVAL

Food has special meanings for people. If you asked students in your school, city, or around the world what food meant to them, you would receive many answers. Some foods mean fun at parties and picnics with your friends. Others suggest comfort and security and remind you of home. Certain foods represent the warmth felt at family gatherings on national holidays or religious celebrations, whereas others recall childhood pleasure when you visited your aunt or grandmother.

One of the best ways to appreciate the meaning of food is to travel away from your home. When you are served strange foods or have to go without your favorite dishes, you long for certain foods again. The food you have may taste good and it may be carefully prepared. It may not be too unusual, perhaps a common food seasoned and prepared in a different way. Yet it is not the same. You might call your feelings a kind of homesickness for the familiar and favorite.

What is food for? If you went about questioning students, the immediate response would probably be "to eat!" Some would say they need food to live, yet many take this basic function of food for granted. You have learned for years that food contributes to health. It has definite purposes in the body that help determine your physical and probably your mental and emotional status. The right kind of food may improve your personal appearance and give you a more alert mind. Yet most people do not give much thought to the reasons why the body needs food. When you think of food, your first thoughts probably concern eating, while later thoughts concentrate on buying, cooking, and preparing it.

In this book, we are going to look at people, food, and science, since they are closely woven together in any study of food. In the beginning chapters you will focus on the relationships of food and people throughout recorded history. You will take a closer look at the Stone Age man and those who followed him. Their dilemma was having enough food to survive, finding it, cooking it, and making it last longer.

In the chapters that follow in Part I, you will investigate your own food needs. Understanding body requirements, needs, and functions is extremely important in our study of *nutrition* which is *the science of food and its relation to health.**

*THE ROLE OF NUTRITION IN INTERNATIONAL PROGRAMS, National Research Council, National Academy of Sciences, Washington D. C., 1961.

2

Hunting Food

If you could turn time backwards and live in the Stone Age, you would probably find that people had many different ideas concerning the nature of food, although their needs were similar to ours. The Stone Age man presumably thought first about the relationship of food and survival. Every day he was faced with the problem of obtaining food which would help him survive. Food held a life or death importance for him.

For you, just as for the Stone Age man, food has meant survival. Wherever and whenever man has lived upon this earth, he has needed food. In Asia, Africa, Europe, or the Americas, and in 500,000 B.C. or 1968, man has required food (as well as air and water) for survival.

Some people today might believe that other things are essential too, like shoes, furniture, and medicine. However, you could live without such things. In the past, man did and he survived. Your life would be quite different, not as comfortable or long, yet you could exist. But you cannot live without food. This you have in common with the Stone Age man who lived on this earth thousands of years ago.

THE SIGNIFICANCE OF FOOD

If you glance through a book on the history of man, you will often see references to food. One of man's problems throughout the ages has been to find enough of the right kind of food. This problem is somewhat different for you today. You don't have to spend every day hunting and searching for food but are more likely to be concerned about getting money to buy food, knowing what food to buy, and preparing it. You may work at a job to earn money which you will exchange for food and other goods and services, but that's quite different from the Stone Age man who spent most of his time and energy hunting for raw food.

The Stone Age man's search for food was long and difficult. He had to spend many hours every day hunting for plants and animals which he could eat. His weapons were his wealth, since without them he could not kill game. Have you ever thought what your life would be like if your father or future husband had to hunt for all of your food?

Then two important discoveries—fire and the cutting edge—were made. People today take fire and knives for granted, but both of these discoveries changed the Stone Age man's way of life. Fire was his first source of power that did not come from his own muscles. It warmed his cave and made him a more successful hunter. He found that animals were afraid of fire, so he used torches to stampede and bewilder game.

Perhaps prehistoric man dropped some food into a fire by accident. Since food was so precious, he retrieved his meal from the fire and discovered, to his surprise, that it tasted good. After that, he cooked with fire. One of the greatest advantages early man had from cooking food was that he spent less time eating. The tough fibers of meat and roots were softened by the fire, making them much easier to chew.

Scientists who have studied the history of man report that "stop-watch studies of man's cousins, the gibbons, show they spend half of their waking hours going through the process of eating and the other half traveling back and forth between their feeding places. Primitive man in the early Stone Age, no matter how strong his jaws or how large his teeth, must have gone through much the same."*

By using fire, man's eating required only a few hours. The remainder of the day could be spent in hunting, tool-making, and other activities. How much time would you need to eat if all of your foods were raw and uncooked?

The invention of the cutting edge enabled man to make several useful tools. He made a spear which served as an important weapon for thousands of years, and when he learned to add a sharp flint to the point of the spear he was able to track and kill animals more successfully.

Man's food supply during this period depended upon hunting, and he travelled extensively to search for fish and game. The abundance of meat varied

*Reprinted by permission of TIME–LIFE BOOKS. From THE EPIC OF MAN, p. 17, © 1961, Time Inc.

with the seasons. As man battled against hunger he found some locations where fish were plentiful year-round and he was able to settle in one place. This establishing of more permanent homes introduced quite a new way of life. Historians have named this period the New Stone Age. During this time, man also learned to store some foods such as seeds, nuts, fruits, and berries. These foods assured him of survival when game was scarce. In addition, man began to farm and till the soil.

Agricultural Revolution

During the New Stone Age, man still faced the problem of having enough of the right food to survive. Two exciting discoveries, however, enabled him to cope with this situation. He found that seeds could be planted to grow food and that animals could be domesticated, or raised and kept for food. These developments led to an agricultural revolution. One way that man's life was changed dramatically by these discoveries was that he had to live in one place to farm his land.

THE SIGNIFICANCE OF FOOD

History suggests that a woman may have been the first to plant seeds to grow food. In all primitive societies, practicing any form of agriculture was mainly the woman's work, since man did the hunting and fishing. The woman also searched for berries, nuts, fruits, and seeds to use as food. Working among the plants and trees, she perhaps observed how they grew and produced fruit. She may have watched grains grow rapidly in the spring and mature in the early summer. These grains or cereals were a dependable source of seeds for food. Perhaps she observed that where grain seeds fell into the soil, plants grew. She may have decided to try placing seeds in the soil to enable more plants to grow. Probably she chose cereals because they grew fast.

At first, the woman had to pull off the head (that part of the plant which contains the seed) of the ripe grains such as wheat, oats, or barley. Then a sickle was invented which made her work easier. The sickle was a sharp flint stone attached to a piece of wood or bone which could cut the stalks of grain. The woman was then able to separate the grains, or seeds, and pound them with stones to make them softer.

Records suggest that agriculture and farming began in this manner. The Agricultural Revolution was one of man's solutions to his problem of securing enough of the right kind of foods. Agriculture spread swiftly across Egypt, Palestine, and Syria, and in addition to cereals and grains, man may have grown onions, lemons, peas, olives, dates, figs, and grapes.

The food supply became more abundant with the development of farming. As a consequence, the human population multiplied about sixteen times between 8000 B.C. and 4000 B.C.

As mentioned before, another important discovery in the New Stone Age was the domestication of animals. Exactly how this happened is not known. All that can be said with certainty is that in the Middle East, man did succeed in taming goats, sheep, pigs, and cattle. Perhaps animals became scarce and man decided to protect them for his own future use. Or the first domesticated animals may have been used as decoys to attract wild animals within the reach of the hunters.

Pottery-making also developed during the New Stone Age. Clay pots were substituted for the animal skins and gourds which had been used as containers. Such a pot may have been used to cook cereal. Meat was roasted on the spit, but cereals required a container both fireproof and waterproof. Pottery-making influenced the art of cookery. With sturdy containers, a woman could prepare food combinations. Cheese-making may have developed during this period, as well as bread baking and meat preservation.

The beginning of villages. Since the man of this time found it more productive to live in one place, the village came into existence. The village was simply a cluster of houses within walking distance of fields and pastures. The village had economic advantages for the people living there which produced a higher standard of living. Ancient records found from these villages suggest peaceful societies, since agricultural life was an improvement over the older hunter existence. Life may have been less exciting but the food supply was more reliable and the land supported a greater number of people. Being able to spend time in ways other than hunting and searching for food was another advantage. Man could engage in religion, politics, business, science, and the arts. Such activities were vital to the development of civilization.

The shift from a hunting society to an agricultural community seemed to affect man's attitude toward woman. Since the woman had an important role in the development of farming, she became the major producer of food. Her independence and authority probably increased. Female priestesses and deities came into prominence and the earth was described in female terms. Numerous female figurines which may have represented the fruitful earth goddess have been unearthed from New Stone Age sites.

As primitive societies grew, the time came when all suitable soil within reach of a given community was depleted. When crops are grown on soil every year, the soil gives to the plants the elements that they need in order to grow. Unless fertilizer is added or the soil is allowed to rest, plants will not grow. The farmer helped solve his problem by not planting some of his land each year. He also discovered the technique of plowing the soil. By using animal power to pull a spade-like tool over the soil, he could dig up more land than he needed for crops. He could use part of his land one year and part another year to increase the soil's fertility.

As farming methods improved, people tried to settle where the land was suitable for growing plants. However, the first small plows could not dig into fertile, heavy soils and people often had to settle in areas where the soil was chalky and light. The use of the plow seemed to reverse the role of the sexes in farming. When animals came into the field to pull plows, men came with them. Women lost their earlier domination over the grain field and once again man became the provider of food.

Irrigation was another discovery which helped man produce more food, and in addition stimulated the development of machines, such as the waterwheel. Fields could be flooded artificially from ditches and canals, and the new plowing and irrigation methods of farming resulted in greater food production. This permitted storage for bad times. Furthermore, everyone did not have to work at hunting and agriculture; some men could become craftsmen and merchants. The surplus grain also could be exchanged for the products of the nomads and mountain dwellers.

Prelude to the Industrial Revolution. Certain discoveries were significant in changing the agricultural society to an industrial one. The wheel was an extremely important invention. The first wheels were solid discs of heavy wood which were fastened together to form a circle. The earliest wheels were used on wagons in Egyptian and Mesopotamian cultures to transport water and merchandise from one village to another. As trade increased with the growth of towns and villages, the need for business records created new methods of writing. The most important application of the wheel itself, however, was in the irrigation of land and the manufacture of pottery.

The Industrial Revolution

Man invented the sailboat which turned the rivers into highways. Accomplishments such as this one were the beginnings of commerce and trade. Towns grew into settled communities where people could work in organized security. Over many hundreds of years, civilization continued to develop. Improved transportation and means of communication extended man's interests throughout the world.

The growth of towns, food production, and commerce and trade led to the next upheaval, the Industrial Revolution. This term usually includes all those changes that occurred as man moved from living in a stable agricultural and commercial society to modern industrialism. Although it is difficult to date the Industrial Revolution accurately, it is possible to say that it extended from about the middle of the 18th century to the end of the 19th century. New inventions changed the world immensely. However, it should be remembered that such great change was the result of man's progress over thousands of years.

Machines, for example, which became so important in the Industrial Revolution had existed before. The Chinese, the Arabs, and the Greeks had taken most of the first steps toward inventing different machines. The Cretans, Egyptians, and Romans also had machines. But the people of Western Europe improved the machine and adapted their style of living to the pace and potential of it. This period climaxed another stage in man's development.

As food surpluses increased and trade was established, man's wealth grew. Hunting weapons had been the wealth for the Stone Age man, but weapons did not represent wealth for the person living in the time of the Industrial Revolution. The latter was no longer a hunter or a farmer but was a businessman, craftsman, and urban man. Man also began to belong to a class according to his heritage and own endeavors. The classes that developed included the royal and aristocratic class, artisans, cultivators of the soil, and the herdsmen.

Long before the Industrial Revolution, man had been seeking wealth through gold and new trade routes. Conflict had occurred. The Industrial Revolution also caused many bitter contests among men of the world. The population had grown and the machine and metal tools increased man's potential for accumulating wealth. Such circumstances sent men from many areas in search of riches. Men found their journeys from Mediterranean shores to the Atlantic coast long and difficult, yet they continued to travel from their homelands to

settle in distant places in the hopes of becoming rich. One country to which men travelled and settled during the Industrial Revolution was America.

An interesting invention produced during the Industrial Revolution was the cookstove. Until this time, fireplaces which used fuel extravagantly and often filled the house with smoke were used for cooking. The new cookstove was a simple cast-iron box with two stove lids at the top. The homemaker could now bake every day rather than once every few days. The new stove also cut down the time necessary for cooking since the heat was easily controlled. Yet many people did not like this invention. They believed that food was not as good when cooked on the stove as in the fireplace.

The problem of food supply had grown very serious in the nineteenth century. Towns and cities were large, and dense populations had concentrated in industrial areas. Food could not be produced locally in sufficient quantities but had to be imported from agricultural areas and other countries. The transportation and preservation of food became major problems.

Once again, to help solve his problem, man experimented, and finally discovered how to can food. The older ways of preserving food were salting, smoking, and drying. By 1840, fish and fruits were being preserved in cans, increasing man's food supply. In fact, it has been speculated by some people that Napoleon would have conquered Russia had he adopted canned food for his army.

Not only did the Industrial Revolution affect food preparation in the home; it also changed agricultural methods. Machines powered by horses had been the first break-through toward mechanization of farming. But the most radical changes came with the steam-powered equipment of the Industrial Revolution. Steam engines were used to power machines to harvest grain. They were harnessed to pull railroad cars in Europe and across the United States. More food and food of greater variety became available throughout the countries. Again man had found solutions to his problem of food for survival.

In the next chapter, you will look more closely at many factors which have influenced food in this country and you will see how patterns of settlement and migration have produced a wide variety of favorite foods. In addition, you will investigate the reasons why the food served in the early days differed from one family to another and from one section of the country to another.

MAJOR IDEAS

The following statements give the main ideas within the chapter you have just studied. Be sure you know the words underscored in these statements and in the questions to follow.

1. Throughout the ages, man has always had the problem of securing enough <u>food for survival</u>.

2. The Agricultural and Industrial Revolutions were two of the most important developments which aided man in solving his food problems.

QUESTIONS TO STUDY

HUNTING FOOD

1. What meaning do the struggles of early man have for us today?
2. Imagine a day in the life of a man in the Stone Age. How would his time be spent?

AGRICULTURAL REVOLUTION

1. Describe the ways in which the Agricultural Revolution helped man to improve his production of food.
2. In what ways did man gradually change his methods of securing and preserving food?

INDUSTRIAL REVOLUTION

1. Explain why the Industrial Revolution did not actually occur until the 18th century even though machines had been invented and used much earlier.
2. How has the Industrial Revolution helped you have enough of the right kind of food?

BIBLIOGRAPHY

BURLINGAME, ROGER, *Machines That Built America*. New York, Harcourt, Brace and Co., 1953.

CRAWFORD, M. D., *The Conquest of Culture*. New York, Fairchild Publishing Co., 1948.

FORBES, R. J., *Man, the Maker*. New York, Abelard–Schuman, Limited, 1950.

MCNEILL, W. H., *The Rise of the West*. Chicago, The University of Chicago Press, 1963.

MUMFORD, LEWIS, *Technics and Civilization*. New York, Harcourt, Brace and World, Inc., 1962.

WELLS, H. G., *The Outline of History*. New York, Doubleday and Co., 1961.

WOOLLEY, SIR LEONARD, *The Beginning of Civilization*, Volume I. New York, Harper and Row, Inc., 1963.

2 INFLUENCES ON FOOD IN THE UNITED STATES

In the last chapter, you followed man through parts of his history to the Industrial Revolution and you looked at answers that man has found to his ever-present problem of obtaining enough food for survival. You will recall that man's struggle was easier after the Agricultural Revolution. After this time, all men did not have to work every day hunting for food as the Stone Age man had done. A number of men had time to think, plan, and work at creating tools and machines. They used their inventions to make work easier and to do jobs which previously had required the labor of many men working together. As a result, the Industrial Revolution speeded its course. Ships were built which carried men around the world. After North America was settled, men were attracted to her by her size and wealth.

Today the United States includes people from all over the world and has the greatest variety of food of any country. When people came to America to live, they brought their favorite foods, recipes, and ways of cooking. Some came during the early years when the country was being settled. Others came later at different times. At one time a map of the United States could show areas where people from certain countries had settled to live together (page 17). Today, however, people have moved about to such a degree that such a map would no longer be accurate. People from one country no longer necessarily stay in one region of this country.

Why did people come to America? What effect did trade routes and commerce have upon the settlement of the country? What caused people to move across what is now the United States? How have the settlement and growth of this country influenced its food supply? To find some answers to these questions, you must go back and look again at the world situation after Columbus discovered America.

Settlement

From the time that Columbus set foot on New World soil, Europeans began to transform the land. In their ships and by foot, they traced the outline of the Atlantic coast and much of the Pacific. Settlements began to develop in the interior parts of the land. The stories of what had been found in America continued to excite the imagination of the men of the Old World.

At the close of the 16th century, the English, French, and Dutch resented their dependence upon southern Europeans who possessed the richer trade routes. These northern European countries became more and more interested

12

in the New World. They realized that it was essential for them to gain access to the rich trading areas just as the Italians and Spaniards had done. Wishing to export the products of their own industries, they knew they had to establish trade routes. Trade routes have often played a significant role in the growth of cities and countries. A map on pages 14–15 shows the major trade routes for shipping food and the countries which developed around them.

Among the first permanent settlers to come to the North American coast were the Pilgrims who arrived in Plymouth in 1620. The Pilgrims were mostly free men who paid their own way across the ocean in order to build their lives anew.

After food and water supplies were found and homes were built, the settlers began searching for ways to earn a livelihood and create an organized way of life in the wilderness. Soon they engaged in commerce and trading. The centers through which overseas trade passed became the first cities of America.

The export of commodities to Europe was the basis for commerce. Food was one product sold abroad. Fishing vessels brought fish, such as cod, which were cured, packed, and shipped abroad. From Connecticut and upper New York, flour and biscuits were sent to Europe. Important non-food items were furs and tobacco. The ships usually headed toward ports where the colonists had business and family connections but trading was also established in the West Indies. The closeness of these rich sugar-producing islands swelled the volume of the colonies' commerce and sustained the life of their towns.

American agriculture was affected by what products could be sold or traded in Europe and the West Indies. Wood was an essential item in the European economy because of the many ships built there. The thick forests of the New World encouraged many men to cut pine and oak trees rather than to farm.

Tobacco was also in high demand in Europe. This plant, however, exhausted the soil. The only tools the farmer had to cultivate his tobacco plants were the spade and hoe, and these devices only scratched the surface of the ground. Raising grapes and flax was also attempted by early farmers but the results were disappointing. Labor was scarce, and the farmers who planted vineyards were unsuccessful.

The development of trade in the West Indies created markets for grain and cattle, and some settlers along the coast discovered that the herring from the rivers and the clams off the seashore could be exported. As the colonists became familiar with the forests, they supplemented their own diets with fish and game. Yet the farmers did not lose sight of the fact that producing staples for overseas markets would yield profits.

Thriving trade and expanding frontiers sustained the agriculture that occupied most of the early settlers' time. The people in the growing cities consumed many of the products produced on the farms; surplus food was shipped to foreign markets. Settlements spread as men attempted to increase the supply of goods and their incomes. Thus the expansion of America began.

MAJOR WORLD ROUTES FOR TRANSPORTING

NORTH AMERICA
1 Quebec
2 Montreal
3 Chicago
4 Duluth
5 Boston
6 Philadelphia
7 Baltimore
8 Atlanta
9 Savannah
10 New Orleans
11 Houston

EUROPE

1	Liverpool	12	Athens
2	Edinburgh	13	Odessa
3	London	14	Novorossisk
4	Bordeaux	15	Batumi
5	Lisbon	16	Oslo
6	Gibraltar	17	Haparanda
7	Málaga	18	Copenhagen
8	Marseille	19	Stockholm
9	Naples	20	Leningrad
10	Venice	21	Gdansk
11	Tirane		

CENTRAL and SOUTH AMERICA
12 Tampico
13 Veracruz
14 Puerto Barrios
15 Guadalajara
16 Acapulco
17 Lima
18 Arica

Reykjavik

Pacific

Ocean

HAWAII

Vancouver
Seattle
San Francisco
Los Angeles

Atlantic

Ocean

Dakar
Abidjan

Panama Canal

CURAÇAO

Georgetown
Belém
Recife
Salvador
Santos
Rio de Janeiro
Buenos Aires
Rio Grande
Valparaiso

New York

OD BY RAIL AND SEA, 1600-1965

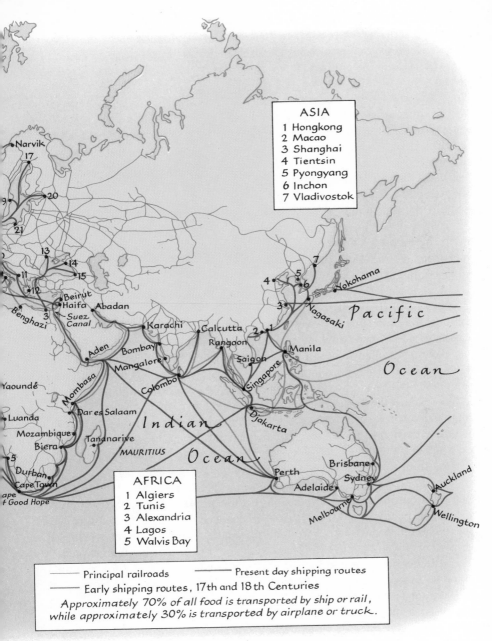

ASIA
1 Hongkong
2 Macao
3 Shanghai
4 Tientsin
5 Pyongyang
6 Inchon
7 Vladivostok

AFRICA
1 Algiers
2 Tunis
3 Alexandria
4 Lagos
5 Walvis Bay

—— Principal railroads   —— Present day shipping routes
—— Early shipping routes, 17th and 18th Centuries
Approximately 70% of all food is transported by ship or rail,
while approximately 30% is transported by airplane or truck.

Expansion

Attracted to the frontier by cheap land and a thirst for adventure, pioneers moved in a series of waves across the country. First came the hunters and the fur traders, seeking wealth in the form of beaver, otter, deer, and buffalo skins. Then came the gold and silver miners who were followed by the cattle ranchers.

The "squatters" followed the ranchers. Lacking capital and energy to tame the wilderness, these people tended small farms and dreamed of wealth. Farmers came after the squatter, bringing equipment, capital, and ambition. They planned to settle in one place, farm their land, and grow with the country.

The early pioneer in this country was faced with the same problem that the Stone Age man and others before and after him had to solve: he had to secure enough of the right kind of food to survive. Men from different parts of the world shared in solving this problem which encompassed interaction between hunting, agriculture, industry, and business. Large cities developed which were centers of trade and commerce, and farms grew in size after machines from the Industrial Revolution enabled farmers to take care of many acres of land. A wide variety of food was grown to satisfy the tastes of the people from many countries.

But how did those first settlers survive? Some of them did not; they starved to death. In Europe, many of the pioneers had never hunted or farmed. Never having searched for food for survival, they did not know how to hunt animals for meat. Being unfamiliar with the wild plants, they did not know which ones could be used for food. Of course, the American Indians had lived here long before the Europeans came. Slowly, the settlers learned from the Indians which native plants could be grown and which animals could be hunted. When they lengthened their short, stubby guns into Kentucky rifles, they could more easily bring down game. They soon became skilled in building log cabins and barns to protect themselves and their animals.

Regional colonization. Expansion of the colonies in the New World depended upon people migrating there to make their homes. The reasons why people came differed. Some were hunting wealth, jobs, and a way to earn a living; others loved the adventure and excitement of exploring unknown territory. Some people were looking for religious freedom. Many were searching for food to escape starvation at home. Some were brought here to work in fields, factories, and homes.

The first permanent settlers to come to North America were the Spanish, English, and French. The early French settlements were mostly in what is now Canada. The first permanent settlements in the United States were

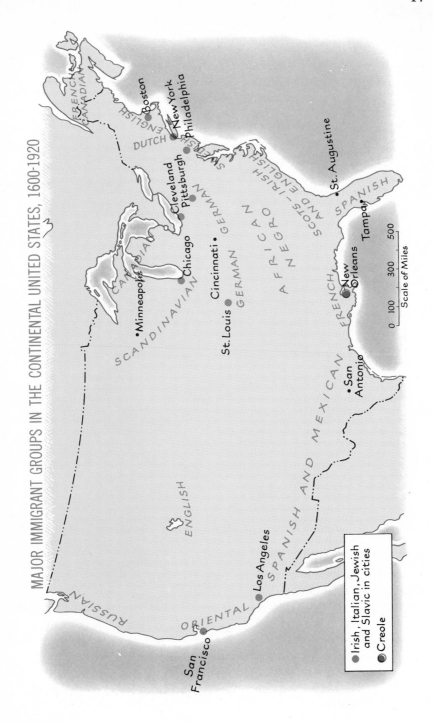

MAJOR IMMIGRANT GROUPS IN THE CONTINENTAL UNITED STATES, 1600-1920

FRENCH CANADIAN

ENGLISH

•Boston

•New York
DUTCH •Philadelphia

SWEDISH

St. Augustine•

SPANISH

Cleveland•
•Pittsburgh

GERMAN

SCOTS-IRISH AND ENGLISH

AFRICAN NEGRO

FRENCH

Tampa•

•Chicago

•Minneapolis

SCANDINAVIAN

•Cincinnati

GERMAN

St. Louis•

GERMAN

New Orleans

CANADIAN

•San Antonio

ENGLISH

SPANISH AND MEXICAN

Los Angeles•

ORIENTAL

San Francisco•

RUSSIAN

Scale of Miles

0   100   300   500

● Irish, Italian, Jewish
   and Slavic in cities
● Creole

THE SIGNIFICANCE OF FOOD

St. Augustine, Florida by the Spanish (1565); Jamestown, Virginia by the English (1607); and Plymouth, Massachusetts by the English (1620). Negroes had arrived in Virginia by 1619. The Dutch were also early settlers. They established the New Netherland colony which was to become New York. The New Sweden settlement was started on the Delaware River. Later, the Germans and the Scotch-Irish ventured further west to areas now known as Pennsylvania.

In the early days, the Spanish dominated the Caribbean area and settled from Florida to California. Agriculture developed in the South and the popularity of tobacco made a number of the southern farmers wealthy, permitting them to live in gracious style on plantations. Negroes from Africa and the West Indies provided a source of labor which enabled southern agriculture to prosper.

The French did not colonize as much in the United States as they did in Canada. However, French fur traders did control the Mississippi valley. At the close of the French and Indian War, French possessions east of the Mississippi River were given to England, and Englishmen began to colonize the area.

From 1840–1880 many Irishmen, Germans, and other people from northern Europe migrated to America. The Irish came in great numbers to escape starvation at home. At that time the Irish depended upon the potato as their staple food. Due to the potato crop failure, famine resulted, causing death and disease.

Germans travelled to the Middle West and settled in the cities of the Ohio and Mississippi valleys, particularly Cincinnati, St. Louis, and New Orleans. The Scandinavians arrived in the Midwest, settling in the area which is now Wisconsin and Minnesota.

After the Civil War, Italians, Slavs (especially from Austria-Hungary and Russia), and Jews left their homes to come to America. These people settled in the East and Midwest.

Spain held most of the West for many years. However, in 1823, Mexico won her independence from Spain. The West, including California, became a territory of the New Republic of Mexico in 1825, but California and all the Southwest were won from Mexico following the Mexican War. By 1860, large groups of Oriental peoples, particularly the Japanese and the Chinese, were brought to this country to work in the gold and silver mines and to build railroads. In the late 1800's, the whole Southwest, including California, experienced a land boom and thousands of people moved to this region. The West also became more popular as irrigation increased the amount and variety of food that could be grown in this area.

This brief review of some of the people who settled in the United States gives a clue to why America's food is so varied. It also reminds us that in the early years of the development of our country, food for survival was one of man's problems.

Food Preparation

When the first settlers arrived along the Atlantic coast they were immediately confronted with the problem of finding three meals a day. Although they were able to catch some fish, get some corn from the Indians and find other grain in the forests near the shore, the winters remained difficult, especially in the northern settlements. Gradually, as land was cleared of rocks and tree stumps, the people found wild berries and fruits and had room to plant vegetable gardens. Seafood was an important part of the diet and was used to make nourishing soups and stews.

As cattle were brought from England and Holland, milk and butter became a part of the diet in colonial times. However, some of the English recipes and ways of cooking that the settlers had brought with them had to be adapted to their new environment. Many persons relied upon the Indians for learning about new foods. For example, the latter taught the settlers how to prepare corn, a food not common in Europe, by roasting it in the husks in an open fire. The natives also taught the newcomers how to grind corn into meal from which cakes could be made. In addition, the Indians demonstrated the method of cooking oysters in stews.

The hardy New Englander of 1620 who had to cope with rocky soil, uncertain climate, and other adverse conditions helped shape today's ideas and attitudes.

The sprawling, lush farms in the Pennsylvania-Dutch area make up some of the most valuable farmland in the United States. It is in this section of the country that the most enduring American regional cuisine developed.

Cookery in settled areas. The main foods in the early colonial days were beans, corn, fish, and game. From these foods the women created many tasty dishes that are still popular today. They cooked pots of baked beans, combined beans and corn to make succotash, and baked corn pudding and johnnycake using cornmeal, flour, and milk. They also made fish chowders from fish, vegetables, and occasionally milk.

Most cooking was done in heavy, black iron pots over an open fire. (As was mentioned earlier, the cookstove was invented in the Industrial Revolution which came later.) The large dinner pot was filled with meat and vegetables and hung over the fire in the fireplace. Bean porridge was made in such a pot.

For sweets, the early settlers used brown sugar and molasses which they obtained through trade with the West Indies. In New England, sap from maple trees was collected in the spring to make maple sugar.

The Pennsylvania Dutch contributed such dishes as scrapple, hasenpfeffer, waffles, apple butter, chicken corn soup, and shoo-fly pie to American cookery. They made use of the local foods, too; cornmeal went into the scrapple and rabbit was used to make the hasenpfeffer. Although the English had brought

Southern history, culture, and cookery are closely related. In the Confederate states, these three areas were influenced by the Anglo-Saxon (symbolizing tradition), Negro (symbolizing primitive strength), and Latin (symbolizing romance).

the idea of pie to this country, the Pennsylvania Dutch cooks did much to develop pie to its present status. These cooks made pie out of anything edible, using meat, vegetables, fruits, milk, eggs, and molasses. They created shoo-fly pie by combining molasses, brown sugar, flour, and spices, baking the mixture in a pastry shell, and topping it with a crumb mixture of flour, sugar, salt, and shortening.

In the South, available foods differed somewhat from the North, as did styles of cooking. One such example was the Creole cooking of the Louisiana area. This type of food combined Spanish, French, American Negro, and Indian ways of cooking. The highly seasoned dishes included meats, seafood, vegetables, and herbs and spices. An example is the gumbo, a type of soup. Gumbo recipes were guarded carefully and handed down from generation to generation. This dish was probably inherited from Africa and the West Indies and adapted in Louisiana. One of the important ingredients of the southern gumbo is filé* powder which thickens soups or stews. The most famous gumbos are made from turkey, chicken, rabbit, squirrel, okra, crab, oyster, shrimp, herbs, or cabbage.

*Pronounced fə´lä . Powdered young leaves of sassafras.

The location of Louisiana also contributed to the development of Creole cookery. Down the Mississippi to New Orleans came the beef and pork, flour and grain of the Middle West. From the nearby river valleys came garden greens and all kinds of vegetables. Fruits and spices arrived from the West Indies, Mexico, and Central and South America. A wide variety of foods were imported, including papayas, cactus fruit, cherries, kumquats, oranges, nuts, pineapples, ginger, onions, mangoes, bananas, avocados, and figs. Also coming into port were garlic, peppers, squash, breadfruit, eggplants, and cassava. Added to all these items were the local game—rabbit, duck and quail, fish from the rivers and lakes, and seafood from the Gulf of Mexico.

Immigrants settling in the Middle West developed what is sometimes called plain, country-style fare. The settlers in this area included the Irish, English, Scandinavians, and people from southern Europe. These people possessed an adventurous pioneering spirit which helped carry them over the mountains and up the rivers where they settled on rich farming land. Today this area helps to provide much of the abundant food supply available to us in the United States. Foods such as wheat from this region are shipped to other countries where food is scarce.

Meat, milk, and eggs were common ingredients in Midwest cookery. Vegetables, fruits, and cereals grown on the farms were used in generous amounts. The people coming to this area brought their own recipes and ways of cooking, adapting them to the foods available, their time, and cooking equipment. This process had happened before in the homes of the settlers along the Atlantic Coast. It occurred over and over again as American cookery developed. Some foods had their origin in Europe, Africa, South America, and Asia and were adapted in this country many times by numerous people according to the local situation.

In the Middle West, the Germans contributed sauerkraut, apfelkuchen (apple cake), kasekuchen (cheese cake), deep dish rhubarb pie, and many kinds of cheeses, including cottage cheese. The Scandinavians in Minnesota added herring, lutefisk (dried cod), limpa (Swedish rye bread), Danish pastry, rich butter cookies, fruit soup, and Swedish meat balls.

The foods of the Far West represented the backgrounds of people from many countries. Again, the Spanish-Mexican influence was present. Trade with Pacific islands brought in tropical fruits. The ocean was a rich source of seafood and the rivers of the Pacific Northwest supplied fish. Rich farming land was found and developed in California and the Pacific Northwest, encouraging fruit to flourish in this climate. On the west coast, the Chinese settlers contributed their specialities, particularly their own fluffy version of cooked rice. Dishes which they and the Japanese probably added to the American diet were sukiyaki, egg foo yong (eggs, vegetables, and chicken, shrimp or meat cooked in hot fat), and their special vegetables which were cooked quickly in special pans, thereby retaining their crispness and flavor.

The Spanish-Mexican influence on the cultural and social traditions and food habits in this country is mainly predominant in the Southwest, where missions still stand and great herds of cattle and abundant fruit trees continue to flourish.

Another region where American food has been influenced by people from other countries and cultures is in the Southwest; Spanish and Mexican dishes are still evident there today. The Spanish brought seeds for growing peaches, figs, oranges, apples, lemons, grapes, apricots, pears, and olives. Foods with a Spanish-Mexican flavor were tamales, enchiladas, chili con carne, tacos, and tortillas. Many of these foods used corn as the foundation. For instance, tortillas are unleavened corn pancakes flattened by pounding between the hands and cooked on an earthernware plate, and tamales are prepared by stuffing corn husks with a cornmeal and meat filling.

The list of people from other countries who contributed to the American diet could go on and on. After the migrations of the 1800's, people continued to arrive. In recent years, Puerto Ricans have settled in the eastern and midwestern sections of the United States. They have contributed their Spanish-Puerto Rican foods such as rice and beans, plantains, and yams.

Hawaii and Alaska have become states, not too long ago. A Spanish immigrant to Hawaii apparently brought the first pineapple seeds there in 1791, and pineapples from Hawaii have been popular in America for years. The foods of Alaska have varied depending on what is available in the area. Fish, especially salmon, have been important. Seals were used as food by some people earlier, but their use as food is more unusual today.

Special religious and cultural rituals have determined certain dietary customs which have involved the selecting, preparing, and serving of food. As people settled here, they brought their dietary customs with them. For example, Jewish dietary laws influenced the acceptability of food as well as the way it was prepared.

Man has found many answers in the United States to his problem of how to have enough of the right kind of food for survival. Many countries in the world have not been so fortunate, for they do not have the wealth of foods that is found here. In the next chapter we will investigate the lack of food in some parts of the world. For many people food is available but it does not provide the nutrients which their bodies need to be strong and healthy.

MAJOR IDEAS

The following statements give the main ideas within the chapter you have just studied. Be sure you know the words underscored in these statements and in the questions to follow.

1. Ways of cooking, recipes, and food customs of many people from different cultural backgrounds have created American cookery.
2. Whenever man moves into new unexplored territories he is faced with finding new foods and food sources, adapting old recipes to accommodate the new foods, and making sure that his food needs can be met.
3. People have their own special food choices which are important to them and kept unchanged if at all possible.

QUESTIONS TO STUDY

SETTLEMENT

1. Give some of the reasons which prompted people to settle in America.
2. Describe a few of the difficulties encountered by the settlers in securing sufficient food for themselves in the New World.
3. What is meant by saying that recipes had to be adapted to meet the conditions of a particular region?
4. What commodities were shipped to Europe?
5. How would a map showing immigrant settlements in the United States look today?

EXPANSION

1. Describe some of the conditions which caused men to move into new territory away from the coastal areas first inhabited by settlers in the New World.
2. What were some of the changes in food supplies resulting from man's move westward?

FOOD PREPARATION

1. How would you explain typical <u>American cookery?</u>
2. Why did adaptations of foreign dishes become important to the early settlers in the New World?
3. Explain how increased trade influenced the availability and variety of foods for people.
4. Consider at least five special dishes or foods. See if you can trace the origin of each.

BIBLIOGRAPHY

The American Heritage Cookbook. New York, American Heritage Publishing Co., Inc., 1963.

BEROLZHEIMER, RUTH, The United States Regional Cookbook. Chicago, Culinary Arts Institute, 1947.

HANDLIN, OSCAR, Immigration As a Factor in American History. Boston, Atlantic Monthly Press, 1959.

HANDLIN, OSCAR, The American. Boston, Little, Brown and Company, 1963.

HUTCHISON, RUTH, The New Pennsylvania Dutch Cookbook. New York, Harper and Row, 1958.

KAUFMAN, WILLIAM, and SISTER MARY URSULA COOPER, O.P., The Art of Creole Cookery. New York, Doubleday and Company, Inc., 1962.

MOSSER, MARJORIE, Foods of Old New England. New York, Doubleday and Company, Inc., 1957.

WEIGLEY, EMMA SEIFRIT, "Food in the Days of the Declaration of Independence." Journal of the American Dietetic Association, Vol 45, July 1964.

WOLCOTT, IMMOGENE, The Yankee Cookbook. New York, Ives Washburn, Inc., 1963.

3 NUTRITION PROBLEMS AROUND THE WORLD

In the first two chapters, you accompanied man in his search for food for survival, travelling with him from all parts of the world to the United States. You have seen how man's search for food in this country during the past four centuries was somewhat easier than that of the Stone Age man. During all those thousands of years separating the two ages, man thought, planned, and worked to solve his food problems. The Agricultural Revolution and the Industrial Revolution were the results of his efforts. Man developed many tools and machines to help him increase his food supply by farming. He planted seeds, raised animals, and transported and preserved his newly produced food and livestock. Because of the many people who have come here and contributed to the food heritage of this country, America's food supply is both varied and plentiful.

However, in some parts of the world, man still searches for food for survival. For many millions of people in the world, food is scarce. Much time and energy is spent by these people in seeking enough food to live. Lacking the right food in adequate amounts causes children to be handicapped all their lives by physical, and probably mental and emotional damage. Nutritious food promotes body growth and maintenance; malnutrition or undernutrition results when food is deficient in quality or quantity.

When the diet lacks the necessary quality of nutrients in relation to body needs, *malnutrition* occurs, regardless of the quantity of food. For example, the diet may be composed chiefly of cereals and starchy foods with few of the essential *protective foods* such as milk, meat, fruit, and vegetables which provide essential nutrients such as protein, minerals, and vitamins. Although cereals and other starchy substances are good foods and rich sources of carbohydrates, the body requires the protective foods for those nutrients which are so important in maintaining good health. The body needs a balanced diet which includes adequate amounts of protein, minerals, vitamins, fats, and carbohydrates.

Undernutrition occurs when the diet lacks a sufficient quantity of food. For example, the diet may consist of the essential nutrients but the amount of food is not enough to produce adequate tissue development and body repair. A combination of undernutrition and malnutrition is also possible.

The map on pages 36–37 shows the distribution of protein around the world. This nutrient is essential for the growth and maintenance of the body. In those areas where protein is scarce, malnutrition and undernutrition are serious problems. These regions are the ones in which cereals are produced in large

26

quantities (map on pages 28–29) and cereals do not provide as much or the same quality of protein as do meat, poultry, fish, milk, and eggs.

Food Preferences

A person selects food, not nutrients, to satisfy his hunger. When he goes to the store, he does not look for proteins or minerals but rather buys the foods which will give him the nutrients he needs. Certain nutrients, which will be studied in detail later, are required by all people, yet what foods people eat in order to fulfill their nutrient requirements will differ. Diets in the United States should not be used as criteria for the foods that people should eat in other parts of the world. Each country has its own native foods which can serve as sources of essential nutrients.

People are healthy and strong only if they have enough of the right kinds of food. Today, inadequacy of nutrients is a world food problem. The United States, which has a surplus of certain foods, has felt a responsibility to take an active part in the task of world food distribution. This effort is greatly influenced by food preferences and habits of people in countries where food is not as plentiful. Understanding these factors is essential if food programs are to be successful.

Diet patterns. Expressing some of man's food preferences are diet patterns, although food choices also depend upon what products are available and what foods an individual has learned to like. Diets can be divided into three general groups: (1) diets of animal foods, (2) diets of plant foods, and (3) diets of plant and animal foods.

The diets composed chiefly of foods of animal sources are found among the Eskimos, Lapps, and the people of Tierra del Fuego. Some American Indians may also have such diets.

H. Armstrong Roberts   Ewing Galloway   Harold M. Lambert Studios

THE STAPLE CROPS USED

GREENLAND

ICELAND

Alaska

CANADA
19.1%

WESTERN EUROPE
1	UNITED KINGDOM	24.7%
2	IRELAND	34.1%
3	W. GERMANY	*
4	NETHERLANDS	25.6%
5	BELGIUM	29.7%
6	FRANCE	35.5%
7	SPAIN	41.3%
8	PORTUGAL	23.3%
9	SWITZERLAND	27.8%
10	ITALY	46.1%
11	AUSTRIA	21.9%
12	DENMARK	13.7%

UNITED STATES
17.6%

Pacific Ocean

Hawaii

Atlantic

MOROCCO 28.4%

ALGERIA 44.4%

MEXICO 45.9%

CUBA 19.2%
HAITI 14.1%

DOMINICAN REP. 13.9%

Staple: Bananas and Plantains

MAURITANIA 40.4%

MALI 40.4%

GUINEA 28.3%

SIERRA LEONE

IVORY COAST 40.4%

DAHOMEY 40.4%

CENTRAL AMERICA
1	GUATEMALA	49.9%
2	BRIT. HOND.	*
3	EL SALVADOR	29.9%
4	HONDURAS	47.7%
5	NICARAGUA	35.0%
6	COSTA RICA	12.7%
7	PANAMA	21.3%

BRAZIL
16.3%

Ocean

SOUTH AMERICA
1	VENEZUELA	15.5%
2	COLOMBIA	20.7%
3	ECUADOR	15.2%
4	GUYANA	*
5	SURINAM	*
6	FR. GUIANA	*
7	PERU	16.2%
8	BOLIVIA	22.3%
9	CHILE	43.1%
10	PARAGUAY	22.7%
11	URUGUAY	31.2%

ARGENTINA
33.2%

* Data on percentage of staple in diet is unavailable.

IN DIETS IN THE WORLD

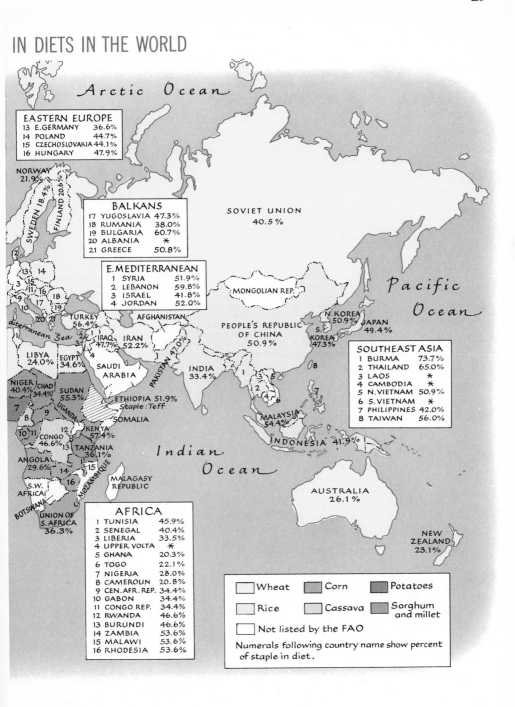

EASTERN EUROPE
13 E.GERMANY	36.6%
14 POLAND	44.7%
15 CZECHOSLOVAKIA	44.1%
16 HUNGARY	47.9%

NORWAY 21.9%

SWEDEN 18.4%

FINLAND 20.6%

Arctic Ocean

SOVIET UNION 40.5%

Pacific Ocean

BALKANS
17 YUGOSLAVIA	47.3%
18 RUMANIA	38.0%
19 BULGARIA	60.7%
20 ALBANIA	*
21 GREECE	50.8%

MONGOLIAN REP.

E.MEDITERRANEAN
1 SYRIA	51.9%
2 LEBANON	59.8%
3 ISRAEL	41.8%
4 JORDAN	52.0%

N.KOREA 50.9%
JAPAN 49.4%

TURKEY 56.4%
AFGHANISTAN
diterranean Sea
IRAQ 47.7%
IRAN 52.2%
PAKISTAN 47.0%

PEOPLE'S REPUBLIC OF CHINA 50.9%

S.KOREA 47.3%

LIBYA 24.0%
EGYPT 34.6%
SAUDI ARABIA
INDIA 33.4%

SOUTHEAST ASIA
1 BURMA	73.7%
2 THAILAND	65.0%
3 LAOS	*
4 CAMBODIA	*
5 N.VIETNAM	50.9%
6 S.VIETNAM	*
7 PHILIPPINES	42.0%
8 TAIWAN	56.0%

NIGER 40.4%
CHAD 34.4%
SUDAN 55.3%
ETHIOPIA 51.9%
Staple:Teff
SOMALIA

UGANDA
KENYA 57.4%
TANZANIA 36.1%

CONGO 46.6%

ANGOLA 29.6%

Indian Ocean

MALAGASY REPUBLIC

MALAYSIA 54.4%

INDONESIA 41.9%

AUSTRALIA 26.1%

S.W. AFRICA
BOTSWANA
MOZAMBIQUE
UNION OF S.AFRICA 36.3%

NEW ZEALAND 23.1%

AFRICA
1 TUNISIA	45.9%
2 SENEGAL	40.4%
3 LIBERIA	33.5%
4 UPPER VOLTA	*
5 GHANA	20.3%
6 TOGO	22.1%
7 NIGERIA	28.0%
8 CAMEROUN	20.8%
9 CEN.AFR.REP.	34.4%
10 GABON	34.4%
11 CONGO REP.	34.4%
12 RWANDA	46.6%
13 BURUNDI	46.6%
14 ZAMBIA	53.6%
15 MALAWI	53.6%
16 RHODESIA	53.6%

☐ Wheat	☐ Corn	☐ Potatoes
☐ Rice	☐ Cassava	☐ Sorghum and millet
☐ Not listed by the FAO		

Numerals following country name show percent of staple in diet.

The diet of the Eskimo is almost exclusively protein and fat. Carbohydrates, if eaten, are obtained largely from berries, roots, and leaves, and compose approximately 10 percent of the diet. The Navajo Indians of New Mexico and Arizona consume all parts of sheep and goats and eat as much meat as they can obtain.

The diets mainly from plant sources are found among people of certain areas of Asia and the rural people of parts of eastern Europe. Rice, wheat, maize, millet, coco-yams, groundnuts, beans, peas, cassava, plantains, gourds, coconuts, and numerous leafy vegetables are the main foods.

Rice is the staple food of the Far East. In Punjab and India, as well as North China, however, wheat is the main cereal. Supplementing these diets are legumes (beans, peas, etc.).

The food energy that a diet provides is measured by *calories*. (You will study calories in Chapter 7.) India has a large population, and the amount of food taken in by her different people varies. Yet, it has been estimated that the caloric intake of an Indian falls short of needs. In addition, the average consumption of protein constitutes only about 11 percent of the total protein requirements for a person. When the protein intake is so low, bodies do not have this essential nutrient for proper growth and maintenance.

The third kind of diet—combining animal and plant sources—is prevalent in Europe, Australia, Canada, New Zealand, Africa, North and South America, and certain regions in Asia. Much variation occurs in these areas. The United States has great variety and abundance of food. Yet, even within this country, many low-income families are not able to secure an adequate diet. This indicates that both malnutrition and undernutrition can still exist in the midst of plenty. However, with all three types of diets, and in all countries, malnutrition and undernutrition can occur.

Did people suddenly decide that they were going to eat certain plants or animals? Examining the history of a region or a country and its people would be necessary to understand why certain people eat the foods they do. Yet different types of diets in the same geographical area have developed. People have chosen to eat specific foods wherever they have lived. We will look later at the food habits of different people and some of the factors that determine these habits.

The problem of increasing the quantity or quality of food in a given area is a complex one. Although man's first need is to obtain energy foods which provide calories, his choice of such food is influenced by his own food preferences and habits. If a man has an acre of land, he may have to make the difficult decision of whether to grow cereals or raise animals. He may know he needs animal proteins, yet his energy requirements come first. The yield of food energy, or calories, from an acre of land is 3 times higher for cereal crops than for legumes which have better-quality protein. Similarly, the yield is 9 times higher for cereals than for meat produced from an acre of land. Where the population is large per acre, the production and consumption of animal products and legumes tend to be economically unfeasible.

How can people improve their food consumption? How can they have enough of the right kinds of food in all countries of the world today? You will remember that this was the problem of the Stone Age man and others who followed him, as discussed in Chapter 1. Because we in the United States will be working to help solve this world problem in the years ahead, we need to understand people. We must attempt to look at their food habits and appreciate them.

Food Habits

Everyone has food habits which include his ideas, beliefs, attitudes, and practices related to food. Like other habits, they are learned very early in life and are extremely difficult to change. The ways in which a child learns to accept or reject foods help to determine how easy change will be later when he is older. In some cases, people are extremely resistant to changes in food habits. For example, staple foods of a diet are often hard to alter. If a person has eaten rice, spaghetti, or potatoes at least once a day for many years, trying to convince him to eat less of those foods and more of others is difficult if not impossible.

Food choices are expressions of ourselves—as individuals and as members of certain groups—and of our philosophy of life. They often reflect a concept of ourselves that we prefer and try to maintain.

Food habits are also dependent upon the food supply. You cannot learn to like milk if it is not available to you where you live. The food supply is determined by many factors, such as the economic situation of the country, climate, agricultural practices, methods of food preparation and preservation, and religious and cultural heritages.

Among many people, food habits are affected by taboos, superstitions, and prejudices. Certain foods may be forbidden because they are flesh or a particular kind of meat. These taboos may be related to religious beliefs that have been passed from generation to generation.

In all parts of the world, people might starve to death rather than eat a food which is unfamiliar to them. This may seem hard to believe. But, for example, when a famine occurs in the rice-eating areas, wheat is often distributed with disappointing results. If the people have never used wheat, it is conceivable that they would not know what to do with it. It is also understandable that they would turn their backs on the bags of wheat to search for their favorite food, rice.

Studies show that starving people undergo behavior changes. They exhibit inability to concentrate, poor judgment, lack of ambition, loss of self-discipline, irritability, and moodiness. When people desperately need food, it is unwise to expect them to be happy or grateful about having a bag of hard,

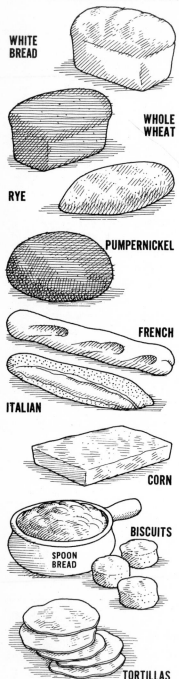

WHITE
BREAD

WHOLE
WHEAT

RYE

PUMPERNICKEL

FRENCH

ITALIAN

CORN

BISCUITS

SPOON
BREAD

TORTILLAS

brown seeds which they have never tasted before and which seem inedible.

Food customs vary from tribe to tribe in Africa. Among certain groups a deep dislike exists for boiled milk. Although this is one of the best ways to assure a safe milk supply for children, these people believe that a cow whose milk has been boiled will yield no more milk and may die. In one African tribe, oranges are not sold to people who throw the skins in the fire since it is thought that such an act might cause the unripe fruit to fall off the trees. Some tribes will not consume milk and meat at the same time, and insist that a considerable interval must elapse between a meal of beef and a meal of milk. This belief is based on the idea that a cow remains in direct physical sympathy with her milk even after she has parted with it, and any such contact of the two foods will injure the animal.

Food habits are based on the customs of tribal family groups, individual class, sex, age, occupation, and special circumstances. For example, a warrior may eat more meat and milk than other family members; the latter may eat more bananas, beans, millet, arrowroots, maize, sugar, and honey. Pregnancy is one of those special circumstances when diet may be affected. Some women will not eat game in the belief that if they do they will bear children who will be difficult to manage. Some will not eat certain foods for fear that their children will have birthmarks. In one tribe, when an animal is killed for food, the men, women and girls, boys and older people eat specific parts of the animal. Children are sometimes forbidden to eat eggs because it is thought this food might cause bladder disease and sterility.

Bread in many forms is a source of food for people all over the world. An Indian diet, in fact, consists mainly of cereals—rice, wheat, sorghum,* bajra,* ragi,* corn, and barley. Meat, fish, and eggs are scarce and a large section of Indians reject animal products because of religious beliefs. The Hindus object to beef; Moslems, to pork. Milk comes from two sources in India—

*Pronounced sor′gəm; bäj′rä; rä′gẽ. Cereal grasses native to India.

goats and buffalo. The Hindus consider the drinking of this liquid a social evil.

For those who do eat meat, certain taboos about cooked meat exist. It is believed by some people that eating the brain of an animal will lead to premature graying, and consuming the tongue of a goat will cause young children to be talkative. Young men are cautioned to avoid eating goat ears, for these may encourage them to be cowards. Young women are told that eating hog stomachs will cause them to have darker complexions, and young girls soon to be married and young married women are discouraged from eating meat from the underside of an animal since it is thought that this meat will interfere with childbearing.

Resistance to corn as a food for humans has occurred in Europe. This attitude is based on the belief that corn is fit only as food for hogs and cattle.

In China, the wheat region (around Manchuria) produces corn, peas, and soybeans. The rice region where the climate is hotter is smaller in area than the wheat area but produces more per acre. Little beef, mutton, pork, or milk is produced. Since the rice loses certain of its nutritive value during the milling process, enrichment has been tried, but this process has not been successful. The enrichment technique used often changed the color of the rice. The people wanted white rice with which they were familiar rather than rice of a yellow or tan color. The soybean, a good source of protein, has been used in China to mix with flour to increase the nutritive value of the latter.

In Indonesia, the people have a fairly sufficient quantity of food, but essential nutrients, especially protein, are lacking. Moslems comprise 93 percent of the population and they will not eat the meat of pork. (However, in Bali, an island off the coast of Indonesia, the religion is Hindu and pigs are kept and eaten.) There is a belief in the rural areas of Indonesia that children will get worms if they eat fish. Some beliefs like this have come from a mother's observations about her child. In this case, it is possible that after the mother weaned her baby from

BEEF

PORK

VEAL

LAMB

VENISON

breast milk, the child began eating more of the common foods, such as fish. The child got worms and the mother associated the worms with the fish the child was eating. This condition could have resulted from eating different kinds of unclean or uncooked food, not just fish.

In South America, the basic food habits are a carry-over from the pre-Spanish period. Corn and beans are dominant in Central Mexico, Yucatan, and the highlands of Guatemala. In the urban areas, rice, wheat bread, tubers, fats, and greater amounts of meat are used.

In Panama, the major staple is rice, although cattle raising by the Spanish introduced meat into the diet. In northeast Argentina, Uruguay, eastern Paraguay, and some areas of Brazil, meat is consumed in considerable amounts.

In the areas of South America where malnutrition is a serious problem, people often do not have the money to buy enough of the foods they require. Some do not know what foods they need; others do not have the foods available to them.

One doctor who has helped children in South America become better nourished stated that malnutrition in the underdeveloped countries is increased because of ignorance, faddism, and quackery. These same factors operate in the United States where food faddists and quacks prey on people. Have any of them ever tried to sell you their special tonics and foods while making all kinds of promises about what these products will do for you? If they haven't yet, they may someday. These people often take advantage of low-income families, elderly persons living alone, and sick people.

Food habits are the products of generations of cultural beliefs. The culture determines what is clean and what is unclean, what shall and shall not be eaten. Food habits grow out of common experiences that people have shared for centuries as they have tried to explain events of life which they don't understand. Why does a child have a birthmark when it is born—could it be a food the mother ate? Why does the baby get worms—could it be the fish he ate? Why is one child brave, another talkative, another hard to manage—could it be the food consumed? The help and knowledge available for today's mother will enable her to find more accurate answers than some accepted previously.

Another association that people have with food concerns the lessening of anxiety. You may have raided the refrigerator or treated yourself to a super-duper sundae when you were upset or unhappy. Eating certain foods with the family or with your friends may relieve tension and encourage sociability. This particular food habit may be more prevalent in the United States, where some food surpluses exist.

Age and maturity are also said to be related to food patterns. In our own country, olives are sometimes called adult food while peanut butter is often referred to as children's food. Some children clamor for tea or coffee because they associate these beverages with maturity or being older in age. Some adolescents may reject cereal and milk because they identify these foods with childhood.

Causes of Malnutrition

Environmental factors are related to nutrition. Food production, population density, food conservation, processing, and distribution play an important role. Malnutrition may be due to insufficient food production. Lack of irrigation and depleted soil may be two factors preventing greater food production. Irrigation might permit more land to be used and chemical fertilizers would make the soil more productive. But pipes for irrigation systems and fertilizers for the soil cost money—how many farmers could afford them in areas where incomes are very low?

The type of plant grown in some areas is another factor affecting food production. Soybeans grow well in a temperate climate but will not grow well in the tropical areas. Some plants that grow well in the tropical areas do not provide the amount of protein that soybeans do. Other plants contain protein but it is not in a form that can be used by the body.

By now, you are probably aware that one of the most serious problems concerning nutrition is the shortage of essential protein. Although animal foods contain more high-quality protein than plants, the former are lacking in many parts of the world. As was mentioned before, more land is required to raise animals, and most countries of the world do not have the necessary amount of land. Climate and cultural beliefs also affect animal production. In tropical climates, cattle raising is difficult because of disease. Taboos relative to killing animals in some areas allow animals to move freely about, consuming and destroying needed plant foods.

In some areas, plant disease is hard to control, and the crop yield is therefore limited. Where malaria is common and food shortages are prevalent, men are often in poor health and physical condition. They cannot work hard or long each day and food production is slowed considerably.

Low incomes are an important cause of malnutrition. In fact, the personal income of people in many of the underdeveloped countries is so low that it is impossible for an individual to spend more money for food or improved food production techniques. Many of the things that a farmer needs to improve food production cost money. He can learn how to do his farming better, but applying what he has learned will require money for machinery, quality seeds, fertilizers, animals, and farm buildings. Only in some areas is the farmer fortunate enough to have government help with these costly items.

The density of population is another problem related to adequate nutrition. Some scientists speculate that if the population continues to grow at the present rate, the availability of food for all the people of the world will pose a serious question for the future. The world's population is growing more than twice as fast today as it did between 1850 and 1950. Half of the world's population is located in four countries: China, India, the Soviet Union, and the United States. The remainder is distributed over approximately 100 countries.

DAILY INTAKE OF

WESTERN EUROPE
1 IRELAND
2 W.GERMANY
3 NETHERLANDS
4 BELGIUM
5 PORTUGAL
6 SWITZERLAND
7 ITALY
8 AUSTRIA
9 DENMARK

CENTRAL AMERICA
1 GUATEMALA
2 BRIT.HOND.
3 EL SALVADOR
4 HONDURAS
5 NICARAGUA
6 COSTA RICA
7 PANAMA

SOUTH AMERICA
1 VENEZUELA
2 COLOMBIA
3 ECUADOR
4 GUYANA
5 SURINAM
6 FR. GUIANA
7 PERU
8 BOLIVIA
9 CHILE
10 PARAGUAY
11 URUGUAY

Based on statistics from *The State of Food and Agriculture -1964* , FAO.

ANIMAL PROTEIN

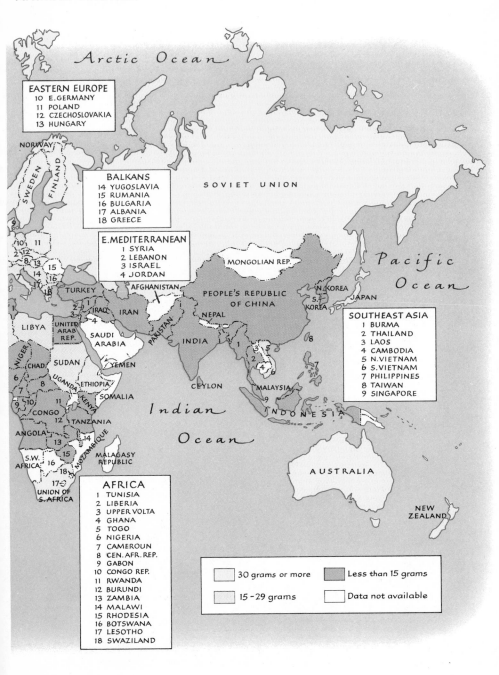

EASTERN EUROPE
10 E.GERMANY
11 POLAND
12 CZECHOSLOVAKIA
13 HUNGARY

BALKANS
14 YUGOSLAVIA
15 RUMANIA
16 BULGARIA
17 ALBANIA
18 GREECE

E.MEDITERRANEAN
1 SYRIA
2 LEBANON
3 ISRAEL
4 JORDAN

SOUTHEAST ASIA
1 BURMA
2 THAILAND
3 LAOS
4 CAMBODIA
5 N.VIETNAM
6 S.VIETNAM
7 PHILIPPINES
8 TAIWAN
9 SINGAPORE

AFRICA
1 TUNISIA
2 LIBERIA
3 UPPER VOLTA
4 GHANA
5 TOGO
6 NIGERIA
7 CAMEROUN
8 CEN.AFR.REP.
9 GABON
10 CONGO REP.
11 RWANDA
12 BURUNDI
13 ZAMBIA
14 MALAWI
15 RHODESIA
16 BOTSWANA
17 LESOTHO
18 SWAZILAND

Arctic Ocean
NORWAY
SWEDEN
FINLAND
SOVIET UNION
Pacific Ocean
TURKEY
AFGHANISTAN
MONGOLIAN REP.
N.KOREA
S.KOREA
JAPAN
PEOPLE'S REPUBLIC OF CHINA
IRAQ
IRAN
NEPAL
PAKISTAN
INDIA
LIBYA
UNITED ARAB REP.
SAUDI ARABIA
YEMEN
NIGER
CHAD
SUDAN
ETHIOPIA
SOMALIA
UGANDA
KENYA
CONGO
TANZANIA
ANGOLA
MOZAMBIQUE
S.W. AFRICA
MALAGASY REPUBLIC
UNION OF S.AFRICA
CEYLON
MALAYSIA
INDONESIA
Indian Ocean
AUSTRALIA
NEW ZEALAND

30 grams or more
15 - 29 grams
Less than 15 grams
Data not available

38

The continents in which the greatest nutritional problems exist include Africa, Asia (other than Japan and Israel), Central America and South America (except for Argentina and Uruguay). These countries, often referred to as underdeveloped, have 55 percent of the world's land area and about two-thirds of the world's population. Their populations have increased faster than their food production. In the developed areas, such as the United States and Europe, food production increases have been greater than population rises. Thus, the underdeveloped countries do not have enough food and the developed countries have a surplus.

What can be done about malnutrition? Many people continue to ask this question. Some of the effects of malnutrition are being investigated and suggestions made regarding what action to take.

Combating Malnutrition

Malnutrition in the preschool child is a serious concern. In developing areas, estimates are that nearly 70 percent of the children may suffer from malnutrition, resulting in the early deaths of millions of children. Those who survive rarely reach their full growth potential, physically, mentally, or emotionally, and become adults who are not as productive as they could be. Preschool malnutrition, therefore, is one factor which slows down the progress of developing countries.

This young girl shows the tragic signs of prolonged malnutrition.

This is the same child after being on a nutritionally adequate diet.

Food for Peace

Food for Peace

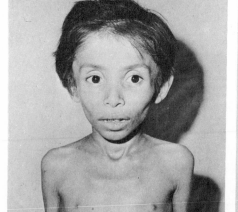
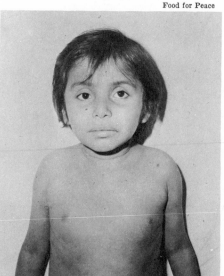

Controlling natural resources is one way of fighting malnutrition. This dam in Korea was built by North Korean refugees who were paid their wages in food. There are thousands of such food-for-work programs currently taking place throughout the world.

Food for Peace

A study of worldwide malnutrition of the preschool child indicated three circumstances which aggravate the problem:

1. Mothers do not know what to feed their children to promote normal growth and development. They do not understand that small children need generous amounts of foods supplying high-quality proteins.
2. Many families cannot afford to buy the food needed by children. Good foods (such as eggs) are often sold for items needed by the adults.
3. Poor crop practices, the raising of non-food cash crops, and lack of transportation, food processing, and preservation are all factors which make essential foods impossible to obtain.

Also mentioned in the study were those reasons which have been previously discussed—cultural factors, social customs, superstitions, taboos, and religious beliefs. All operate together to prevent the preschool child from receiving the food he desperately needs.

Any kind of program to combat malnutrition will have to take all these factors into consideration; a plan will have to include agricultural, educational, health, and economic measures. Both the wishes and the capabilities of the people will have to be considered. Not only will food production have to be increased, but more of the much needed proteins will have to be produced and distributed. A few high-protein foods are being developed which should be available at low cost and in a form acceptable to the people. Their use must be promoted. Education will be necessary to help people know what foods they need and how they can prevent loss of food by spoilage and destruction by rodents and insects. Financing may be necessary for farmers.

AID

Above: A school lunch program in Taiwan.
Left: A school garden in Taiwan.

AID

A significant program in the United States has been the Food for Peace Program. This plan has made possible overseas distribution of American surplus foods to food-deficient countries. The program has been carefully structured to promote the development of the receiving country and to improve its own food production. Food for Peace has enabled many countries to establish their own school lunch programs. In this way, children receive additional nutritious food. In some areas, the students plant gardens and raise chickens and rabbits for food to be used in their school lunches. They also help prepare and serve the meals.

Malnutrition produces suffering and slows down human progress; it is a problem that must not be ignored. When you consider that nearly 70 percent of the children in the underdeveloped countries are suffering from malnutrition, you can only guess at the consequences. The amount of suffering and damage to human beings, when this many children are involved, is staggering. How many adults could be included is not known.

In the next chapter you will learn of some of the agencies which are actively concerned with solving the world's food crisis.

MAJOR IDEAS

The following statements give the main ideas within the chapter you have just studied. Be sure you know the words underscored in these statements and in the questions to follow.

1. Understanding food preferences and habits helps one appreciate the meanings that food holds for people.
2. Malnutrition occurs when the quality of food is poor.
3. Undernutrition indicates a lack of quantity of food.
4. Malnutrition is one of the most serious food problems of our time.

QUESTIONS TO STUDY

FOOD PREFERENCES

1. Distinguish between malnutrition and undernutrition.
2. Describe the general types of food patterns; explain what influences the establishment of these patterns in various countries.
3. What do calories measure?

FOOD HABITS

1. Give several reasons why food habits are difficult to change.
2. Consider two of your own food habits which you would find hard to change. Try to determine why this would be true.
3. What factors most strongly influence one's food habits?

CAUSES OF MALNUTRITION

1. Explain why insufficient protein may produce malnutrition.
2. Discuss the statement, "Environmental factors influence the quality of nutrition."
3. How may food faddism lead to malnutrition?

COMBATING MALNUTRITION

1. Describe the Food for Peace Program.
2. Outline the steps you might take if you were sent to another country to help the people there combat malnutrition.
3. Why is the diet of the preschool child of such great importance?

BIBLIOGRAPHY

BABCOCK, CHARLOTTE, "Food and Its Emotional Significance." *Journal of the American Dietetic Association*, Vol. 24, May 1948, pp. 390–393.

BEATON AND MCHENRY, *Nutrition*, Vol. II. New York, Academic Press, 1964.

BURGESS, A., and DEAN, R. F. A., (editors), *Malnutrition and Food Habits*. London, Tanistock Publications, 1962.

COWAN, J. W., SURRINDER, CHOPRA, and HOURY, GLADYS, "Dietary Survey of Rural Lebanon." *Journal of the American Dietetic Association*, Vol. 45, August 1964, pp. 130–133.

DONAHUE, HAYDEN and FOWLER, PHOEBE, "Some Problems of Feeding Mental Patients." *American Journal of Clinical Nutrition*. Vol. 5, No. 2, March-April 1957, pp. 180–183.

ENGEL, R. W., "Food Faddism." *Nutrition Review*, Vol. 17, No. 12, December 1959, pp. 353–355.

Ethiopia Nutrition Survey. Interdepartmental Committee on Nutrition for National Defense, September 1959.

FRAZER, J. C., *Folklore in the Old Testament*. London, Macmillan and Co., 1923.

HOELZEL, FREDERICK, "Dr. A. J. Carlson and the Concept of Hunger." *American Journal of Clinical Nutrition*, Vol. 5, No. 6, November–December 1957, pp. 659–662.

JANSSEN, WALLACE F., "Food Quackery—A Law Enforcement Problem." *Journal of the American Dietetic Association*, Vol. 36, February 1960, pp. 110–113.

KAUNITZ, HANS and JOHNSON, RUTH ELLEN, "Manipulation of Food Intake by Man." *Experimental Medical Surgery*, Vol. 20, 1962, pp. 50–54.

Kingdom of Thailand Nutrition Survey. Interdepartmental Committee on Nutrition for National Defense, November 1961.

LOEB, M. B., "The Social Function of Food Habits." *Journal of the American Academy of Applied Nutrition*, No. 4, 1951, p. 1.

Malnutrition and Disease: A Major Problem of the Human Race. World Health Organization, FFCH Basic Study No. 12, Geneva, 1963.

MONTAGU, ASHLEY M. F., "Nature, Nurture, and Nutrition." *American Journal of Clinical Nutrition*, Vol. 5, No. 3, May–June, 1957.

MOORE, HARRIET, "The Meaning of Food." *American Journal of Clinical Nutrition*, Vol. 5, No. 1, February 1957, pp. 77–82.

MORGAN, AGNES FAY, "Interactions of Food Technology with Nutrition During the Last Twenty-five Years." *Food Technology*, September 1964, pp. 1314–1318.

"The Nutritional State of the World." Ohio University Symposium, 1963.

PRUGH, DAVE, "Some Psychologic Considerations Concerned with the Problem of Overnutrition." *American Journal of Clinical Nutrition*, Vol. 9, September–October 1961, pp. 538–542.

RICHARDSON, H. L., "What Fertilizers Could Do To Increase World Food Production." *Advancement of Science*, Vol. 12, January 1961, pp. 472–480.

SIMON, JUSTIN, "Psychologic Factors in Dietary Restriction." *Journal of the American Dietetic Association*, Vol. 57, August 1960, pp. 109–114.

SLATER, W. K., "The World's Food—The Problem." *Food Technology*, December 1964, pp. 1891–1894.

STEIBELING, HAZEL K., "Our Share in Better World Nutrition." *Journal of the American Dietetic Association*, Vol. 45, October 1964, pp. 315–320.

4 AGENCIES WORKING ON NUTRITION PROBLEMS

Many persons find it difficult to understand why people in some parts of the world do not have enough food. In Chapter 3, you considered some of the reasons why such hunger exists: (1) unequal distribution of food, (2) rapid population growth, (3) competition for land, and (4) lack of education.

One of man's most critical problems today is providing food for every human being. This problem is so complex that it will be with us for years to come. You are part of the generation that will have to help solve this crisis.

Food production has increased faster than population growth in the United States. Although our farmers are fewer in number, they produce more food than ever before by using machines, improved plants and animals which give a high yield, and fertilizers. In fact, it is estimated that a United States farm worker feeds 37 people, nearly twice as many as ten years ago. The farmer has had to become educated and skilled in scientific methods of farming.

This is not true in many parts of the world where the population has increased faster than the food production. In these areas especially, children are suffering from malnutrition and undernutrition. It may seem to some people that hunger in these countries could be reduced or totally eliminated if the farmers followed the example of American farmers and used their available money to buy equipment and used scientific agricultural methods to produce more food. Yet the farmers are faced with agonizing decisions.

If your children were starving, could you bear to sell the rice you had grown for money to buy machinery or fertilizer? If your children were going to bed hungry, would you be able to improve your land by not growing anything on it for a year? These are the decisions that people must consider in countries where the food supply is inadequate.

A start has been made by a number of agencies to increase food production and eliminate malnutrition. Some are international agencies supported by many countries around the world; others are supported by national governments; still others are private organizations, sponsored by groups of people who want to help in this activity.

International Agencies

The United Nations has been one of the agencies that has brought hope to countless numbers of people. In 1945, the UN grew out of the deep desires of men from many countries for peace and a better way of life. The UN has labored toward these goals for over 20 years. Since malnutrition is usually found with poverty, ignorance, and disease, the member countries and the

44

agencies of the UN have had to attack several problems at one time. Four important agencies of the United Nations which are helping to solve the immense food crisis are the Food and Agriculture Organization (FAO), the World Health Organization (WHO), the United Nations International Children's Emergency Fund (UNICEF), and the United Nations Educational, Scientific, and Cultural Organization (UNESCO).

FAO. Hunger is the special problem of the Food and Agriculture Organization. This agency sends experts to countries that want technical advice concerning the best ways to grow more food. These skilled people assist countries in controlling pests and plant and animal diseases. They advise on how to protect food in storage and help countries increase their food production from farms, fisheries, and forests.

World Food Surveys have been conducted by the FAO. The World Food Survey in 1963 showed that some 60 percent of the population in the less-developed areas suffered from undernutrition or malnutrition or both.

FAO experts have aided people in Ceylon to improve their fishing boats, helped Egyptians double their rice production, assisted the Mexicans in improving the poultry industry, and helped Indonesians develop their trees and fish ponds. In several countries nutrition workers have taught mothers to feed their families a better diet. In addition, the FAO has fought to rid huge areas of Africa and Asia of swarms of locusts which destroy essential green plant life. It has been estimated that one swarm of these insects weighs about 80,000 tons.

An FAO trainee works in a pilot market vegetable garden in Gabon.

United Nations

THE SIGNIFICANCE OF FOOD

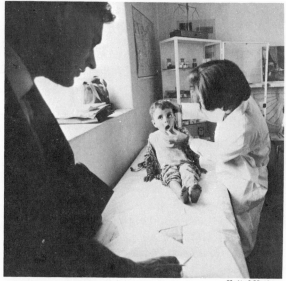

The Government of Iran created The Food and Nutrition Institute for the purpose of studying the nutritional problems of the country and the possibilities for solving them. FAO, WHO, and UNICEF are jointly providing the Institute with expert services. Here a WHO visiting consultant from the United Kingdom watches as a pediatrician examines a child in a village near Teheran.

United Nations

WHO. The World Health Organization works closely with the FAO on many projects. WHO is a specialized agency which advises member countries on public health and the control of disease. It attacks the widespread plagues such as malaria, tuberculosis, yaws, and syphilis. Nutrition problems accompany such infections and diseases.

In 1955, WHO undertook a worldwide campaign to eliminate malaria. This campaign has made an interesting story and it has been called "the greatest challenge in the history of humanity's fight for health." One of the most important discoveries of this battle against malaria was the fact that a mosquito which bites a malaria patient will rest on the nearest wall to digest the meal. If the inside walls of the houses are sprayed with DDT, the disease-carrying mosquitoes will get it on their legs and die. DDT teams were sent out, and by the end of 1959 almost 280 million people had been reached with malaria protection. At that time, about 1.4 billion people lived in malaria country.

Sometimes the activity of WHO overlaps the work of FAO and they operate together. This is advisable since, after all, health and food problems are often closely related. Both of these agencies have cooperated in the attack on hunger, poverty, and disease.

UNICEF. The United Nations International Children's Emergency Fund was created by the General Assembly of the United Nations in 1946. This agency is not supported by the UN budget but by voluntary contributions from governments and individuals and through sale of UNICEF Christmas cards.

The Fresh Water Fisheries Project is part of the Indonesian Government's attempt to improve Indonesian nutrition as a whole. The Project maintains three hatcheries in Central Java which supply small fish to various village, community, and school ponds. Six months later, the fish are given to the poor. The boys in the photograph are collecting the fish from one village pond where they were delivered six months earlier. The catch will be given to the poor. UNICEF has contributed tractors, bicycles, and nylon nets to the Project.

United Nations

UNICEF also specializes in the supply of medicines, foods, and equipment for services to mothers and children. Concerned primarily with control of diseases especially affecting children, UNICEF has also improved the diets of millions of children.

When attacking nutrition problems, the work of UNICEF often overlaps the tasks of FAO and WHO. The three agencies share the job whenever possible, each supplying what it can do best. The Protein Advisory Group is a food and nutrition department sponsored by UNICEF, WHO, and FAO. This group has been active in promoting the use of high-quality protein foods for infants and preschool children.

Starting in 1956, UNICEF, FAO, WHO, and a number of scientific and industrial groups have been working on the development of new high-protein foods. Cottonseed flour, peanut flour and fish flour are now in experimental stages as possible foods for people in areas where milk and other protein-rich foods are not available. A "soymilk" plant has been built with the assistance of UNICEF in Indonesia. In India, with the help of FAO, programs called "backyard" or "kitchen gardens" have been developed to increase village production of vegetables, fruits and other foods. A great deal of malnutrition results from unscientific beliefs about child feeding, traditional eating habits, and general ignorance. To help overcome this, UNICEF is increasing its training program for local nutrition workers.

During the post-war years, UNICEF shipped skim milk powder donated by the United States and other countries to developing countries. The distribution of skim milk powder through schools and health centers has helped show people what better nutrition can do for their children and has stimulated support for the development of local dairy industries. UNICEF now ships about 100 million pounds of skim milk powder to the developing countries every year for use in nutrition and health education programs.

But what happens after a mother has skim milk or a protein-rich food for her hungry child? What occurs if she mixes the skim milk in an unclean container and the child becomes ill? This has happened and the mother may blame the child's illness on the milk. She doesn't know about the bacteria that can get into milk from dirty containers and make her child sick. Education must go along with the skim milk and the protein-rich food. Another United Nations agency—UNESCO—has been dedicated toward this goal.

UNESCO. Recognizing the immediate need for an agency to encourage educational and cultural development, the delegates to the conference that created the United Nations organized the UN Educational, Scientific and Cultural Organization in 1945.

According to the latest statistics (1964), about 750 million adults—almost 40 percent of the adults in the world today—are illiterate. Pilot projects of UNESCO are gradually reducing this distressingly high figure. Today, literacy projects are being launched in Algeria, Iran, and Mali. The efforts to educate illiterate people in these areas are aimed at improving the market gardens and

FAO Photo

This is the Iranian version of American 4-H Clubs. They are called 4-D Clubs in Iran— "Donesh" for head, "Del" for heart, "Dast" for hand, and "Davam" for health. This photograph was taken in Khak Ali village which was near the center of the disastrous 1963 earthquake. Many of the villages in this area, including much plant and animal life, were destroyed. Here the 4-D leader teaches fruit tree grafting to this 25-boy club.

groves in Algeria, irrigation canals and agricultural areas in Iran, and cotton and rice districts in Mali. It is evident, therefore, that UNESCO and UNICEF can work closely together.

One cause of the illiteracy problem is that less than half of the world's children go to school. A result of the lack of schools in so much of the world is that most of the human race cannot read or write. Progress cannot go far in communities where hardly anyone can read.

But UNESCO has found that where most of the people cannot read, learning the alphabet is not usually what they need first. They need simple, practical improvements in their daily life that they can understand and accept. Perhaps the first thing the people must learn is to boil the water before drinking it. Or they may be taught how to improve their food supply by planting a garden. When the people have tried a few simple changes and found them acceptable, learning to read may seem easier. Then, if a teacher with modern visual aids and other equipment is available, this educational step will be simpler. Once the people of a community can read, a giant step has been made toward helping them to help themselves.

Think a minute of the mother we talked about who mixed the skim milk powder in an unsafe way and made her child ill. When this mother is able to read, one way she can learn more quickly how to provide safe food for her family is by following clearly written directions.

UNESCO helps train teachers who can teach this mother and others like her to read. UNESCO does not have the money to hire teachers to send around the world but it does show countries how to train their own teachers and helps by contributing certain kinds of equipment.

National Agencies

The underdeveloped countries are making efforts for improving the health, education, and economic level of their people. Their task is tremendous and requires support from many of their neighbors. Most of the underdeveloped countries are assisted by other countries or the United Nations in some way. The problems of the various developing countries are similar, yet different, too. In many countries, rapidly increasing populations and inadequate food supplies are threatening people's health, education, and economic progress. The details differ depending on the size of the country and its resources.

India is an example of how one country is attacking the critical problems relative to food supply. India's third Five-Year Plan (1961–66) for development allotted more than $3.5 billion for agriculture, irrigation, and community development, and India's Minister of Food has often expressed the hope that by 1971 India's food production will be adequate for her population. Heretofore the food production has been inadequate and could not keep up with the annual population increase. India has been working on her own food problems and in addition has also sought assistance from the United Nations and other countries.

Although the United States does not face the food crisis of some other countries, she does have problems regarding an adequate food supply for all her citizens. As mentioned previously, even in this country which has the reputation of being a "land-of-plenty," malnutrition exists. For example, as late as 1966, the production of milk decreased to what leaders believed to be distressing levels, since high beef prices encouraged farmers to slaughter cows at a high rate. In addition, the difficulties of managing a small farm successfully have made many farmers in this country go out of business.

In our own country, a number of agencies have been involved with worldwide nutrition problems.

The Agricultural Research Service. If you were to visit Beltsville, Maryland, you would find the laboratories of this agency fascinating. The Agricultural Research Service is part of the United States Department of Agriculture, and its responsibility is to conduct research into all areas of agriculture. Involved in all types of scientific study of animals and plants and, of course, food, ARS hopes that such research will be part of the answer toward eliminating the world problem of hunger and malnutrition. The ARS also cooperates with the State Agricultural Experiment Stations in a wide variety of projects.

The Nutrition Foundation. Some exciting work has been encouraged and supported by this organization. One example which has worldwide implications is that a protein-rich food, "Incaparina," has been developed by the Institute of Nutrition of Central America and Panama (INCAP) (financed by The Nutrition Foundation), to help fight malnutrition in Central America. Incaparina resembles dry milk powder or flour, but it compares favorably with milk in all the essential nutrients. Incaparina helps children to grow and be healthy since many children in Central America do not have enough food or enough protein. These protective foods—milk, meat, eggs, and fish—are scarce. Vegetables and plant protein have previously provided the main diet, limiting the essential nutrients which all bodies need.

The challenges faced by INCAP scientists when creating high-protein foods were to (1) determine what local foods would provide the hungry children with the protein they needed, (2) make sure that foods could be grown or found locally, (3) keep food costs extremely low, and (4) provide the finished product in a form acceptable to the people.

After much investigation and experimentation, the INCAP scientists developed Incaparina, a light yellow mixture of vegetable proteins. To this mixture the experts added corn flour, sorghum flour, cottonseed flour, torula yeast,

A mother prepares to give her children Incaparina in Santa Caterina Barahona, a village near Antigua, Guatemala.

United Nations

vitamin A, and calcium carbonate. Each of these ingredients had some value of its own, and when blended together they made a good quality high-protein food. Incaparina could be added to the common Central American dishes, just as dry milk is added to many dishes we cook and bake, and could be mixed with water and used as a beverage. Incaparina even had a pleasant taste.

The next problem the INCAP scientists faced was to encourage people to try a new food like Incaparina. If you have studied Spanish, you know that the Spanish word for flour is "harina." The agency used their initials—INCAP— and combined them with harina to create the name Incaparina, since it was hoped that the people in Central America would be more receptive to a food which had a Spanish-sounding name. They used all possible means to tell the village people that Incaparina would make them healthier. They put up posters with pictures, since many people could not read, and gave out free samples for people to try. They talked about Incaparina and showed movies about it.

The Nutrition Foundation helped to start the INCAP project that resulted in Incaparina in two Central American villages. Tons of this food are now being produced in Central America. Other countries in South America, Asia, and Africa have learned from INCAP. They are creating their own high-protein low-cost products from foods that can be produced locally. This is only one example of how the Nutrition Foundation has functioned in helping to solve nutrition problems.

The Food and Nutrition Board of the National Research Council. You have probably seen tables which show how many calories and certain nutrients such as protein, calcium, or iron are recommended for a teen-ager. If you look at Table 2 on page 74, you will see that the information was taken from the "Recommended Daily Dietary Allowances" prepared by the Food and Nutrition Board of the National Research Council. This agency has prepared this guide to help us know more about the kinds of nutrients which can keep us healthy.

The Food and Nutrition Board was organized to help coordinate and apply the findings of nutrition research for the benefit of Americans. The members of this board are concerned that findings in the laboratory be put into practice in the community and in the home. This group cooperates with international and private agencies such as the Rockefeller Foundation (a private agency) which has provided funds for the Food and Nutrition Board to study possible sources of high-quality protein foods. This research is being done in cooperation with three UN agencies—FAO, WHO, and UNICEF.

The Agency for International Development. This organization helps develop leadership in the developing countries. For example, at the request of an African country, AID might set up a program in education or agriculture and send experts from this country to the area to train the African leaders. When the experts were no longer needed, they would return to the United States. The African people who had worked with them would continue the work the AID experts had helped to organize.

This girl is one of 600 children in Santiago, Chile, who receive a daily hot lunch under the Food for Peace program.

Food for Peace

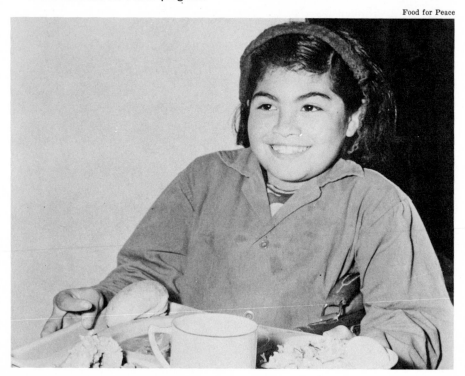

U. S. Interdepartmental Committee on Nutrition for National Development. ICNND has conducted some 24 nutrition surveys in newly developing countries. These studies have been useful in demonstrating what special nutrition problems exist in a particular country. The surveys have also generated interest within a country to do something about these problems.

Food for Peace. This program was mentioned previously in Chapter 3. Food, seeds, and tools are distributed in an effort to encourage people of the developing countries to consume a better diet. It is hoped that the efforts of this program to help under-developed countries will reduce the amount of conflict between those nations which have enough food and those countries which need food supplies.

Private Agencies

A number of private agencies have been attempting to improve the well-being of people. Two examples are the Rockefeller Foundation and the Ford Foundation. Both were created by men who played an important part in shaping the history of the United States—John D. Rockefeller, Sr., and Henry Ford, Sr.

One of the most dramatic accomplishments of the Rockefeller Foundation was the program of crop improvement in Mexico in cooperation with the Mexican government. Because of this effort Mexican food production increased greatly; wheat, corn, and bean crops doubled, broiler production

The Rockefeller Foundation is helping farmers in Mexico to improve the quality and supply of their corn (page 450). This farmer is inspecting his new crop.

The Rockefeller Foundation

The Rockefeller Foundation

These Philippine agricultural extension workers learn the methods they in turn will teach farmers. Here they weed one of their maximum yield trial production plots at The International Rice Institute.

tripled, and egg production went up two and a half times. Even though the Mexican population increased, the people had more food to eat and more animal-protein foods.

Using this experience in Mexico and similar efforts in other countries, the Rockefeller Foundation and the Ford Foundation joined forces in a larger program. They cooperated to set up the Rice Research Institute near Manila in the Philippines which offers great hope to the people in this area.

Rice is the staple diet of half the world's people. The rice project is attempting to demonstrate how the amount of rice grown on each acre of land can be increased. Another goal is to find ways to enrich the protein content of the rice. In Southeast Asia, a region where people don't have enough food or protein, these findings would help hungry people to be better fed. Important work such as that sponsored by the Rockefeller and Ford Foundations can help immensely to ease the food crisis.

There are many other agencies in the world working to find answers to nutrition problems, yet all of them cannot be included here. Most of the agencies have similar aims; they want to do something about the terrible suffering caused by hunger, poverty, and disease. A child suffering from malnutrition is not a pleasant sight. How can we end hunger? How can we help other countries achieve a balance between food and people? The task of your generation will be to help such agencies as these described by supporting them in their efforts to solve these critical problems.

MAJOR IDEAS

The following statements give the main ideas in the chapter you have just studied. Be sure you know the words underscored in these statements and in the questions to follow.

1. Several organizations have been sponsored through the United Nations which are concerned with improving nutrition, the food supply, and health on an international scale. These agencies are FAO, WHO, UNICEF, and UNESCO.
2. Nationally, both government and independent agencies engage in or sponsor nutrition and agricultural research and conduct surveys concerning the food supply and the nutritional status of people.
3. We should have a deep concern for people who have inadequate food, live in poverty, and suffer from numerous diseases which can be controlled with proper care.
4. We must support agencies which are working to seek causes, develop answers, and mobilize resources to improve the world's food supply.

QUESTIONS TO STUDY

INTERNATIONAL AGENCIES

1. What is the purpose of FAO?
2. Explain the ways in which science and technical knowledge can help a developing country.
3. Describe the kind of work sponsored by WHO.
4. Describe the work done by UNICEF.
5. What are the goals of UNESCO?
6. Why do you think the work of these agencies might be hampered?

NATIONAL AGENCIES

1. Describe ways in which certain government agencies have helped to improve the nutritional status of people in the United States.
2. Explain how the work of the Interdepartmental Committee on Nutrition for National Defense could help end hunger.
3. What special programs does AID sponsor?
4. Cite a current problem relative to food in the United States.

PRIVATE AGENCIES

1. How do the kind of programs sponsored by the Rockefeller Foundation and Ford Foundation help to improve nutrition?
2. Why are these agencies interested in rice research?

BIBLIOGRAPHY

BERRY, FRANK B. and SCHAEFER, ARNOLD, "Nutrition Surveys in the Near and Far East—Report of the Interdepartmental Committee on Nutrition for National Defense." *American Journal of Clinical Nutrition*, Vol. 6, No. 4, July–August 1958, pp. 342–353.

Century of Service—The First 100 Years. Centennial Committee, U. S. Department of Agriculture, 1963.

COYLE, DAVID C., *The United Nations and How It Works.* New York, The New American World Library of World Literature, 1960.

DEUTSCHMAN, PAUL, "IRRI Fills Empty Rice Bowls." *Saturday Review*, August 6, 1966, pp. 16–17, 39.

FAO, What It Is, What It Does, How It Works. United Nations Pamphlet, 1964.

The First Ten Years of the World Health Organization. World Health Organization, Geneva, 1958.

MEAD, MARGARET, *Cultural Patterns and Technical Change.* New York, The New American Library of World Literature, 1963.

The Nutrition Foundation Inc., 1963–1964. The Nutrition Foundation, New York, 1964.

Pre-school Child Malnutrition. National Academy of Sciences, National Research Council, Washington, D. C., 1966.

SHAPLEN, ROBERT, *Toward the Well-Being of Mankind.* New York, Doubleday and Company, Inc., 1964.

STEIBLING, HAZEL K., "Improved Use of Nutritional Knowledge —Progress and Problems." *Journal of the American Dietetics Association*, Vol. 45, October 1964, pp. 315–320.

Toward a Better World for Children, The Work of UNICEF. United Nations Children's Fund, Dobbs Ferry, New York, Oceana Publication, Inc., 1963.

"UNESCO and Literacy: Progress Report." *Saturday Review*, July 30, 1966, p. 24.

UNICEF, What It Does, How It Works for a Better World for Children. United Nations Pamphlet, 1965.

5 CONTRIBUTORS TO THE SCIENCE OF NUTRITION

In the previous chapters, you investigated man's individual and collective search for food for survival. In this chapter you will study about some of the scientists who have tried to make man's pursuit easier and more fruitful.

For centuries, man has asked questions about food, the human body, and disease. Men have spent their lifetimes seeking understanding of the mysterious relationship between life, disease, and food. You, too, have probably asked questions such as "What foods will keep me healthy?" and "What foods will help me live longer?"

All the knowledge that man has acquired in trying to answer questions concerning food and its relationship to the living body has led to the development of the science of nutrition. As mentioned in Chapter 1, *nutrition* can be defined as *the science of food and its relation to health*. Stated in another way, it is the science concerned with providing the nourishment needed by the body for growth, maintenance, repair, and regulation of body processes.

Since the science of nutrition developed after chemistry (the science of the composition of substances and how they are transformed) and physiology (the science of the functions of living things), it is often called a twentieth century science. For the most part, the development of this science came through the work of chemists and physiologists. As the science of chemistry progressed, man learned about the composition of air, water, and food. He was able to study the chemistry of proteins, fats, and carbohydrates. The science of physiology also advanced, permitting man to discover, in part, how the human body works. In turn, man began to understand certain functions of the heart, lungs, and muscles, all of which need nutrients to operate.

Although words such as *nutritive, nutrify,* and *nutriment* were in existence by the fifteenth century, the word nutrition did not originate until a century later and was rarely used until about 1898. Before this time, the term *dietetics* was used to refer to problems related to food.

Biographical Sketches

Many people have contributed to the development of the science of nutrition. Application of the findings of research in the area of nutrient requirements, body processes, and caloric needs has made men healthier and able to live longer.

Vitamin research is one example of how nutrient deficiencies were discovered by scientists and efforts made to correct them. James Lind, a Scotch

An early photograph of
Elmer Verner McCollum.

Brown Brothers

physician, cured scurvy* in 1753 by giving lemon juice (which is rich in vitamin C) to British sailors in controlled experiments. Christian Eijkman, a Dutch
physician, and G. Grijns, a Swedish biologist, demonstrated how brown rice
could cure or prevent beriberi,† a disease which was prevalent in predominately
rice-eating countries. The unpolished or brown rice contained thiamine, part
of the vitamin B complex, whereas the white rice was lacking in this essential
nutrient. Joseph Goldberger, an American pathologist, was criticized for his
belief that pellagra‡ was a dietary problem, but he was finally able to prove it.
He showed that niacin, thiamine, and riboflavin (vitamin B complex factors)
could prevent or cure this disease.

ELMER VERNER MCCOLLUM (1879–1967) was an American physiological chemist who specialized in the study of vitamins and the relationship of diet to growth.
He and another scientist, MARGUERITE DAVIS, isolated vitamin A in butterfat,
located vitamin B in lactose which had not been sufficiently refined, and recognized the importance of vitamin D in the treatment of the bone disease rickets.§

CASIMIR FUNK (1884–1967) was a Polish-American chemist who tried to isolate
the substance from unpolished rice which would prevent beriberi. He had rea-
soned that if there were something in food which could forestall beriberi,

*A disease which is characterized by swollen bleeding gums, loose teeth, and muscular weakness.
†A disease of muscular and nervous fatigue, pains and finally paralysis in the legs.
‡A disease which is recognized by neurologic symptoms, gastrointestinal disturbances, and red, scaly, rough skin.
§A childhood disease characterized by faulty forming of bones.

The Bettmann Archive, Inc.

An experiment on respiration being conducted in Lavoisier's laboratory.

pellagra, and scurvy, it was necessary to define it and apply it to other aspects of life and disease. His laboratory preparation, which was effective in curing beriberi in birds, was an amine compound; he therefore coined the name "vitamine."

Vitamin research is, however, only a small part of the past and current investigation in the field of nutrition. The following biographies indicate the varied areas of interest. It should be remembered that these biographies represent a minute fraction of scientists who have been (or are) active in this area.

ANTOINE LAURENT LAVOISIER (1743–1794) was a French chemist who is often referred to as "the father of nutrition" because of his work on respiration and oxidation. Lavoisier demonstrated that the life process is one of respiration, and that as oxygen is taken in by the body, carbon dioxide is exhaled. By measuring those gases he was able to calculate the body's heat production, and he determined that the working man expended more calories and therefore needed more food than the person who was less active. His extensive work helped to establish the foundations upon which the modern science of chemistry relies.

WILLIAM BEAUMONT (1785–1853) was a U. S. Army surgeon and physiologist who was able to examine a stomach directly through an external opening in a patient. He observed the rates of dissolution of foods and recorded the effect of emotions on gastric secretion and digestion.

CONTRIBUTORS TO THE SCIENCE OF NUTRITION

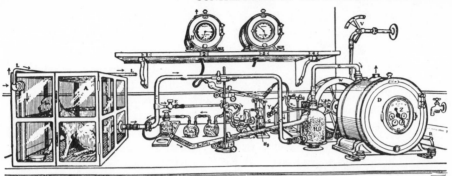

From Tigerstedt, New York, D. Appleton & Co.

Basal metabolism is usually defined today as the amount of energy which is required by the body when it is lying at rest in a pleasant environmental temperature, relaxed, and without food (that is, 12 to 15 hours after the last meal). The illustration above shows the respiration apparatus of Max van Pettenkofer and Carl von Voit. Compare this machine with the more modern one illustrated on page 75.

JUSTIN VON LIEBIG (1803–1873) was a German chemist who was active in providing adequate educational laboratories for students of chemistry so that they could obtain the best possible training. In addition, he studied animal physiology to determine the chemical and physiological laws relative to the maintenance of health and life. He also categorized various foods according to their functions in the animal system. Contrary to the ideas which were believed at the time, Liebig taught that the combustion and oxidation performed within the body caused the body's heat. His work was later to lead to the science of biochemistry.

CARL VON VOIT (1831–1908) was a German physiologist who was instrumental in establishing some of the fundamental principles of metabolism and nutrition. He and another scientist, MAX VAN PETTENKOFER, built the first metabolism machine capable of holding a human being. With this device they demonstrated that the rate of carbon dioxide production is proportional to the rate of muscular activity. They were also the first men to accurately determine the energy requirements of man (relating to necessary caloric intake).

FREDERICK COWLAND HOPKINS (1861–1947) was an English biochemist who did extensive work in the study of proteins. In 1906 he published evidence which proved the existence of essential amino acids in foods as well as those accompanying factors which were later to be known by the name of vitamins.

LAFAYETTE BENEDICT MENDEL (1872–1935) was an American physical chemist, physiologist, and biochemist. While doing research at Yale University, he and THOMAS BURR OSBORNE discovered the existence of a fat-soluble factor required for the growth of animals. This substance was subsequently named vitamin A.

HENRY CLAPP SHERMAN (1875–1955) was an American biochemist who studied the mineral elements in food and their function in nutrition, the digestive enzymes, protein requirements of man, the efficiency of food proteins, and the functions and effects of different intake levels of vitamins. He maintained that old age could be postponed by eating a diet abundant in the protective foods such as fruits, vegetables, and milk in their various forms.

HELEN K. STIEBELING (1896–　) is a recently retired research administrator who was influential in establishing a working pattern of the amounts of food and nutrients needed by individuals of different ages, sex, and activities, on a daily basis. Dr. Stiebeling guided a nationwide survey of food consumption of Americans during the mid-1930's. The study was concerned with the adequacy of the diets as compared to a standard of requirements. Her report aroused widespread concern and encouraged President Franklin Roosevelt to take action in advising people of the prevalent nutritional deficiencies and the best ways to correct them.

E. NEIGE TODHUNTER (1901–　) is an American nutritionist who has traced the history of the science of nutrition. Her diagram,* which outlines the evolution of concepts of food and nutrition through history, is an important contribution to the understanding of the way ideas have changed in emphasis through the ages.

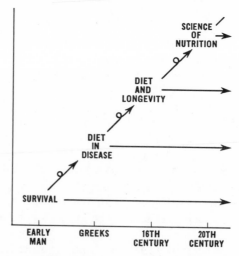

*Reprinted by permission. JOURNAL OF THE AMERICAN DIETETIC ASSOCIATION, Vol. 44, No. 2, August, 1963, p. 107.

These are only a few of the many scientists who have contributed to the development of the science of nutrition. Brief biographies indicate only a minute part of each person's endeavors. They do not convey the beliefs, emotions, and struggles of each scientist as he searched for knowledge in the area of nutrition and, more broadly, in its relationship to life. It is valuable, therefore, to consider at least one nutrition scientist in greater detail.

LYDIA JANE ROBERTS (1879–1965) died at the age of 86 after an incredibly full and rewarding life. She studied at the University of Chicago, receiving her Bachelor of Arts, Master of Arts, and Doctorate degrees there. Until her retirement in 1944, she taught nutrition at that university. Her students were many and she became widely known as a nutrition scientist.

Dr. Roberts' experimental work centered around good nutrition for children and she extensively studied the nutrient and food requirements of this particular age group. She investigated the effect of supplementing diets of children with different foodstuffs. Dr. Roberts directed the nursery school at the University of Chicago and offered the first university course which gave college students an opportunity to deal directly with the important problems of nutrition in childhood.

The nutritionist was a prolific writer. Probably her best-known publication was her book, *Nutrition Work with Children*, published in 1927. She also wrote journal articles, bulletins, and pamphlets and shared her depth of knowledge about nutrition through her writing with many people—teachers, nurses, social workers, and parents.

After her retirement, Dr. Roberts was invited to join the faculty of the University of Puerto Rico. For more than twenty years she lived and worked in Puerto Rico and made it her adopted home. With amazing energy and drive she worked constantly to improve the lives of the Puerto Rican people. She demonstrated how nutrition ideas could be applied on this island. Government officials in many countries asked for her help in improving the lives and health of their own people. As a result, Dr. Roberts helped train workers from Mexico, the Caribbean Islands, and every country in Central and South America.

Dr. Roberts was especially proud of Puerto Rico's many accomplishments. She loved the small island and its people. One of her own great accomplishments was the Government's adoption of her plan for improving the nutrition of families in the remote rural areas in the island. Dr. Roberts became the first director of the program which was later to reach far beyond the borders of Puerto Rico.

The first target was a tiny mountain barrio known as Doña Elena. The plan which Dr. Roberts designed called for a concentrated program of nutrition services provided by existing agencies for families in this community. Soon the program was expanded to include advancement of other aspects of living.

Lydia Jane Roberts

Moffett-Russell

The Governor of Puerto Rico watched the project closely to determine whether it could be applied to other isolated areas, and in 1960, with the Governor's influence, the legislature voted funds for extending the work. The legislature also established a "Commission for Improvement of Isolated Communities" to conduct the program, and the Governor made Dr. Roberts its first chairman. To date, some thirty or more programs have been undertaken in the image of Doña Elena.

Scientists and educators from around the world travelled to Puerto Rico to observe the methods Dr. Roberts had developed to attack nutritional problems. These people had to rise early in the morning if they wanted to ride with Dr. Roberts to visit families in the remote areas. When the mountain roads became impassable because of weather conditions, Dr. Roberts walked, and her visitors and students did, too.

Lydia Roberts is an example of a nutrition scientist of our century who has helped develop present concepts of nutrition. Because of scientists like her, our knowledge of food and nutrition has grown greatly since the time of early man.

In Chapters 6–9 you will study the essential nutrients in food which are one key to the understanding of man's body and all of life. These nutrients were discovered only after the diligent work of many scientists such as those mentioned in this chapter.

MAJOR IDEAS

The following statements give the main ideas in the chapter you have just studied. Be sure you know the words underscored in these statements and in the questions to follow.

1. Many people have searched for answers concerning the complex and mysterious relationship of food, life, and disease.
2. The science of nutrition developed from the work of chemists and physiologists.

QUESTIONS TO STUDY

BIOGRAPHICAL SKETCHES

1. Which nutrients were lacking in the food of people who suffered from scurvy, beriberi, and pellagra?
2. Why does an active person need more food than one who is less energetic?
3. How was the word vitamin coined?
4. How can the work of Lydia Jane Roberts be applied to other countries today?

BIBLIOGRAPHY

BAKER, E. M., and others, "Vitamin B6 Requirements for Adult Men." *American Journal of Clinical Nutrition*, Vol. 15, No. 2, 1964, p. 59.

BOGERT, JEAN, *Nutrition and Physical Fitness.* Philadelphia, W. B. Saunders Company, 1960, p. 131.

COOPER, LENNA, and others, *Nutrition in Health and Disease.* Philadelphia, J. B. Lippincott and Company, 1963, p. 65.

FLECK, HENRIETTA and MUNVES, ELIZABETH, *Introduction to Nutrition.* New York, The Macmillan Company, 1962.

Food—The Yearbook of Agriculture. United States Department of Agriculture, Washington, D. C., 1959.

TODHUNTER, E. NEIGE, "Some Classics of Nutrition and Dietetics." *Journal of the American Dietetic Association*, Vol. 44, No. 2, 1962, p. 107.

6 PROTEINS

Gerardus Mulder, a Dutch scientist, is credited with recognizing that a certain substance is essential to life in every living cell. He called this substance *protein* which comes from the Greek word meaning "to take first place." The word defines the substances in the body tissues which contain nitrogen, in addition to carbon, hydrogen, and oxygen. Some proteins also contain sulfur, phosphorus, iron, or iodine. Proteins are in every living cell and are a vital part of the nucleus and the protoplasm of each cell. Essentially, proteins are made up of amino acids. Some 20 amino acids have been identified and have been classified as being *essential* or *nonessential*. Essential amino acids are those which must be provided preformed in food because they are not formed in the body. The amino acids classified as nonessential are ones which can be made in the body if not supplied in sufficient amounts in food. In a sense, all amino acids are essential since they are needed for building and repair of body tissues.

Table 1
Amino Acids

Essential		*Nonessential*	
Valine	Lysine	Glycine	Citrulline
Threonine	Leucine	Tyrosine	Aspartic Acid
Isoleucine	Tryptophan	Cystine	Proline
Phenylalanine	Methionine	Glutamic Acid	Hydroxyproline
Arginine	Histidine	Alanine	Serine

The last amino acid to be identified, threonine, was isolated in 1935. Each amino acid is equally important in terms of building protein in the body. All must be supplied in some way—either from protein foods as eaten or as the result of various chemical changes which occur during digestion and assimilation. When the amount of nitrogen (or protein) taken into the body is practically equal with that burned up or kept in the body, there is a *nitrogen balance*. When the amount burned or used is greater than that taken into the body, there is a *negative balance*. If the intake is greater than the amount used, there is a *positive balance*. By experimentation it has been shown that the removal of an essential amino acid from one's food intake results in a negative nitrogen balance. The body has the ability to adjust the amount of protein it uses for growth and repair of body tissues if energy needs are not met by the intake of

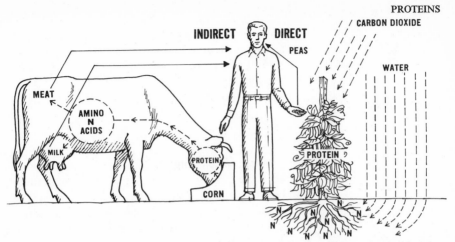

Adapted from Bogert, Briggs and Callaway, *Nutrition and Physical Fitness*, 8th edition
Philadelphia, W. B. Saunders Co., 1966.

fats and carbohydrates. In addition, all protein taken over the minimum amount needed is burned or changed to fat and stored.

A protein which supplies all the amino acids needed for growth is said to be a *complete* protein. One which is lacking in any one of the essential amino acids is an *incomplete* protein. Few proteins are incomplete but some may contain a low quantity of a certain amino acid. These deficient amounts affect the efficiency with which various proteins are able to meet body needs.

Requirements

It is very difficult to predict the exact amount of protein that a particular person is likely to need. The amount needed is affected by the nature of the particular protein, the body's ability to digest it, and the size and age of the person. However, there are some general standards which are recommended to maintain the body in a satisfactory manner.

The Food and Nutrition Board of the National Research Council has established recommendations which are set forth in a guide known as "Recommended Daily Dietary Allowances" (page 74). The recommended amounts of protein are based on studies of nitrogen balance of adults and children who seem to be thriving and in good health. These recommendations allow a certain "margin of safety" to accommodate differences in individual needs. Seventy grams of protein for men and fifty-eight grams for women (over 18 years of age) are recommended. These figures represent 10 to 15 percent of the total daily caloric requirement or 1 gram of protein for every kilogram (2.2 pounds) of body weight. The protein allowances for children, pregnant women, and nursing mothers are somewhat higher per kilogram of body weight. Demands for protein for children are greater because of the rapid rate of growth

which must be supported. A pregnant woman needs added protein to maintain her own body plus the body of her developing baby. A nursing mother requires additional protein in order to support the production of milk for her new baby.

Sources

When discussing the food sources of protein, both the quality and quantity of the protein must be considered. This means that the nutritive value or *biological value* of the protein in the food must be estimated. This is the percentage of nitrogen from the protein that will be absorbed and retained by the body. In a given food, biological value is determined by its amino acid content. The nitrogen of egg protein has been found to be almost completely absorbed and retained. It has been assigned a biological value of approximately 100. This is the standard used for measuring the biological value of other protein foods.

Animal sources. Egg and milk proteins have the highest biological values in animal sources. Next come the proteins of certain organs—liver, kidney, and heart. Third are the muscle proteins of meat, fish, and poultry. Some animal proteins lack certain essential amino acids. Gelatin, for instance, which is a protein derived from the connective tissue of meat, is lacking in tryptophan and tyrosine but is rich in lysine. It could not support life it if were the only source of protein eaten.

Plant sources. Plant proteins are, in general, of lower biological value than animal proteins. However, plant proteins can supplement each other and when mixed in certain proportions do have high nutritive value. In an effort to find a means of supplying more protein-rich foods in countries where there is a protein deficiency, various combinations of plant protein foods have been tried. Incaparina (pages 50–51) is an example. A similar product is made of peanut protein combined with dried milk (or the milk protein, casein), lysine, and methionine. Since animal proteins are not available in sufficient quantities for human needs in some areas, products of this kind are important.

The animal foods which contain the essential amino acids and are of high biological value are eggs, milk and milk products, meat, fish, and poultry. Those from plant sources with lower biological value are legumes, nuts, cereals, and cereal products such as bread. Plant foods are not adequate sources of protein unless they are supplemented by animal foods or combined with each other so that the amino acid content is adequate.

Functions

Proteins are essential in the body because they (1) furnish animo acids necessary for the building and maintenance of body tissues, (2) furnish fuel for energy when sufficient carbohydrates and fats are lacking, (3) carry certain minerals and vitamins which are essential to body functions, and (4) act as buffers to help prevent the accumulation of too much acid or base which would interfere with normal body functioning.

From the amino acids which result after protein has been digested, body tissues select the particular acids needed as they are circulated in the blood. No two types of tissues have exactly the same composition. Muscle, liver, kidney, blood, skin, and so forth must have its specific type and quantity of amino acids to use for building and repair. Each cell within the tissue has to have such material to maintain its structure and body function. For example, cells must constantly be repaired and new cells must be developed if the tissue is to grow. There is a constant interchange of amino acids and other nutritive substances between the blood and the tissues. This process goes on all the time in the body's effort to maintain its own working conditions in the best way possible.

Hemoglobin of the blood is a protein form. Its function is to transport oxygen from the lungs to

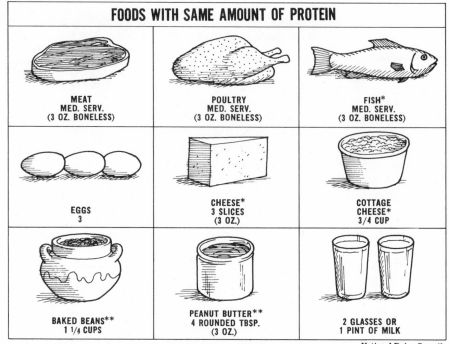

FOODS WITH SAME AMOUNT OF PROTEIN

MEAT MED. SERV. (3 OZ. BONELESS)	POULTRY MED. SERV. (3 OZ. BONELESS)	FISH* MED. SERV. (3 OZ. BONELESS)
EGGS 3	CHEESE* 3 SLICES (3 OZ.)	COTTAGE CHEESE* 3/4 CUP
BAKED BEANS** 1 1/4 CUPS	PEANUT BUTTER** 4 ROUNDED TBSP. (3 OZ.)	2 GLASSES OR 1 PINT OF MILK

National Dairy Council

*Advise iron-rich foods with these, as greens, eggs, prunes.
**Advise milk, cheese, or another food from animals with these to improve the quality of their protein.

the tissues and bring carbon dioxide back to the lungs where it can be expelled from the body. There are also other proteins present in the blood as antibodies which protect the body against disease and infection.

Protein's unique function is to build and repair tissues. However, protein can be a source of fuel for energy. Although carbohydrates and fats serve chiefly as energy sources, if the food one eats does not supply enough calories from these sources, tissue protein will be used to provide the energy needed. The body's need for energy is of first importance.

MAJOR IDEAS

The following statements give the main ideas within the chapter you have just studied. Be sure you know the words underscored in these statements and in the questions to follow.

> 1. The primary use of protein is to build body tissue. The amount needed is dependent upon the nature of the particular protein, the body's ability to digest it, and the size and age of the person.

2. All amino acids are equally important in <u>protein synthesis</u>. The <u>biological value</u> of any protein depends upon the amount of its nitrogen absorbed and retained by the body.
3. <u>Plant proteins</u> are, in general, of lower biological value than <u>animal proteins</u> but can be mixed in certain proportions so that they supplement each other and have a higher biological value.
4. Protein is used to supply energy for the body in the event that <u>carbohydrates</u> and <u>fats</u> are not present in sufficient quantity.

QUESTIONS TO STUDY

REQUIREMENTS

1. What are the factors which influence the amount of protein a person requires?
2. Explain what is meant by "a margin of safety."

SOURCES

1. Explain what is meant by the biological value of protein. How is this determined?
2. Explain why plant food proteins are of lower biological value than are animal foods.
3. Explain what is meant by saying that plant proteins can <u>supplement</u> each other. Indicate where this knowledge has been applied to improve diet.

FUNCTIONS

1. Explain the relationship of <u>amino</u> acids to a state of good health.
2. Describe the primary function of protein in the body. Under what conditions is protein used as a source of energy?

BIBLIOGRAPHY

BOGERT, L. JEAN, BRIGGS, GEORGE M., and CALLOWAY, DORIS, *Nutrition and Physical Fitness.* Philadelphia, W. B. Saunders Company, 1966.
COOPER, LENNA F., and others, *Nutrition in Health and Disease.* Philadelphia, J. B. Lippincott Company, 1963.
MARTIN, ETHEL AUSTIN, *Nutrition in Action.* New York, Holt, Rinehart and Winston, 1963.

7 CARBOHYDRATES AND FATS

The body's first need for food is to furnish energy for internal work and external or physical work and to maintain normal body temperature. Carbohydrate foods, especially cereals and breads, provide a significant portion of food energy. An examination of the dietary patterns at the lower end of the economic scale in economically poor populations shows a marked increase in the intake of carbohydrates and a corresponding decrease in fats and proteins. In the average American diet, carbohydrates supply about one half of total energy needs.

The total energy needed by the body depends on the amount required to carry on all the body's various functions. When one breathes, when the heart pumps blood through the body, as well as when any physical exercise is done, energy is used. To keep the body warm requires energy. If the body is required to do any of these tasks vigorously, the energy demand is greater.

Measurement of energy in food. The potential energy value in food is measured in *calories*. This measure is equivalent to the amount of heat necessary to raise the temperature of 1000 grams of water 1° centigrade. For example, one tablespoon of butter provides about 100 calories. That is the amount of potential food energy from that tablespoon of butter after it is oxidized by the body. The body requires energy 24 hours a day. When energy is needed and no food is available, the body's own tissues are burned or oxidized to supply the energy. Thus, the body—especially its fat—is a reserve supply of food for energy. When the energy supplied in food is not used, it is stored in the body in the form of fat.

By using an instrument called a *calorimeter* the number of calories obtained from a particular food can be measured. A known amount of the food is placed in the calorimeter and burned. The heat given off during the burning is measured and the amount of potential energy in that food is calculated. The caloric values of many foods have been determined. These known values make it possible to plan a daily diet so that it meets the caloric needs of the body. Recommended dietary allowances for calories and nutrients are given in Table 2 on page 74.

Three classes of foods are main sources of energy when oxidized—carbohydrates, fats, and proteins. Each of these nutrients has other specific functions in the body besides being potential sources of energy. Carbohydrates yield about 4 calories per gram; fats, 9 calories; proteins, about 4 calories.

72

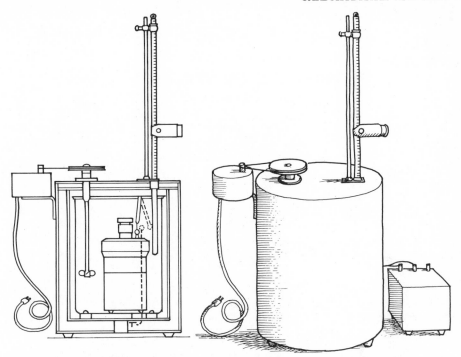

The number of calories in a food can be measured in a calorimeter such as the one above. The device on the left fits into the structure on the right.

The number of calories a food can provide depends upon how much carbohydrate, fat, and protein it contains. Some foods are classified as high-calorie foods because they possess large amounts of these three nutrients, especially of fat. Others are low-calorie because they have less fat, carbohydrate, and protein but more water and fiber.

For example, celery contains much water and fiber but little of the energy-producing compounds. Skim milk has less of the energy-producers than whole milk because the fat has been removed. This makes a significant difference since fat is a concentrated source of energy. One gram of fat yields over twice as many calories as 1 gram of protein or carbohydrates.

Foods that yield fewer calories may be described as watery, bulky, coarse, or fibrous. Those which have many more calories packed into small portions can be designated as oily, greasy, sweet, sticky, compact, or concentrated.

Metabolism

Basal metabolism involves the body's use of just enough energy to maintain its vital cell activity, respiration, and circulation. In other words, it is the

Table 2 Recommended Daily Dietary Allowances* (Revised 1963)

FOOD AND NUTRITION BOARD, NATIONAL ACADEMY OF SCIENCES—NATIONAL RESEARCH COUNCIL

	Age† Years from–to	Weight kg. (lbs.)	Height cm. (in.)	Calories	Protein gm.	Calcium gm.	Iron mg.	Vitamin A Value I.U.	Thia- mine mg.	Ribo- flavin mg.	Niacin Equiv. mg.	Ascorbic Acid mg.	Vitamin D I.U.
Men	18–35	70 (154)	175 (69)	2,900	70	0.8	10	5,000‡	1.2	1.7	19	70	
	35–55	70 (154)	175 (69)	2,600	70	0.8	10	5,000	1.0	1.6	17	70	
	55–75	70 (154)	175 (69)	2,200	70	0.8	10	5,000	0.9	1.3	15	70	
Women	18–35	58 (128)	163 (64)	2,100	58	0.8	15	5,000	0.8	1.3	14	70	
	35–55	58 (128)	163 (64)	1,900	58	0.8	15	5,000	0.8	1.2	13	70	
	55–75	58 (128)	163 (64)	1,600	58	0.8	10	5,000	0.8	1.2	13	70	
	Pregnant (2nd and 3rd trimester)			+200	+20	+0.5	+5	+1,000	+0.2	+0.3	+3	+30	400
	Lactating			+1,000	+40	+0.5	+5	+3,000	+0.4	+0.6	+7	+30	400
Infants	0–1	8 (18)		kg.x115 ±15	kg.x2.5 ±0.5	0.7	kg.x1.0	1,500	0.4	0.6	6	30	400
Children	1–3	13 (29)	87 (34)	1,300	32	0.8	8	2,000	0.5	0.8	9	40	400
	3–6	18 (40)	107 (42)	1,600	40	0.8	10	2,500	0.6	1.0	11	50	400
	6–9	24 (53)	124 (49)	2,100	52	0.8	12	3,500	0.8	1.3	14	60	400
Boys	9–12	33 (72)	140 (55)	2,400	60	1.1	15	4,500	1.0	1.4	16	70	400
	12–15	45 (98)	156 (61)	3,000	75	1.4	15	5,000	1.2	1.8	20	80	400
	15–18	61 (134)	172 (68)	3,400	85	1.4	15	5,000	1.4	2.0	22	80	400
Girls	9–12	33 (72)	140 (55)	2,200	55	1.1	15	4,500	0.9	1.3	15	80	400
	12–15	47 (108)	158 (62)	2,500	62	1.3	15	5,000	1.0	1.5	17	80	400
	15–18	53 (117)	163 (64)	2,300	58	1.3	15	5,000	0.9	1.3	15	70	400

*The allowance levels are intended to cover individual variations among most normal persons as they live in the United States under usual environmental stresses. The recommended allowances can be attained with a variety of common foods, providing other nutrients for which human requirements have been less well defined.

†Entries represent allowances for the midpoint of the specified age periods, i.e., line for children 1–3 is for age 2 years (24 months); 3–6 is for age 4½ years (54 months), etc.

‡1,000 IU from preformed Vitamin A and 4,000 IU from beta-carotene.

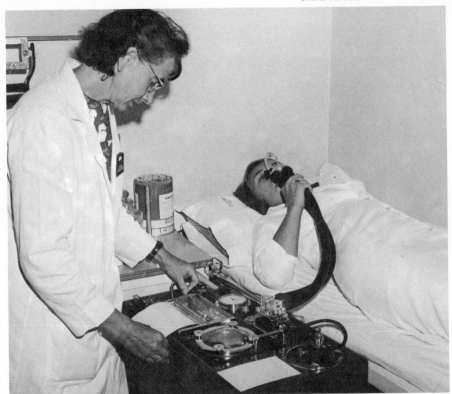

Peter Bent Brigham Hospital

A basal metabolism test being administered in a hospital clinic. Compare the machine in this photograph with the first basal metabolism machine illustrated on page 61.

basic energy needed to sustain life and the normal functioning of the involuntary workings of the body. *Metabolism* is concerned with all of the energy required to sustain internal functions and to meet the needs for external work. The more external work done, the more calories are required to provide needed energy. If insufficient energy is supplied, the body will use protein or fat for fuel, that is, will draw on its own tissues to meet the demands for more energy.

As mentioned previously, the total energy needed by the body depends on the amount needed to carry on the body's functions and activities. The energy actually expended by the body throughout a given period can be determined. In brief, the amount of oxygen a person breathes in is measured by a special respiration apparatus. From the oxygen consumed in a given number of minutes the energy expenditure can be calculated. The amount of energy expended indicates the number of calories that must be available in the food intake to provide this amount of energy. In other words, the food eaten should equal in

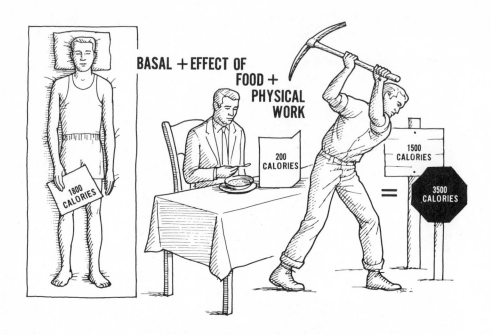

caloric value the energy units used by the body if the same weight and body conditions are to be maintained. The weight of the person and the number or size of muscles involved in an action also influence the number of calories required. For example, a man doing sedentary work may require only 2500 calories per day whereas a man doing ditch digging may require as much as 4000 calories.

In "Recommended Daily Dietary Allowances" the suggested number of calories and the nutrient allowances for persons of different ages and sexes are shown. These allowances apply to individuals engaged in moderate physical activity.

Carbohydrates. The major carbohydrates are found in cereals and cereal products, some vegetables, fruits, and concentrated sweets such as candy, honey, and sirup. Of these, the cereals and their products form the largest part of the carbohydrates in the human diet. Roots and tubers—beets, potatoes, carrots, turnips, and squash—supply considerable amounts and also contain other important nutrients. Dried beans, peas, and lentils supply carbohydrates as well as certain amino acids. Bananas, dates, and figs contain considerable amounts of carbohydrates, while rhubarb, strawberries, and watermelon have limited amounts. The carbohydrate content may vary as much as from 5 percent in fresh fruit to 60–80 percent in dried fruit, due to the difference in water content.

Sucrose is the chief source of sweetening used in most desserts, ice creams, and candies. This is the common white granulated sugar. The average consumption of this sugar in the United States has been estimated to be about 2 pounds per person per week.

Most animal foods—meats, poultry, and fish—contain only traces of carbohydrates. These are often in the form of glycogen or animal starch. In all animals the liver serves as a temporary storehouse for the quickly available fuel, glycogen, for the body. The amount stored depends on the daily intake of carbohydrates.

Fat. The amount of fat in the diets in different countries varies. In any country, however, the social requirements for fat for "good living" are far higher than physiological requirements for good physical health.

There are only two fatty acids which can be said to be essential: linoleic acid and arachidonic acid. Linoleic acid is quite widely distributed in both animal foods and plant foods while arachidonic acid is synthesized from linoleic acid by animals and is found in animal tissues. At the present time no deficiencies in fatty acids in adult humans have been recognized.

There are few foods, except butter, margarines, vegetable oils, and shortenings, which are composed solely of fat. Usually fat is combined with proteins and carbohydrates. Meat, fish, poultry, whole milk and milk products, and egg yolks are some of the richest sources of fats, as are some vegetables and fruits such as avocados, olives, and nuts.

Fat not only supplies energy but also increases the palatability of foods, partly because of its lubricating quality. Since fat absorption requires about a $3\frac{1}{2}$-hour period after eating, the feeling of hunger hours after eating is lessened.

While carbohydrates and fats are main sources of food energy for the body, protein is used when the demand for energy is greater than the energy being supplied by these nutrients.

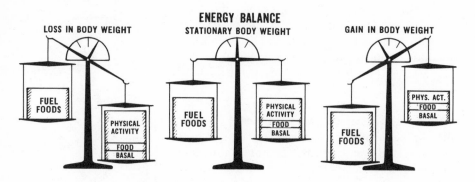

Calories and weight. Weight is a topic of constant concern. The relationship between calories and weight is primarily one of energy balance. If the food being eaten yields about the same number of calories that the body uses, the body weight will normally stay about the same. If the food is supplying more energy than is being used, there may be a weight gain because the excess energy is stored as fat tissue. If the food, on the other hand, provides fewer calories than the body demands, there will be a loss of weight because body fat will be oxidized to supply the needed energy. Therefore, *energy balance* is equalizing the intake of calories with the expenditure of energy.

A pound of fat has the energy value of about 3500 calories. The gaining of one pound of weight requires that enough food be taken in to give the body 3500 calories more than it uses. This extra energy is stored as fat. To lose one pound, less food must be taken in than the body demands. The body will oxidize stored fat to make up the shortage.

At each stage of life, there is for each individual a desirable body weight to maintain. This is true for infants, children, adolescents, adults, and elderly people. In general, when the age of twenty-five is reached, a person should have attained the weight that it would be desirable to maintain as an adult.

Terms frequently used to describe a deviation from the desirable weight are overweight, obesity, and underweight. *Overweight* is defined as an excess of 10 to 20 percent in body weight. *Obesity* indicates that the excess body weight is more than 20 percent of the person's desirable weight. *Underweight* means that the actual weight of an individual is 20 percent or more below the weight he should have.

Overweight is considered one of the most important health problems in the United States, especially among adults. All age groups have overweight persons but underweight persons are apparently less prevalent among adults in this country.

Factors affecting energy requirements. One factor, already mentioned, is that of the kind and amount of muscular activity in which a person engages.

Table 3

Desirable Weight for Height for Adults

	Height (without shoes)	Weight (without clothing)
	Inches	Pounds
Women:	60	100–118
	62	106–124
	64	112–132
	66	119–139
	68	126–146
	70	133–155
	72	140–164
Men:	64	122–144
	66	130–154
	68	137–165
	70	145–173
	72	152–182
	74	160–190

A second factor is the size of the person. A large person uses more energy than a small person in performing activities because a larger mass of body is involved.

Many household tasks have been studied to determine the energy expended during such activities. The results have been used to design household equipment and work areas. Some of the tasks studied have been food preparation, dishwashing, cleaning, bedmaking, utensil storage, and laundering. The energy expenditure varies depending on how a person reaches, bends, stoops, and twists. For example, if you reach from the floor to a specific height at a particular rate, an extra expenditure (over that required for standing) of calories an hour is needed.

The energy expenditures for many activities have been estimated. The extra energy used per hour by a man weighing about 154 pounds in performing certain tasks is given in Table 4, page 80.

The caloric requirements to perform these activities would vary with the size of the individual and the speed or intensity with which he does the work.

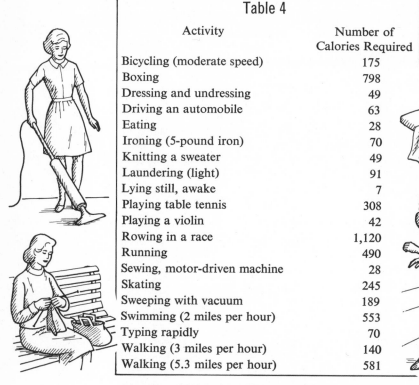

Table 4

Activity	Number of Calories Required
Bicycling (moderate speed)	175
Boxing	798
Dressing and undressing	49
Driving an automobile	63
Eating	28
Ironing (5-pound iron)	70
Knitting a sweater	49
Laundering (light)	91
Lying still, awake	7
Playing table tennis	308
Playing a violin	42
Rowing in a race	1,120
Running	490
Sewing, motor-driven machine	28
Skating	245
Sweeping with vacuum	189
Swimming (2 miles per hour)	553
Typing rapidly	70
Walking (3 miles per hour)	140
Walking (5.3 miles per hour)	581

Adapted from FOOD—THE YEARBOOK OF AGRICULTURE, U. S. Department of Agriculture, Washington, D. C., 1959, p. 49.

MAJOR IDEAS

The following statements give the main ideas within the chapter you have just studied. Be sure you know the words underscored in these statements and in the questions to follow.

1. Food is the source of energy for sustaining the body's <u>vital internal functions</u> and its external muscular activity.
2. Carbohydrates provide energy which is immediately available to the body. When converted to glycogen and body fat and stored in the body, carbohydrates also provide potential energy.
3. Fats provide energy and also improve food <u>palatability</u>.

QUESTIONS TO STUDY

METABOLISM

1. Define metabolism and basal metabolism.
2. By what means is the energy potential of food measured?
3. Explain why it is very important that one's diet have a sufficient amount of carbohydrates.
4. What are the major food sources of carbohydrates?
5. What is glycogen? Where is it found in the body?
6. Explain ways in which the body takes care of excess amounts of carbohydrates.
7. What are the major food sources of fat? With what other nutrients are fats often combined?
8. What purpose does fat have in the body?
9. Explain how the body reacts to the lack of sufficient carbohydrates and fats in order to maintain its energy.
10. What are the factors which influence energy requirements in the body?
11. What are some of the reasons for conditions of overweight and underweight?
12. Give some examples illustrating the differences in energy requirements for various persons.
13. Find examples of ways in which cultural background may influence the amount and kinds of fats used in daily diets.

BIBLIOGRAPHY

BEATON, GEORGE and MCHENRY, EARL, "Macronutrients and Nutrition Elements." *Nutrition*, Vol. 1, New York, Academic Press, 1964, p. 254.

HODGES, ROBERT E., and KREHL, W. A., "The Role of Carbohydrates in Lipid Metabolism." *American Journal of Clinical Nutrition*, Vol. 17, November 1965, p. 334.

LOPEZ, ALFREDO, HODGES, ROBERT E., and KREHL, WILLARD A., "Some Interesting Relationships Between Dietary Carbohydrates and Serum Cholesterol." *American Journal of Clinical Nutrition*, Vol. 18, February 1966, p. 149.

MARTIN, ETHEL AUSTIN, *Nutrition in Action*. New York, Holt, Rinehart, and Winston, 1963.

SINCLAIR, H. M., "Carbohydrates and Fats." *Nutrition*, Vol. 1, New York, Academic Press, 1964, pp. 71–72.

8 MINERALS

Even though mineral elements are needed in small amounts and compose only 4 percent of the body weight, they are very important to the body. They are needed for both hard and soft tissue and for body fluids. In body fluids they are important for movement of water into and out of the tissues (osmotic pressure), the normal functioning of nervous and muscular tissues, the clotting of the blood, the maintaining of body neutrality (concerning acids and bases), and oxidation processes. Although minerals have specific functions, they rarely work alone. Each is needed in varying amounts. For example, iron is required in making hemoglobin, the pigment in red blood cells. Copper is also indispensable for forming hemoglobin. Thus, animals that get too little copper develop anemia although plenty of iron is supplied.

It is impossible to say that certain minerals are more important than others despite the fact that some are required in much larger amounts. In general, the minerals needed by the body are divided into two groups. The first group includes those that occur in the body in relatively large amounts. Calcium, phosphorus, iron, sodium, potassium, magnesium, sulfur, chlorine, and inorganic carbon compounds belong to this group. The second group includes fluorine, copper, manganese, zinc, cobalt, molybdenum, iodine, and selenium. These minerals are needed in very small amounts. In the past, the terms "trace minerals" and "minor elements" were used to designate this group since methods had not yet been developed to measure the minute amounts of these nutrients accurately. Today, it has become acceptable to use the term *micronutrient elements*.

Fortunately, almost all the micronutrient elements are found in minute amounts in so many foods that they are not apt to be lacking in the diet. On the other hand, iron, calcium, iodine, and phosphorus are either distributed unevenly in foods or found in such small amounts that a freely chosen diet may provide less than is required.

Calcium

The name calcium is derived from the Latin word "colx" which means chalk. This name was probably chosen because calcium is a white, powdery, chalk-like substance. Almost all of the calcium in our bodies is found in the bones and teeth, providing their strength and rigidity; the remaining percent is present mostly in the soft tissues and body fluids.

82

Calcium requirements. The minimum requirement for calcium, 500 milligrams per day for adults, is the amount needed to balance the loss of calcium from the body through excretion. Therefore, the Food and Nutrition Board of the National Research Council recommends a daily allowance of 800 milligrams per day for an adult. There are some persons who believe that this allowance is too high, since there is much individual variation in the amount of calcium required. However, while a part of any population might subsist well on less than the recommended amount, it is entirely possible that a large proportion of the population may require much more. Even though there are differences of opinion at present regarding the needed amount of calcium, it would seem that the standard recommended by the National Research Council should be used as a guide to allow for a margin of safety. For pregnant women, the daily allowance for calcium during the latter half of the pregnancy is nearly double that of non-pregnant women. This is also true during the lactation period when the mother's body is producing milk for her baby; the additional calcium is a necessary factor in insuring that the baby will have strong teeth and bones. Children continue to need relatively large amounts of calcium to support growth and development of strong bones and teeth. The amounts needed are greater in proportion to body weight than those needed by adults.

Sources of calcium. The outstanding sources of calcium are milk and dairy products, which supply 75 percent of the calcium in the diet of Americans. Vegetables, especially the leafy green type, and fruits supply about 15

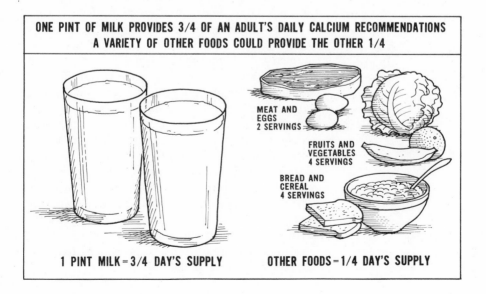

ONE PINT OF MILK PROVIDES 3/4 OF AN ADULT'S DAILY CALCIUM RECOMMENDATIONS
A VARIETY OF OTHER FOODS COULD PROVIDE THE OTHER 1/4

MEAT AND
EGGS
2 SERVINGS

FRUITS AND
VEGETABLES
4 SERVINGS

BREAD AND
CEREAL
4 SERVINGS

1 PINT MILK = 3/4 DAY'S SUPPLY   OTHER FOODS = 1/4 DAY'S SUPPLY

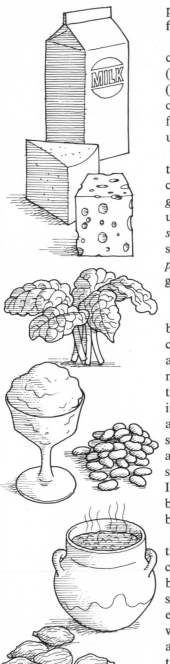

percent. The balance comes from the meat group, fish, poultry, and eggs.

In planning a diet that will furnish enough calcium, one must take into consideration the following: (1) the amount of calcium present in the food, (2) the foods which furnish calcium in a form that can be easily utilized by the body, and (3) the foods which are rich enough in calcium to contribute substantially to the daily diet.

Foods can be grouped according to their contributions of calcium as *excellent sources*—hard cheese, milk, and most dark green leafy vegetables; *good sources*—ice cream, softer cheese, dried legumes, broccoli, baked beans, and dried figs; *fair sources*—cottage cheese, light cream, oranges, dates, salad greens, nuts, lima beans, parsnips, and eggs; *poor sources*—most other fruits and vegetables, grains, and meats.

Calcium functions. Calcium is essential for the building of strong bones and teeth. Ninety-nine percent of the calcium in the body is found in these two areas. The other 1 percent is carried in the blood. If more calcium than is needed is supplied to the body, the excess amount is stored in the bone tissue where it can be drawn upon as needed. The stored calcium also helps to provide added strength. If there is insufficient calcium, the bone tissue will become thin and weakened. Calcium deficiency in children causes stunted growth and poorly formed bones and teeth. In older persons it has been found that if there has been a low calcium intake over a long period of time, bone tissue is apt to be weak, porous, and fragile.

In addition, calcium is necessary in the blood for the process of clotting. Further, it is an important constituent of fluids that function in the rhythmic beating of the heart, the response of nerve tissue to stimuli, and the contraction of muscles. Calcium is essential to control the passage of fluids through cell walls in the process of osmosis. According to some authorities, a liberal amount of calcium may reduce the amount of radioactive Strontium 90 that may be deposited in the body.

Table 5

Foods That Furnish Adult Standard Calcium Allowance (800 mg. daily)

Calcium, (1) 855 mg.		*Calcium,* (2) 821 mg.		*Calcium,* (3) 808 mg.		*Calcium,* (4) 809 mg.	
Milk, 1½ pts.	855	Milk, 1 pint	570	Milk, ½ pint	285	Cheese, Am.	
		Cottage		Cheese, Am.		Cheddar,	
		cheese,		Cheddar,		1½ oz.	337
		2 rd. tbsp.	52	1 oz.	225	Ice cream,	
		Bread, w. w.,		Bread, w. w.,		plain, ⅙ qt.	123
		4 slices	92	4 slices	92	Bread, w. w.,	
		Orange,		Orange juice,		4 slices	92
		1 med.	62	8 oz.	24	Turnip	
		Green beans,		Broccoli,		greens,	
		¾ c, cooked	45	⅔ c	88	½ c, cooked	138
			821	Carrots,		Beans,	
				diced, ⅔ c	33	baked, with	
				Cream, light,		molasses, ½ c	82
				4 tbsp.	61	Egg, 1 med.	27
					808	Hamburger,	
						lean, 85 gm.	10
							809

Adapted from Bogert, Briggs, and Calloway, NUTRITION AND PHYSICAL FITNESS, 8th edition, Philadelphia, W. B. Saunders Co., 1966, p. 158.

Phosphorus

Phosphorus is the most widely distributed mineral in the body, yet 80 percent of the body's phosphorus is found in the teeth and bones. The other 20 percent is found in the soft tissue of the body and is vitally involved in the body processes. There are 2 to 3 times as much phosphorus and calcium in the body as the rest of the minerals combined. Phosphorus is an essential part of protein of the nuclei of all cells, as well as of phospholipids which are fat-like substances that play an important role in metabolism.

Phosphorus requirements. The allowance for phosphorus was formerly given as 1.32 grams per adult per day, but in the most recent recommendations by the Food and Nutrition Board no allowance for phosphorus is included. This is due to the fact that research has shown that diets which supply the recommended amounts of protein, calcium, and iron are practically certain to provide plenty of phosphorus.

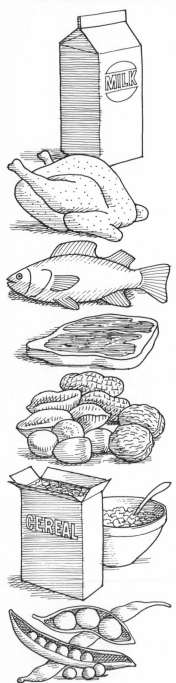

Phosphorus is associated chiefly with protein-rich foods—milk, poultry, fish, meat, nuts, cereals, and legumes. Dried fruits and vegetables contribute lesser amounts to the diet. The phosphorus element is carried more liberally in foods than is calcium.

Phosphorus functions. Phosphorus aids several essential functions in the body. It is important, together with calcium, in maintaining the acid-base balance of the body. Calcium is an inactive substance while phosphorus is very active chemically and causes other compounds with which it combines to become active too. It combines readily with proteins, fats, carbohydrates, and calcium. Phosphorus is necessary for the normal response of nerves to stimulation and for muscular contraction.

When discussing proteins, it was mentioned that proteins have a part in regulating the neutral reaction of the blood by acting as "buffer" substances capable of uniting with either acids or bases to prevent them from affecting blood neutrality (page 69). Mineral elements also participate in regulating blood neutrality in that they give rise in metabolism to both acidic and basic substances called salts Phosphorus is an acid-forming element which helps to maintain the neutrality of the blood.

Iron

Although the quantity of iron in foods is much less than calcium and phosphorus, it is a very valuable element to the body and small amounts of it are needed daily. Without iron, the blood does not have enough hemoglobin, and a type of anemia may develop.

Iron requirements. The recommended allowance for iron, established by the Food and Nutrition Board, is 10 milligrams per day for men and 15 milligrams for women. The amount of iron absorbed by the body from food varies according to the amount needed by the body at a particular time, the presence of iron in food in a form most readily used by the body, and the general condition of the body's intestinal tract where substances may be present which form insoluble compounds with iron, thus limiting possible absorption.

The age and stage of life influences the iron needed by the body. The higher allowance for women compensates for the loss of iron through menstruation. Any time in which growth takes place calls for an additional allowance of iron. Infancy, childhood, and adolescence are all such periods. The recommended allowances for children are calculated for each age group on the basis of body weight: infants, 1 milligram per kilogram (2.2 pounds); children aged one to nine years, 8–12 milligrams; boys and girls, aged nine to eighteen years, 15 milligrams.

The quantity of iron in foods is much less than calcium and phosphorus, ranging from .2 milligrams in 1 cup of milk (a trace) to 19.2 milligrams in $3\frac{1}{2}$ ounces of raw pork liver. Excellent sources of iron are eggs, lean meats, legumes, nuts, dried fruit, whole grains or enriched cereal foods, and all green leafy vegetables. When consumed in large amounts, foods of low content may provide an adequate intake. On the other hand, dark molasses, raisins, and nuts, all rich sources of iron, when used infrequently are not important sources of iron in the diet.

Iron functions. Iron is found in every living cell and is responsible for stimulating vital processes in the cell itself. The highest percentage of iron is found in the hemoglobin of the blood. Hemoglobin in the red blood cells combines with oxygen in the lungs to form oxyhemoglobin, and as such, travels in the blood stream to the body tissues where the oxygen is released to take part in oxidative processes. Part of the carbon dioxide formed is carried back by the hemoglobin to the lungs where it is expelled and a new load of oxygen is picked up. Iron is also found in muscle cells in the form of myoglobin. This substance acts to store the oxygen necessary for muscle operation or contraction. The amount of

THE SIGNIFICANCE OF FOOD

iron in the body is regulated by control of absorption and it is stored in two forms—ferritin and hemosiderin. Once it is absorbed into the blood stream, the iron travels to the bone marrow and liver in combination with protein and transferrin.

If the diet is poor in iron content, nutritional anemia may result. Nutritional anemia is a condition in which the hemoglobin in the red blood cells is abnormally low. Thus, the oxygen-carrying capacity of the blood is lowered. Nutritional anemia may be evident in young girls whose diets are on the borderline of iron deficiency, since menstruation causes increased loss of iron.

Anemia may also result from an excessive loss of blood such as might occur following a serious accident. This condition necessitates improving the diet with regard to iron as well as increasing all the substances required to build whole blood.

Pernicious anemia results from a lack of some substance or substances required by the body for the production and development of red blood cells. Though these three types of anemia have different causes, only the nutritional one is due to the dietary lack of iron in sufficient amounts to meet body needs.

Table 6

Recommended Daily Iron Allowances

	Age Years from–to	Iron (in mg.)	
Men	18–75	10	
Women	18–55	15	
	55–75	10	
	Pregnant (2nd and 3rd trimester)	20	(maintenance + 5 mg.)
	Lactating	20	(maintenance + 5 mg.)
Infants	0–1	1.0 mg. per kg. wt.	
Children	1–3	8	
	3–6	10	
	6–9	12	
	9–12	15	
	12–15	15	
	15–18	15	

Food and Nutrition Board, National Academy of Sciences, National Research Council, Pub. 1146, 1964.

Other Essential Minerals

The minerals sodium, potassium, magnesium, chlorine, and certain carbonates will be considered only briefly because of the limited information now available.

Sodium. Sodium is a base-forming mineral. It acts with the chlorides and bicarbonates for the regulation of osmotic pressure and the acid-base equilibrium. Sodium is important for maintaining the proper water content in the body. It also functions in preserving the normal irritability of the muscle tissue. The most common source of sodium is ordinary table salt, sodium chloride. Additionally, foods which use salt brine (pickles, for example) are very high in sodium content.

Potassium. The potassium requirement is approximately 4 grams per day. Since this mineral is so widely distributed in natural plant foods, a deficiency is unlikely. Similar to sodium, potassium has the function of regulating osmotic pressure and maintaining acid-base balance in the body. It, too, is a base-forming element. A small amount of potassium in the extracellular fluid is necessary for normal muscular activity.

Magnesium. Magnesium is similar to potassium in its distribution within the body, with concentration in the cells exceeding the quantity outside by a wide margin. Highest concentrations are in the bones, soft tissues, and blood. Magnesium is relatively abundant in food. Green plants contain large amounts, owing to magnesium's presence in chlorophyll. A daily intake of 250 to 300 milligrams for an adult is considered adequate. During pregnancy and lactation 400 milligrams are believed to be required.

Sulfur. Sulfur is found in every cell, generally in connection with amino acids. In addition, sulfur is present in a number of the body's secretions, such as saliva and bile. It is also a constituent of insulin which is necessary for carbohydrate metabolism. No definite human requirement has been established for sulfur. Foods which are rich in this mineral are lean beef, cheese, peanuts, clams, and lentils.

Chlorine. Chlorine is the acid-forming element most commonly combined with sodium in the extracellular fluid and with potassium in the cells. During digestion, some of the chlorine of the blood is used for the formation of hydrochloric acid in the gastric glands and is secreted into the stomach. Here it functions temporarily with the gastric enzymes and is then reabsorbed by the blood. The only time when the body may be depleted of chlorine is after the loss of gastric contents due to vomiting.

Micronutrient Elements

The minerals in this group are needed in very small amounts by the body. They are usually referred to as "trace" or "minor" elements although the term "micronutrient" is now acceptable.

Fluorine. Fluorine, a pale greenish-yellow gas, is chemically active and has a strong tendency to combine with other elements to form fluorides. This element is widespread in nature and is present in nearly every human tissue.

Most foods contain fluorides but the greatest concentrations are found in tea, seafood, bone meal, spinach, and gelatin. Citrus fruits, vegetables, eggs, and milk contain the least quantities of fluorides. The amount of fluorides actually taken into the human system is unpredictable. It is dependent on numerous factors pertaining to the food—its processing and preparation—and the food habits of the individual. When food is boiled in fluoride-ion-containing water, its fluoride concentration is increased. The amount of fluoride in water depends largely upon its source. Sea water is relatively high in fluoride content while surface waters—lakes, rivers—are generally lower.

Copper. Until recently, the micronutrient copper received comparatively little attention in relation to humans but is now regarded as essential, although copper deficiency has not been demonstrated in adults. Copper is found widely distributed in food and water, the quantity depending on the soil's content.

It has been estimated that of the 2 to 5 milligrams of copper taken into the body daily, 0.6 to 1.6 milligrams are absorbed. Copper balance is maintained with an intake of about 2 milligrams of copper daily. Therefore, this amount approximates the daily minimum requirement. Seemingly, even a mediocre diet would not lead to a copper deficiency of any major importance. An insufficient quantity is more likely the result of a combination of low intake, poor absorption by the body, and increased excretion.

Copper occurs along with other mineral elements in most natural foods. The richest sources are in oysters, cocoa, chocolate, beef or calf's liver, and mushrooms. Copper is necessary for the utilization of iron in producing hemoglobin in the blood even though copper is not present in hemoglobin. This mineral is also a part of many enzymes which are involved in metabolism.

Manganese. The body contains about 12 to 20 milligrams of manganese, but little is known of its distribution. Man's requirement has not been established. Manganese is found in many foods and for this reason it is unlikely that human deficiency of this mineral occurs. The functioning of enzymes concerned with digestion and metabolism of carbohydrates and fats and the formation of blood seem to be affected by manganese. Blueberries and wheat bran are the richest known sources of this element.

Zinc. The presence of zinc in living organisms and its role as an essential nutrient for plants and animals was discovered in 1869. However, satisfactory confirmation did not occur until 40 years later.

The amounts needed are small, and normally the human diet provides ample quantities to prevent deficiencies. Zinc functions in the transportation of carbon dioxide by the blood and in the secretion of hydrochloric acid in the gastric digestive juice. It also seems to be a metal that activates enzymes which function in the digestion of proteins.

Cobalt. Cobalt does not appear to have any function in the body other than that involved with the formation of red blood cells. There is ample cobalt present in the average diet and there is no danger of deficiency occurring.

Molybdenum. Molybdenum is accepted as a micronutrient associated with or functioning as a part of two or more oxidative enzymes. The few foods known to contain molybdenum are legumes, cereals, organ meats, and yeast. Need for this element is minute and human deficiencies do not occur.

Iodine. Iodine, one of the first micronutrients to be isolated, is essential for normal nutrition. The adult body normally contains 20 to 50 milligrams of iodine. About 8 milligrams of this amount is concentrated in the thyroid gland. Since the thyroid normally weighs only 0.2 percent of the whole body, it is evident that this concentration of iodine is intense. It is found in the hormones secreted and stored by the thyroid gland and is the substance on which the hormone activity depends.

The adult requirements for iodine are estimated at 0.15–0.30 milligrams per day. This amount needs to be increased for women during pregnancy and lactation. No definite amount has been established for children. Iodine content of plant foods on land depends on the nature of the plant and its ability to take iodine from the soil. Spinach is especially competent in this respect. The richest sources of iodine in the plant world are the seaweeds.

Widely distributed throughout the animal world, iodine is found in substantial amounts in fish—especially salt-water ones. The cod fish contains considerable amounts of iodine because it feeds on algae and other marine life. It may be reasonably said that the iodine content of food is in almost direct relation to the iodine content of the soil from which the diet, whether plant or animal, comes.

The addition of iodine to salt has helped supply iodine in the diets of persons living in areas where the soil does not contain large amounts of this mineral. Were it not for the existence of goiter, there would probably be little interest in the nutritional aspects of iodine. Goiter, an enlargement of the thyroid gland, is due to an insufficient supply of iodine. The gland enlarges in an attempt to compensate for the storage of necessary material for making

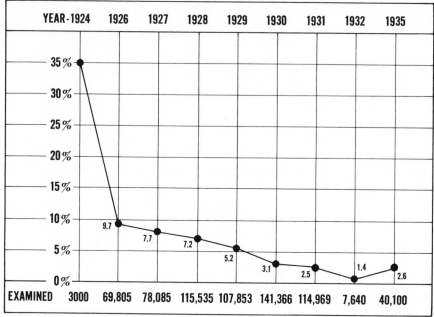

YEAR-1924	1926	1927	1928	1929	1930	1931	1932	1935

35%
30%
25%
20%
15%
10% 9.7
5%   7.7   7.2
     5.2
0%   3.1   2.5   1.4   2.6

EXAMINED	3000	69,805	78,085	115,535	107,853	141,366	114,969	7,640	40,100

(From Kimball, O.P. *Journal of American Medical Association, 1937*.)

The incidence of goiter among Detroit school children declined dramatically between 1924–1935 when iodized salt was added to their diets.

its hormones, thyroxine and triiodothyronine. This disorder was common for many centuries before its cause was recognized. If the diet includes iodized salt, there is assurance that the daily quota will be met for this particular mineral.

Selenium. Selenium joined the group of essential micronutrients within the last decade. The exact role of selenium is not known but it is thought to be closely associated with vitamin E.

MAJOR IDEAS

The following statements give the main ideas within the chapter you have just studied. Be sure you know the words underscored in these statements and in the questions to follow.

1. Even though underscored minerals represent a very small percentage of total body weight, they serve many different purposes which are vital to the functioning of the body.
2. Minerals provide the necessary environment in living cells for normal chemical reactions to occur.
3. If calcium, iron, and phosphorus requirements are met, other mineral requirements are usually satisfied at the same time.

QUESTIONS TO STUDY

MINERALS

1. What is the general role of minerals in the body?
2. Why is calcium in the blood necessary?
3. What is the relationship of phosphorus to the acid-base balance of the body?
4. What is the relationship of iron to hemoglobin?
5. What is nutritional anemia? What is the relationship of iron to this disease?
6. Describe the role that each of the following minerals play in body processes: sodium, potassium, magnesium, chlorine.
7. Why are some minerals called micronutrient elements? How do these differ from the essential minerals?
8. What is the relationship of copper to iron with regard to body processes?

BIBLIOGRAPHY

BOGERT, J. and others, *Nutrition and Physical Fitness.* Philadelphia, W. B. Saunders Company, 1960, p. 131.

CARTWRIGHT, G. E. and WINTROBE, M. M., "The Question of Copper Deficiency in Man." *American Journal of Clinical Nutrition,* Vol. 15, August 1964, p. 99.

CARTWRIGHT, G. E., and WINTROBE, M. M., "Copper Metabolism XIII, Hepatolenticular Degeneration." *American Journal of Clinical Nutrition,* Vol. 14, 1964, p. 224.

COPPER, L., and others, *Nutrition in Health and Disease.* Philadelphia, J. P. Lippincott and Company, 1963, p. 65.

HATHAWAY, MILLICENT L., and LEVERTON, RUTH, "Calcium and Phosphorus." *Food, The Yearbook of Agriculture,* U. S. Department of Agriculture, Washington, D. C., 1959, p. 117.

MARTIN, D. J., "The Evanston Dental Caries Study VIII, Fluorine Content of Vegetables Cooked in Fluorine-containing Water." *Journal of Dental Research,* Vol. 30, 1951, p. 676.

SMITH, H. V., and VARRCH, M., "Fluorine in Milk, Plant Foods and Food Cooked in Fluorine-containing Water." University of Arizona Agriculture Experiment Station, Report No. 77, 1952.

WACKER, WARREN, "Magnesium Metabolism." *Journal of the American Dietetic Association,* Vol. 44, No. 5, November 1963, pp. 362–367.

WALDBOTT, GEORGE, "Fluoride in Food." *American Journal of Clinical Nutrition,* Vol. 12, June 1963, p. 460.

9 VITAMINS, WATER, AND FIBER

The year 1968 marked the fifty-sixth anniversary of the use of the term "vitamine," coined by Casimir Funk, a scientist from Poland. He advanced the idea that certain diseases, such as beriberi, known to occur as the result of faulty diet, were due to a diet deficiency rather than to a poison or toxin as was generally believed. He stated that certain substances which he called "vitamines" could prevent and cure deficiency diseases.

Funk's research and papers have inspired many scientists to study vitamins. We will consider the vitamins according to their solubility in water and fat. Vitamins A, D, K, and E are fat-soluble while the B complex vitamins and vitamin C are water-soluble.

Vitamins are organic compounds different from any of the other nutrients. They are needed in only small amounts but are essential for normal growth and health. Their functions in the body are regulatory ones. Vitamins are secured from plant foods or from animals which have fed on plant foods. The vitamin content of a plant food may vary, depending on cultural conditions, the stage of ripeness when picked, the conditions under which it is stored, how it is processed, and the ways in which it is prepared for consumption. The vitamin content of animal foods is influenced by what the animal has been fed. For example, the vitamin A content in eggs varies according to the amount of vitamin A the hens have had in their diet. Organs where animals store these food materials become excellent sources of vitamins for human consumption.

The fat-soluble vitamins are found, of course, in fatty foods while water-soluble vitamins are found in vegetables, fruits, cereals, and lean meats. Both are present in whole milk. The recommended allowances for vitamins allow for a margin of safety as is the case with other nutrient allowances. Allowances vary somewhat from one country to another. However, daily allowances established for the United States are generous so that deficiencies can be prevented, vitality increased, and better growth promoted for all individuals.

In general, a good way to make sure that sufficient vitamins are included in the diet is to have the recommended amounts of milk, whole grain cereals or enriched breads and cereals, fruits, vegetables, butter or fortified margarine, eggs, and meats. By following the "Daily Food Guide" recommendations (pages 336–337) and making proper selections of foods, an adequate amount of the vitamins as well as the other essential nutrients can be achieved.

Fat-soluble Vitamins

Fat-soluble vitamins are stable and not likely to be lost during the cooking of foods. Because they are absorbed in the intestines along with fats, any interference in fat adsorption affects the utilization of these vitamins. Since they are not soluble in water, they cannot be excreted in the urine. Fat-soluble vitamins can be stored in the body in large amounts which, if excessive, can produce toxicity.

Vitamin A. This vitamin is an important one. It is found in plant foods as vitamin A and in the plant pigment carotene. The latter is converted into vitamin A in the body when eaten. This process occurs mainly in the intestinal wall during digestion. Because of its ability to change from carotene to vitamin A, carotene is known as a *provitamin*. The relationship of vitamin A to the pigment carotene was demonstrated in 1920. Research showed that the vitamin A potency of vegetable foods was closely related to their carotene content. In 1957 the final proof was presented that carotene is the "pro-vitamin" of vitamin A.

The total vitamin A contribution of a food is referred to as its vitamin A value. There are differences in individuals as to how well they use carotenes but it is usually estimated that less than half of the carotene intake may be expected to be transformed into vitamin A. Foods that contain carotenes are said to have vitamin A value even though they do not carry this vitamin in a preformed condition.

Vitamin A values both for requirements and in food are stated in International Units (I.U.) rather than by weight. One International Unit is defined as equivalent to 0.6 micrograms of pure beta-carotene or 0.3 micrograms of pure vitamin A.

The amount of vitamin A in foods varies widely. Primarily, vitamin A is supplied from the fat of dairy products and from egg yolks. Skimmed milk contains only traces. Margarines which have been fortified by having vitamin A added to them in the production process are sources of this vitamin.

Vitamin A also occurs in the livers of many fresh-water fish and in fish liver oils. Green and yellow vegetables are important plant sources of vitamin A. Here the vitamin value is due to the presence of yellow carotenoid pigment. The intensity of the yellow and green color is a reliable indication of vitamin A value in vegetables.

Vitamin A is needed for the normal functioning of the eyes, the maintenance of the epithelial tissue, and the promotion of growth.

Vitamin A is needed for vision. The eye is one of the first organs affected by the lack of vitamin A because this vitamin is a part of the pigment in the retina of the eye. This pigment is called visual purple. When light falls on the retina the visual purple is changed to another pigment known as visual yellow. As a result of this change, images are transmitted to the brain through the optic nerve. In darkness the visual purple is rebuilt. New supplies of vitamin A must be available in order for this accommodation to light and dark to occur in the eye properly. When a person moves from a light area to a dark area the eye must adjust to the light change. If vitamin A is low in the blood stream, normal vision will be restored slowly and the adaptation or adjustment of the eye will be faulty.

Another function of vitamin A is the maintenance of the epithelial tissues, namely the skin and the mucous membranes of the body. Where a deficiency of vitamin A exists, there is a change in the membranes. They become thin, dry, porous, and flaky. Whenever such changes occur, the skin is less able to perform its protective function against infection.

Vitamin A is also essential for the formation and maintenance of tooth enamel and healthy gums.

Excessive amounts of vitamin A may lead to a number of abnormalities. There may be thickening of the skin, interference with normal development of the bones leading to softness and fragility, tendency to bleed, and interference with normal reproduction. Conditions of excessive vitamin A have been observed in man in the Arctic regions when he has eaten large amounts of polar bear liver or seal liver. Similar conditions may result from an over-dosage of vitamin A tablets. It is not difficult to get the recommended allowance of vitamin A from natural foods in the average diet. In the United States, on the average, persons are getting enough vitamin A. Among infants the intake is more than ample. For pregnant women and adolescent girls the average intake is low.

Vitamin D. This vitamin is referred to as the "antirachitic" (rickets-preventing) vitamin. Vitamin D occurs in foods in 2 forms—as preformed vitamins and as precursors.* These latter substances are altered chemically by light so that they become capable of functioning as vitamins in the body. Vitamin D

---

*A substance which is converted into another.

has at least ten known forms which show vitamin D activity but D_2 and D_3 are of major importance. The precursor of D_2 is found in plants and that of D_3 is found in animal sources. Vitamin D is measured in terms of International Units. An International Unit of vitamin D is 0.025 micrograms of vitamin D_3. Four hundred I.U. of vitamin D per day are recommended for infants, children, boys, girls, and pregnant and lactating women.

Egg yolk and liver, as well as fish oils, contain vitamin D. Fortified milk—milk to which vitamin D has been added—is available to most people in the United States. This milk is fortified or enriched by 400 I.U. of vitamin D per quart.

The main function of vitamin D is to aid in the absorption and excretion of calcium and phosphorus. Several investigators have shown that vitamin D promotes the absorption of calcium. Although the effect of vitamin D on intestinal absorption of calcium seems to be definitely established, there is still question as to whether vitamin D also has a direct effect on calcification and bone structure.

Vitamin D, like other fat-soluble vitamins, can be stored in the body. The small child in a state of rapid growth will not store quantities of vitamin D because his body demand for the vitamin is great. However, an adult will store the vitamin in greater reserve so that probably no deficiency will exist.

Overdosage of all forms of vitamin D may be dangerous. Too much vitamin D is characterized by deposits of calcium phosphate which affect the joints, kidneys, heart, parathyroid glands, pancreas, skin, lymph glands, arteries, eyes, and the acid-secreting portions of the stomach. In advanced or extreme stages, demineralization of bones (withdrawal of minerals) may occur.

Vitamin K. This vitamin was isolated in 1935 by Carl Dam of Copenhagen. Vitamin K is fairly widely distributed in food. It appears abundantly in cauliflower, cabbage, spinach, pork liver, and soybeans. The main function of this vitamin is for the normal clotting of the blood.

Official minimal requirements or recommended allowances of vitamin K have not been established.

Vitamin E. This vitamin was discovered in 1923. However, it was not until 1936 that vitamin E was isolated. The main function of vitamin E involves its ability to act as an antioxidant. It seems to be the protector of vitamin A and keeps its precursor, carotene, from being oxidized. Vitamin E also protects the blood of newborn, full-term infants from the blood-destroying action of hydrogen peroxide.

The requirements for vitamin E have not been established because of the lack of supporting evidence to suggest a specific need for this vitamin. Green leafy vegetables, corn oil, dairy products, butter, eggs, liver, and fruits are all excellent sources of vitamin E.

Water-soluble Vitamins

Water-soluble vitamins make up a large group, all of which, with the exception of one, belong to the B complex. The remaining one is vitamin C (ascorbic acid). These vitamins are not stored in the body so the possibility of over-dosage is eliminated.

Vitamin B complex. At least eleven vitamins compose the vitamin B complex. Seven of these are essential and should be provided in the daily diet. The various vitamins within the complex are all water-soluble and contain nitrogen; other than these characteristics they have little in common.

Beriberi, the disease which is now known to be due to *thiamine* deficiency, was recognized for many centuries. In fact, it was described by the Chinese as early as 2600 B.C. In a study of diets among Japanese and British sailors in the latter part of the nineteenth century, it was found that beriberi could be eliminated by a well-balanced diet. Since that time many men have worked on the anti-beriberi factor known as thiamine. The symptoms of beriberi include numbness in toes and feet, cramps in

legs, difficulty in walking, and finally paralysis of the legs. Various nerves are also affected in the later stages of the disease (page 59). This association caused vitamin B_1, or thiamine, to be known as the antineuritic vitamin.

The most important function of thiamine seems to be in its role in the digestion and absorption of carbohydrates. Glucose is oxidized in the tissues to supply energy. This occurs through a series of reactions, each requiring specific enzymes. Thiamine is a part of the enzyme structure essential to this activity.

Other functions ascribed to thiamine are varied and seemingly unrelated. This vitamin seems to be necessary in maintaining a normal functioning nervous system. However, it has not been shown that nervous disorders are due to thiamine deficiencies. In the United States, diets supply enough thiamine so that beriberi does not occur often. Thiamine is present in all plants and animals. In addition, the enrichment of bread has contributed significantly to the intake of this vitamin.

The requirement for thiamine is related to the metabolic rate, body size, physical activity, temperature, and general physical state of the individual. Physical state includes age, functioning of the thyroid gland, pregnancy, lactation, and fever. Numerous studies have shown that thiamine requirement is so related to carbohydrates that for practical purposes it can best be expressed in terms of caloric intake. The minimal need in adults is approximately 0.2 to 0.3 milligrams per 1000 calories. The allowance recommended by the National Research Council is 0.4 milligrams per 1000 calories for adults on ordinary caloric intake but at least 0.8 milligrams if the intake yields less than 2000 calories. For infants and children the recommendation is the same. Organ meats, whole grains, enriched bread and cereals, legumes, and pork are the best sources of thiamine.

Riboflavin, or vitamin B_2, is another of the B vitamins. A deficiency of this vitamin is characterized by a sore mouth, cracked lips at the corners, denuded areas on the lips, and a shiny tongue with purplish color.

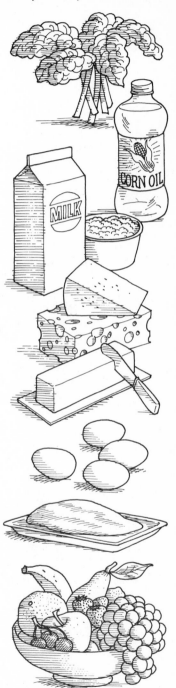

Riboflavin is found in tissues where it seems to combine with protein to form a number of important enzymes known as flavoproteins which are necessary in tissue metabolism. Riboflavin is also thought to be a part of the retinal pigment of the eye where it participates in the eye's adaptation to light differences.

In combined forms, riboflavin is widely distributed in both plants and animals. As in the case of thiamine, the amount of riboflavin required by the body is based on the total caloric intake per day. The recommended allowance is 0.6 milligrams of riboflavin per 1000 calories. Milk, liver, kidney, heart, egg white, and green leafy vegetables are excellent sources. Lean meats, pork, veal, beef, poultry, cheese, dried apricots, and tomatoes contribute worthwhile amounts.

Niacin, another of the B vitamins, is an essential part of certain enzymes which are important in energy metabolism. Its presence is necessary for healthy tissues.

The discovery of this vitamin is related to the deficiency disease pellagra (page 59). This disease is characterized by rough, darkened skin, sore mouth and tongue, and inflammation of the intestinal tract. Pellagra was first described in 1730, but it was not until 1937 that researchers demonstrated that a substance, nicotinamide, isolated from liver, could cure pellagra patients. This was after the treatment had been tested on dogs suffering from "black tongue," the canine equivalent of pellagra.

The amount and quality of protein in the diet appears to influence niacin requirement. Recommended allowances are expressed as niacin equivalents. The protein, tryptophan, is considered the precursor of niacin, and it is assumed that 60 milligrams of tryptophan may be converted to 1.0 milligrams of niacin in the body. Niacin allowances for infants have been determined as 6–7 milligrams per 1000 calories. For safety, the recommended daily intake of niacin is 13–14 milligrams for women, 15–19 milligrams for men, and 6–22 milligrams for children depending on their ages.

The best food sources of niacin are yeast, liver, lean meat, poultry, peanuts, and legumes. Fair sources are potatoes, whole wheat cereal, and whole wheat or enriched bread. Cornmeal and refined white flour are very low in niacin. These, however, may be enriched by having niacin added during the milling process.

Vitamin B₆ (pyridoxine) is the name given to an unidentified factor necessary for growth and the prevention of a type of skin disorder in rats. Two other forms of this vitamin have been identified from natural resources—pyridoxal and pyridoxamine.

Vitamin B_6 occurs in the enzyme system involved in the metabolism of amino acids and so is essential to the normal metabolism of proteins. A variety of central nervous system disorders may result from a lack of this vitamin. A deficiency of B_6 also results in characteristic symptoms evident from a lack of other B vitamins.

The exact daily requirement for vitamin B_6 has not yet been established for man. However, it seems that a daily intake of approximately 2 milligrams is sufficient. The richest food sources are pork, glandular meats, legumes, potatoes, oatmeal, and bananas.

For scientists interested in the study of vitamins, it was apparent that liver and liver concentrates contained some substance that was potent in restoring a normal blood condition in people with pernicious anemia. After many chemical purifications, chemists succeeded in isolating this active substance from the liver, and gave it the name *vitamin B_{12}*.

The human requirement of B_{12} has not been firmly established. For adults, 3–5 micrograms per day is a reasonable estimate.

Sources of vitamin B_{12} have not been fully investigated but at present there is a high content indicated in liver and kidney. Vitamin B_{12} has other nutritive uses besides its anti-pernicious anemia effect. It is thought that this vitamin is required for reproduction at least in all the species of experimental animals investigated.

Folic acid, another of the B complex vitamins, has been the subject of much investigation involving several animal species. It was isolated from spinach and named for the Latin word "folium," meaning leaf. Although folic acid is obviously an essential nutritional factor, it has not yet been established to what extent man is dependent upon it. It is probable that 0.1 to 0.2 milligrams daily will maintain good health. Probably under normal conditions the amount synthesized by intestinal bacteria fulfills the need. Folic acid is found in liver, kidney, yeast, mushrooms, and green leafy vegetables.

Pantothenic acid was discovered in 1933 during the investigation of an acidic substance that was required as a growth factor for yeast. It was given its name from the Greek word meaning "everywhere."

A definite requirement for this vitamin has not been established. However, there seems little doubt that it plays an important part in human nutrition.

Deficiency of pantothenic acid seldom occurs in man except under the most unusual circumstances or as a result of excessive metabolic demands by the body. The best food sources for this vitamin are liver, kidney, heart, salmon, and eggs. Fruits are relatively poor sources.

Another B vitamin found as a growth factor for yeast cells was isolated in 1936. The requirement for *biotin* has not been established. Most American diets contain 150 to 300 micrograms of biotin which seems adequate for good health. Good food sources of biotin are liver, kidney, molasses, and egg yolk. To a lesser degree, vegetables, nuts, and grains are also sources. Biotin deficiency has been recognized in man only when diets have included large amounts of raw egg white. This is due to the fact that an anti-vitamin that inactivates biotin, avidin, is found in egg white.

Vitamin C. Scurvy, a disease characterized by weakness, anemia, spongy gums, and bleeding of the mucous membranes, results from a deficiency of vitamin C, ascorbic acid (pages 58–59). As early as 460–370 B.C. this disease was described by Hippocrates. High incidence of scurvy was noted in the early Roman army and the disease was also prevalent during the Renaissance. With the coming of long sea voyages, scurvy was frequently found among ships' crews.

Sixteenth century writers made reference to the therapeutic use of scurvy grass, water cress, and oranges to combat the condition of scurvy. By 1600 A.D. the British navy was experimenting with the use of lime juice for this purpose. In 1753 James Lind established the curative effect of citrus juices in the treatment of scurvy and in 1932 vitamin C was isolated from lemon juice.

Vitamin C performs several functions in the body. One of its most important roles is involved in the formation and maintenance of the substances which hold the body cells together. This explains why it is essential for the healing of wounds. Further, it strengthens the blood vessels and influences the

Table 7 Functions and Sources of Selected Vitamins

Vitamin	Primary Functions	Important Sources
Vitamin A	To help keep the skin clear and smooth To help keep the mucous membranes firm, healthy, and resistant to infection To help prevent night blindness To help control growth of bones and teeth	Liver, eggs Butter, margarine, whole milk, cream, Cheddar-type cheese Dark green and deep yellow vegetables Deep yellow fruits, such as cantaloupe
Thiamine (Vitamin B₁)	To help promote normal appetite and digestion To help keep the nervous system healthy To help the body release energy from food to be used for work	Meat, especially pork, liver, heart, and kidney Fish, poultry Eggs Enriched or whole grain breads and cereals Dried beans and peas
Riboflavin (Vitamin B₂)	To help the cells use oxygen To help keep the skin, tongue, and lips normal To help prevent scaly, greasy skin around mouth and nose	Milk, cheese, ice cream Meats, especially liver, heart, kidney, and tongue Fish, poultry, eggs Dark green vegetables Enriched breads and cereals Dried beans
Niacin or its equivalent	To help keep the nervous system healthy and normal To help keep the skin, mouth, tongue, and digestive tract in healthy condition To help the cells use other nutrients	Peanut butter Meat, fish, poultry Milk Enriched or whole grain breads and cereals Dried beans and peas
Ascorbic Acid (Vitamin C)	To help make cementing materials that hold body cells together and make walls of blood vessels firm To help in healing wounds and broken bones To help protect against infection	Citrus fruits—oranges, grapefruit, lemons, limes Strawberries, cantaloupes Vegetables (especially raw) including green peppers, cauliflower, broccoli, kale, Brussels sprouts, cabbage, tomatoes, and potatoes
Vitamin D (The Sunshine Vitamin)	To help absorb calcium from the digestive tract and build calcium and phosphorus into bones and teeth.	Milk with added vitamin D Eggs Sardines, salmon, tuna (Sunshine on skin also produces vitamin D in the body)

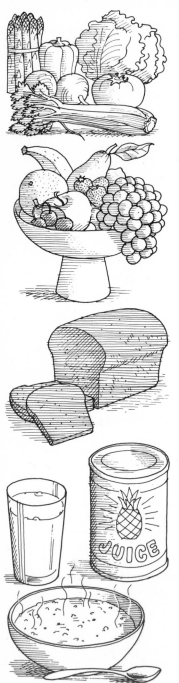

formation of hemoglobin. It also seems likely that it plays a part in the maintenance of a normal hemoglobin level. Although not fully understood, vitamin C also protects the body against infection.

When a deficiency of vitamin C exists, there are indications of listlessness, lack of endurance, pains in the legs and joints, signs of hemorrhaging under the skin's surface, and gums which bleed readily. There has been some disagreement as to the amount of vitamin C which is needed by the human body. The suggested allowance of 70 milligrams is based on the maintenance of a level of saturation in the blood. Very few American diets today have such limited amounts of vitamin C to cause a condition of scurvy, but a significant number may be considered inadequate.

The richest sources of vitamin C are citrus fruits— lemons, oranges, limes, and so forth—and tomatoes. Some vegetables, such as potatoes and cabbage, if eaten in relatively large quantities, are also good sources.

Water and Fiber

Water does not have nutritive value but it is extremely essential in the proper functioning of the body. Although a person can live without food for a few weeks, without water he can live only a few days.

Most authorities recommend that 6 to 8 glasses of water be consumed daily. However, the amount of water a person actually needs daily is affected by his environment, particularly by the temperature and humidity. A person living in a hot or warm climate requires more water than a person living in a cold climate because he perspires more and therefore loses more water.

Water, present in all foods, varies in amount. Fresh fruits and vegetables are foods which contain large amounts. All liquids—tea, coffee, soup, and carbonated beverages—furnish large quantities of water for the body.

Water serves several functions in the body. It is the medium in which the various chemical changes of the body take place. As a carrier, it aids in digestion, absorption, circulation, and excretion. Each step in the process of converting food into tissue and energy is facilitated by water. For example, the digestive secretions are largely water. Water acts as a solvent for nutrients. It softens, dilutes, and liquefies the food so digestion can be accomplished readily. Water also aids in moving food along the alimentary canal. The absorption of nutrients by osmosis through the intestinal wall is facilitated by water. Finally, the blood and lymph carry the nutrients in solution or suspension to the cells where needed.

Water also forms one of the end products after fats, carbohydrates, and proteins have been metabolized. The water which is not used is excreted as urine by the kidneys and as perspiration by the skin. Through perspiration, water acts as a thermostat for the body and helps to maintain the proper body temperature.

The indigestible vegetable *fiber* should not be confused with the digestible animal fiber found in meats. The vegetable fiber is composed of cellulose, whereas the so-called fiber in meats (connective tissue) consists primarily of collagen, a protein-like substance which can be absorbed by the body.

Although fiber in food is not considered a nutrient, it is very necessary in the diet to promote the proper excretion of waste materials from the body. The presence of a considerable amount of fiber aids in the absorption of nu-

From *Nutrition in Health and Disease* by Cooper, Barber, Mitchell, Rynbergen and Greene adapted and reproduced by permission of J. B. Lippincott Company.

FUNCTIONS OF WATER IN THE BODY

WATER INTAKE

BLOOD 3500 CC

INTESTINAL JUICE 3000 CC

WATER EXCRETED

2000 - 4000 CC

| PRESENT IN FOODS |
| FORMED IN METABOLISM |
| CONSUMED AS FLUIDS |

GASTRIC JUICE 2500 CC

SALIVA 1500 CC

BILE & PANCREATIC JUICE 1500 CC

2000 - 4000 CC

| BY LUNGS AS WATER VAPOR |
| BY SKIN AS SWEAT |
| IN STOOLS |
| BY KIDNEYS AS URINE |

THE SIGNIFICANCE OF FOOD

WATER CONTENT OF FOODS	
VEGETABLES, FRESH	90%
MILK, WHOLE	87%
FRUITS, FRESH	85%
OATMEAL, COOKED	85%
EGGS	74%
BEEF, MEDIUM LEAN	60%
BREAD, WHITE	36%
OATMEAL, UNCOOKED	8%

From *Nutrition in Health and Disease* by Cooper, Barber, Mitchell, Rynbergen and Greene adapted and reproduced by permission of J. B. Lippincott Company.

trients in the small intestine. It also promotes a favorable growth of bacteria in the intestine.

Significant amounts of fiber—also called cellulose, roughage, and bulk—in a normal diet are found in vegetables, fruits, whole grain (dark) breads or cereals, and bran.

In Chapters 6–9 you have learned that the functioning of the human body and consequently life itself, depends upon an intricate and complex system of chemical and physiological processes. Each nutritional element found in food has its own important role as well as interrelated ones with other nutritional elements. You have studied some of the ways in which these elements are used by the body in maintaining its life functions.

In the last chapter of Part I you will study some of the food faddisms which are based on incorrect conceptions of food and body needs.

MAJOR IDEAS

The following statements give the main ideas within the chapter you have just studied. Be sure you know the words underscored in these statements and in the questions to follow.

1. Vitamins are extremely important for the normal functioning of the body.
2. Eating a well-balanced diet assures a person of a sufficient amount of the various vitamins needed by the body.

3. Certain vitamins are closely associated with certain deficiency diseases. These diseases can be cured or prevented by supplying the necessary vitamins in sufficient amounts.
4. Some vitamins occur as <u>preformed</u> substances in foods while others occur as <u>precursors,</u> or <u>provitamins</u>, from which the vitamins are <u>synthesized</u> by the body.
5. Each vitamin has specific functions in the body.
6. Water is not a nutrient in itself but is absolutely essential if the body is to survive.

QUESTIONS TO STUDY

VITAMIN A

1. In the preparation of food why is it important to know that certain vitamins are soluble in fat and that others are soluble in water?
2. What is a provitamin?
3. Why are <u>carotenes</u> referred to as precursors of vitamin A?
4. Explain the relationship of the human requirement for vitamin A to the precursors of this vitamin.
5. What is an <u>International Unit</u>?
6. Describe the part that vitamin A plays in the function of the eyes.
7. What are major sources of vitamin A?
8. What special functions does vitamin A have in the body?
9. Can one have too much vitamin A?

VITAMIN D

1. Why is this vitamin referred to as the "<u>antirachitic</u>" vitamin?
2. Explain the relationship between vitamin D and the use of calcium in the body.

VITAMIN K

1. What main function does vitamin K serve?

VITAMIN E

1. Explain the relationship between vitamin E and carotene.

VITAMIN B COMPLEX

1. In what way are vitamins B_1, B_2, and <u>niacin</u> related?
2. Why is thiamine often added to certain cereals and cereal products?
3. Why is niacin closely associated with the amount of <u>protein</u> one eats?

THE SIGNIFICANCE OF FOOD

4. What are some deficiency diseases associated with the lack of various vitamins?
5. Explain the relationship between vitamin B_6 and protein metabolism.

VITAMIN C

1. Why are citrus fruits used in the treatment of the deficiency disease, scurvy? How was this treatment discovered?
2. Why does one have to take care in preparing foods that are rich in vitamin C?

WATER AND FIBER

1. Explain in detail why water is so necessary to the body.
2. What factors influence the amount of water a person needs each day?
3. Explain why it is important to eat the non-digestible fibers found in foods.

BIBLIOGRAPHY

"Are Vitamin Pills Necessary?" *Consumer Bulletin*, Vol. 48, April 1965, pp. 18–21.

BAKER, E. M., and others, "Vitamin B_6 Requirements for Adult Men." *The American Journal of Clinical Nutrition*, Vol. 15, No. 2, 1964, p. 59.

BOGERT, L. JEAN, *Nutrition and Physical Fitness*. Philadelphia, W. B. Saunders, 1966.

COOLEY, D. G., "What Is A Vitamin?" *Today's Health*, Vol. 41, January 1963, pp. 20–3.

DOWLING, J. E., "Night Blindness." *Scientific American*, Vol. 215, October 1966, pp. 78–84.

DREYFUS, R. M. and VICTOR, M., "Effects of Thiamine Deficiency on the Central Nervous System." *American Journal of Clinical Nutrition*, Vol. 9, 1961, p. 414.

Facts about Nutrition. U. S. Department of Health, Education, and Welfare, Washington, D. C.

Food for Family Fitness. The Nutrition Foundation, Inc., New York, 1963.

"Four Roles Found For Vitamin B_{12} Coenzymes." *Science News Letter*, Vol. 83, June 8, 1963, p. 360.

GUTHRIE, HELEN A., *Introductory Nutrition*. Saint Louis, The C. V. Mosby Company, 1967, pp. 176–265.

HARDY, B., "Do Milk Cows Need More Vitamin A?" *Farm Journal*, Vol. 86, November 1962, p. 49.

"Hypervitaminosis A: Its Broadening Spectrum." *American Journal of Clinical Nutrition*, Vol. 6, 1958, p. 335.

MADDOX, G., "Vitamin Pills Are Not A Food Substitute." *Today's Health*, Vol. 39, November, 1961, pp. 38–39.

MALENA, D., "Vitamin A, How Much Is Too Much?" *Successful Farming*, Vol. 63, March 1965, p. 124.

MAYNARD, LEONARD A., "An Adequate Diet." *Journal of the American Medical Association*, Vol. 170, 1959, pp. 457–458.

"New Form of Vitamin K Found in Spinach Study." *Science News Letter*, Vol. 86, August 22, 1964, p. 119.

Nutrition Handbook for Family Food Counseling. National Dairy Council, Chicago.

OLSON, J. A., "The absorption of beta-carotene and its conversion into Vitamin A." *American Journal of Clinical Nutrition*, Vol. 9, 1961, p. 1.

"Packaged Potatoes Cheat Family of Vitamin C." *Science News Letter*, Vol. 83, April 20, 1963, p. 248.

Recommended Dietary Allowances, 6th Revised Edition. Publication 1146, National Research Council, National Academy of Science, Washington, D. C., 1964.

ROELS, O. A., "Present Knowledge of Vitamin A." *Nutrition Review*, Vol. 24, 1966, p. 129.

"Too Much Vitamin D?" *Consumer Reports*, Vol. 31, February 1966, pp. 52–54.

WHITACRE, J., McLAUGHLIN, L., Futriel, M. F., and Grumes, E. T., "Human Utilization of Vitamin C." *Journal of the American Dietetics Association*, Vol. 35, 1959, p. 139.

10 FOOD FADDISM

False and misleading advertising and the promotion of drugs, health devices, and reducing aids is one of America's primary social problems. Government experts estimate that consumers in this country spend more than 500 million dollars every year on unnecessary or falsely represented vitamin and mineral products and so-called health foods. Food faddists spread erroneous ideas about food while they try to sell the public their products which are sometimes offered as cure-alls for many disease conditions. People who may have serious medical problems may be tricked into making their own diagnosis, using these cure-alls, and delaying medical attention.

Food Faddists and Their Theories

Today's food faddists seem to be of two types. The first truly believes that certain foods have miracle qualities or religious significance; the other exploits misinformation about certain foods for financial profit. Faddists carry on the superstitions, taboos, and myths that started with the caveman. The Egyptians considered garlic a miracle strength-giving food and fed this herb to

Vendors of health foods use all available media to sell their merchandise. The results of their appeals may be confusion, loss of money, and at times added sickness.

the laborers who built the pyramids. The Romans believed that lettuce would clear the mind of all confusion. Ideas such as these, and countless others, have persisted because of ignorance, food habits, religious beliefs, and the advertised claims of the patent medicine vendors. For example, even today some people persist in believing that garlic can reduce high blood pressure and honey and vinegar can relieve the pains of arthritis. Food quacks often prey on the elderly (who may be experiencing some kind of physical discomfort), people who are insecure, those who seek to remain young and youthful, and men and women who are seriously or incurably sick and therefore seek any kind of help.

Promoters of food fads often base their food beliefs on the theory that chemical imbalance in the body because of a faulty diet is the primary cause of almost all diseases, including arthritis and rheumatism. They therefore recommend that certain food supplements (which they usually sell) be consumed to correct this imbalance. Actually, there are very few diseases in the United States today which are caused by dietary deficiencies. This country's food supply is satisfactory in volume, variety, and nutritional value. An adequate diet can be secured from eating a variety of foods (pages 336–337); many food supplements that the faddist tries to sell are expensive, unnecessary, and perhaps even dangerous.

Another theory promoted by the food faddists is that chemical fertilizers poison the land and the crops grown on it. They warn people that the only way to avoid such evils is by "organic farming,"* eating so-called natural foods, and supplementing the diet with their various products. No scientific basis exists for this theory. Some soils have been depleted and produce poor yields of crops; yet most of our soils are capable of providing abundant food supplies. Furthermore, the nutritive value of foods produced on different soils does not vary greatly, except in the case of iodine. In fact, the only disease in man which is known to be linked to a deficiency of soil is simple goiter due to lack of iodine in certain areas. The deficiency of this element in the diet can be corrected by using iodized salt.

Faddists also contend that white flour, refined cereals, and canned food lose their nutritive value when they are milled, processed, kept in storage, exposed to daylight, and then cooked. Some recommend that raw sugar be used in place of refined sugar, lemon juice be substituted for vinegar, and sea salt used instead of common table salt. However, modern food processing methods have been devised to preserve or restore nutritional value to foods. For example, fruits and vegetables are canned and frozen at the peak of nutritional perfection, and flour, bread, milk, and margarine are fortified with vitamins and minerals. These additions to certain foods have been carefully calculated by scientific authorities so that the amounts added supply known dietary requirements.

*In organic farming, organic matter (humus and vegetables) is used for fertilizer. Pesticides and commercial fertilizers are not used.

THE SIGNIFICANCE OF FOOD

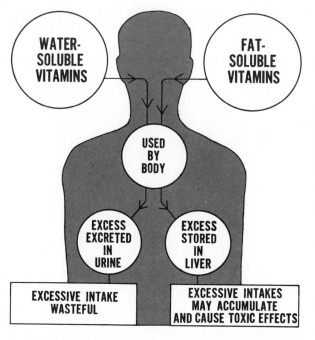

The body can use only limited amounts of water-soluble vitamins; any extra vitamins which the body cannot use are excreted. An overdose of fat-soluble vitamins, on the other hand, can lead to toxicity. Eating wisely selected foods is therefore much more sensible than depending upon expensive, high-potency vitamin supplements.

Adapted from Bogert, Briggs and Callaway, *Nutrition and Physical Fitness*, 8th Edition. Philadelphia, W. B. Saunders Co., 1966.

How successful this scientifically guided food-improvement program has been is demonstrated by the fact that the once-prevalent deficiency diseases such as rickets and pellagra are now rare in the United States.

Deploring the idea of pasteurization, food faddists insist that during this process milk loses its nutritive value. Although there is some loss of ascorbic acid when milk is pasteurized, a person receives the recommended amount of this nutrient from other foods. When the protection that pasteurization gives to milk from pathogenic bacterial growth is considered, this process should be considered essential and indispensable.

Some food quacks maintain that in addition to food processing and pasteurization, cooking as practiced in the home destroys nutrients, especially vitamins and minerals. They recommend the use of special equipment to minimize these losses. Claiming that Americans suffer from "subclinical deficiencies," a lack of the necessary vitamins and minerals which causes fatigue or aches and pains, they encourage the use of some "medicine" to combat this general feeling of tiredness. They also recommend the eating of "natural" foods. According to scientific research, however, it is agreed that no person can live without experiencing some aches in the body or fatigue. Furthermore, such symptoms, when they do occur, can be the result of many causes, not necessarily a deficiency of vitamins and minerals. A competent physician should recommend any extra food supplements; buying pills without such advice may be expensive and unwise.

Miracle foods. Still another belief of some people is the existence of miracle foods. Some claim that blackstrap molasses, yeast, and wheat germ are miracle foods that can correct various difficulties, including insomnia, undesirable hair and skin coloring, digestion problems, and aging. The first food is also falsely thought to be a cure for anemia and rheumatism.

Yogurt is another food which is thought by some people to contain special qualities not found in other foods. In fact, however, yogurt has the same food value as any sour milk of the same butterfat content. Unfortunately, the people who believe that yogurt is a miracle food are willing to pay up to four times the price of ordinary buttermilk for the same amount of yogurt.

"Royal jelly," a special food substance prepared by worker bees for the queen bee, is another food supplement which has received attention during the last few years. Manufacturers have obtained this jelly, inserted it into bottles, and sold it, claiming that the substance will restore beauty, youth, and vitality. Science has investigated royal jelly and found it to be helpful for bees but not for people.

A cult which has become prominent in parts of this country is based on religious beliefs. Grain soup with wheat noodles and lily roots, steamed wheat, mealy bread with a pasty substance spread over the top, seaweed, tea, and brown rice are the "foods" which make up the devotee's meal. It is claimed that this food combination can cure asthma, headaches, and backaches, in addition to reducing the amount of sleep needed every night. The people who maintain their existence by this diet also contend that the foods drastically reduce weight, expand thought and depth of concentration, and may even stimulate religious hallucinations. They believe that all illnesses are caused by living in extremes and eating meals too rich in "yin" foods such as fruit and ice cream and "yang" foods such as meat. Grains are found in neither extreme and are therefore the staple of the meals. A number of deaths have been attributed to this diet.

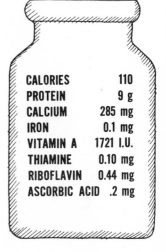

BUTTERMILK (1 CUP)

CALORIES	110
PROTEIN	9 g
CALCIUM	285 mg
IRON	0.1 mg
VITAMIN A	1721 I.U.
THIAMINE	0.10 mg
RIBOFLAVIN	0.44 mg
ASCORBIC ACID	.2 mg

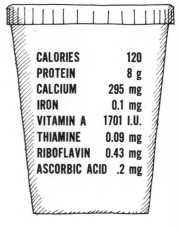

YOGURT (1 CUP)

CALORIES	120
PROTEIN	8 g
CALCIUM	295 mg
IRON	0.1 mg
VITAMIN A	1701 I.U.
THIAMINE	0.09 mg
RIBOFLAVIN	0.43 mg
ASCORBIC ACID	.2 mg

Food fallacies. There are many other beliefs concerning food which have occupied people's imaginations. Some of these superstitions are the following:

1. The combination of milk and oysters, milk and fish, ice cream and oysters, milk and cucumbers, and milk and lettuce are harmful.

    No evidence demonstrates that combinations of natural foods such as those mentioned above are detrimental to good health.

2. Brown eggs are less nutritious than white eggs.

    The nutritive quality of an egg is not related to the color of the shell. Color is determined by the breed of hen.

3. Raw eggs are more nutritious than cooked eggs.

    The method used for cooking eggs influences the rate of digestion but only slightly affects the nutritive value of the eggs in the body.

4. Vegetable juices have disease-curing properties.

    No vegetable juices have special health-giving qualities.

5. Wine makes blood.

    There is no single food which is responsible for making blood.

6. Vitamin E is valuable for fertility, muscular strength, and control of heart disease.

    There is no evidence that this vitamin is helpful for any of these various conditions.

7. Heart disease can be caused by drinking ice water.

    Drinking this liquid will not cause heart disease.

8. Vegetables of the onion and cabbage families, in addition to cucumbers and radishes, are indigestible.

    This generalization cannot be made. Whereas some people may be sensitive to these foods, all people have personal idiosyncrasies concerning food and its ease of digestibility.

9. Margarine is harder to digest than butter.

    The body digests and utilizes all food fats equally well.

10. The constant use of margarine has an adverse effect on secondary sex characteristics, such as the depth of the voice.

    It has not been shown that margarine contains any substance that adversely affects the secondary sex characteristics.

Perhaps, as people become more educated in this country as well as others these false beliefs will disappear as nutritional facts replace them.

Weight Reduction Fads

Food faddists also capitalize on the desire of many men and women to lose weight quickly and without any effort. Lacking the will power to adhere to a carefully planned low-calorie diet, these overweight people listen to charlatans and buy their pills and devices.

The pills which the faddists sell are usually nothing more substantial than a placebo,* and are usually accompanied by a warning to eat low-calorie foods which will stimulate the effectiveness of the pills. It is obvious, however, that the recommended diet would be sufficient to allow loss of weight; the pills are an expensive deception.

Federal agencies are investigating promoters who claim that weight can be reduced merely by having the patient lie on a vibrating sofa. Other faddists contend that they possess power to reduce weight in special places so that bulges will disappear. Recommendations to join weight-reducing gyms are also suspect; baths and vigorous exercise for overweight people who are not accustomed to this type of activity can be dangerous.

Following abnormal diets publicized in mass media can also be unwise since the creator of the diet cannot possibly know of an individual's particular weight problem, to what foods he may be sensitive or allergic, what foods he prefers, how much money he can afford to spend on "special" foods, and which foods he may or may not be able to obtain locally.

Strange diets are also in fashion at certain times, such as the lamb chop and pineapple diet, the green-vegetable diet, the all-fruit diet, etc. These diets may not reduce weight but do limit the intake of essential nutrients. They can also become monotonous and take any pleasure out of eating, a factor which is psychologically important.

Some manufacturers persist in promoting laxatives as remedies for reducing weight. Such medicines interfere with the normal utilization of food. In addition, many valuable food nutrients are lost since the food is rushed through the digestive tract and cannot be absorbed properly. This can cause a weakened condition and lowered resistance to diseases.

In this first part of the book, you have studied the food habits of people and the essential nutrients which are so important in maintaining good health. In the next part, you will examine the characteristics of plant and animal cells, the structure and composition of food, and the scientific principles which govern food processing, preparation, and storage.

MAJOR IDEAS

The following statements give the main ideas within the chapter you have just studied. Be sure you know the words underscored in these statements and in the questions to follow.

> 1. Consumers in this country spend more than a half billion dollars on unnecessary or falsely represented vitamins, minerals, and so-called health foods.

*An inert or innocuous medication.

2. It is dangerous for people with serious diseases to subscribe to the theories of the food faddists, buy their products, and delay essential medical attention.
3. Education is needed to impress people with scientific facts concerning food and medicine.
4. Food faddists' expensive weight-reducing pills and devices cannot take the place of a carefully selected low-calorie diet under a physician's supervision.

QUESTIONS TO STUDY

FOOD FADDISTS AND THEIR THEORIES

1. Why do food fads persist even though scientific evidence is available to refute them?
2. Why are food faddists incorrect when they maintain that most foods are nutritionally deficient by the time they are consumed?
3. Name some food fads or false beliefs about food which are now popular.

WEIGHT REDUCTION FADS

1. Why do people turn to food faddists to help them lose weight?
2. Why is it unwise to follow weight-reducing techniques sponsored by faddists or advertised in mass media?
3. What is the best and safest way to lose weight?

BIBLIOGRAPHY

"False Advertising and Products for the Overweight." *Consumer Reports*, Vol. 24, November 1959, p. 612.

"Food Additives, Facts for Consumers." Food and Drug Administration, U. S. Department of Health, Education, and Welfare, Washington, D. C., 1964.

"Food Facts vs. Food Fallacies." Food and Drug Administration, U. S. Department of Health, Education, and Welfare, Washington, D. C., 1964.

"Food Quackery." *Consumers All—The Yearbook of Agriculture.* U. S. Department of Agriculture, Washington, D. C., 1965, pp. 414–416.

"Food Quackery Costs Americans $500 Million a Year." *Science Digest*, Vol. 51, March 1962, pp. 50–51.

MARTIN, ETHEL AUSTIN, *Nutrition in Action.* New York, Holt, Rinehart and Winston, 1963, pp. 231–238.

MAYER, JEAN, "Food Fads for Athletes." *Atlantic Monthly*, Vol. 208, December 1961, p. 50.

MITCHELL, HELEN S., "Don't Be Fooled by Fads." *Food—The Yearbook of Agriculture*, U. S. Department of Agriculture, Washington, D. C., 1959, pp. 660–668.

Nutrition Handbook for Family Food Counseling. National Dairy Council, Chicago, 1965.

"Nutrition Nonsense." *Consumers All—The Yearbook of Agriculture*, U. S. Department of Agriculture, Washington, D. C., 1965, pp. 660–668.

"Self-Dosing and Fad Diets Can Have Harmful Effects." *Science Newsletter*, Vol. 78, November 26, 1960, p. 344.

SMITH, RALPH LEE, "The Bunk About Health Foods." *Today's Health*, Vol. 43, Oct. 1965, pp. 27–30.

"Yin, Yang, and MB." *Newsweek*, Vol. 65, April 5, 1965, p. 90.

Part II The Nature of Food

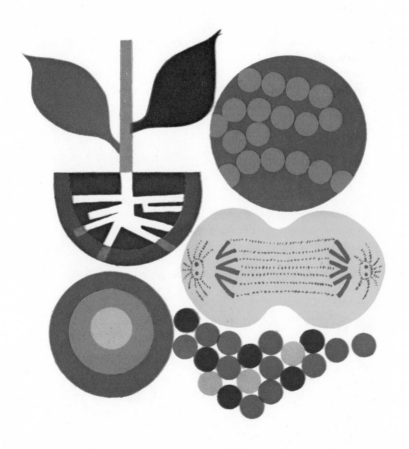

11 LIVING CELLS

All living matter is made up of living cells. These cells, though very small, are extremely complex. They must include a mechanism for obtaining and using energy, for reproducing, and for carrying food materials in and waste material out of the cell.

Cells differ in size, in shape, and in their internal structures. Study the diagrams of a "typical" plant cell and a "typical" animal cell. The structures in these diagrams are not to be found in all cells nor are all the structures found in these particular cells included. Only those components which have importance in our food study are shown here.

Cell Structure

Parts of cell. An individual cell consists of the protoplast, the cell membrane, and the inclusions. The *protoplast* includes the nucleus, the cytoplasm, and all the other living content of the cell. The *nucleus*, which is present in nearly every plant and animal cell although its position may vary in different

All living matter is made up of cells. Each of the cell's activities is coordinated by its nucleus.

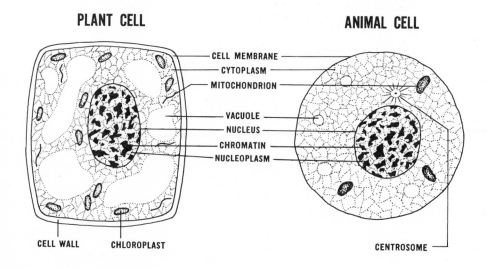

PLANT CELL   ANIMAL CELL

CELL MEMBRANE
CYTOPLASM
MITOCHONDRION
VACUOLE
NUCLEUS
CHROMATIN
NUCLEOPLASM

CELL WALL   CHLOROPLAST   CENTROSOME

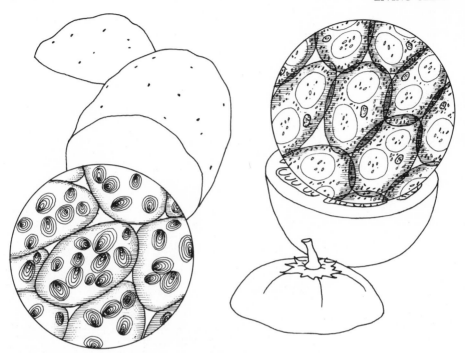

Cell structure of a crosscut of a potato and tomato showing the leucoplasts in the potato and the chromoplasts in the tomato.

types of cells, seems to coordinate the cell's many activities. It is bound by a thin, living *nuclear membrane* which controls the passage of material to the nucleus from the cytoplasm and vice versa. The coded instructions which are developed in the nucleus are referred to by scientists as DNA.* The molecules which act as messengers, moving out of the nucleus to one of the various structures of the cell, are referred to as RNA.† The DNA of the nucleus also controls the process of cell reproduction. As scientists unlock more of the mysteries of DNA and RNA, fruits, vegetables, and animal foods of the future may be developed with entirely different characteristics.

All the protoplast outside the nuclear membrane is the cytoplasm. It surrounds the nucleus and contains a variety of structures. For our purpose we are concerned with two of these, the mitochondria, which control the amount of energy available for cell activity, and the plastids, which are the source of color in all plants. The major plastids are chloroplasts, chromoplasts, and leucoplasts.

*DNA, deoxyribonucleic acid, a sugar ribose without one of its oxygens, combined to form a nucleic acid. Nucleic acids are the molecules that exert primary control over the basic life processes.
†RNA, ribonucleic acid, a nucleic acid that contains ribose sugar.

Chloroplasts, occurring in most green plant cells, are the most common of the three kinds of plastids. The green color of chloroplasts is caused by *chlorophyll* (green coloring), a mixture of two slightly different forms of a pigment called chlorophyll a and chlorophyll b. (Carotene and xanthophyll are also present in chloroplasts, but their colors are usually masked by that of chlorophyll.)

The *chromoplasts* are red, yellow, or orange and are related to the color of tomatoes, carrots, corn, and red peppers. The characteristic color of chromoplasts is attributed to the presence of two pigments (coloring matter), carotene and xanthophyll, respectively deep yellow and pale yellow. Carotene is converted into vitamin A by animals.

Leucoplasts are colorless plastids occurring most commonly in storage cells of roots and underground stems. The leucoplasts are centers of starch formation in the storage cell. White onions, potatoes, and cauliflower are examples of this group.

As mentioned before, chloroplasts contain the green pigment chlorophyll which is important in the process of *photosynthesis*. This is the process by

The process of photosynthesis.

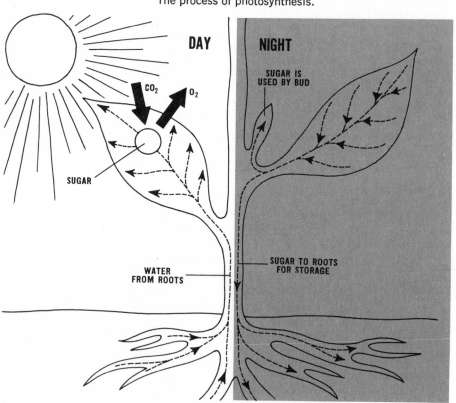

which certain living plant cells combine carbon dioxide, water, and light energy, in the presence of chlorophyll, to form glucose and release oxygen as a waste product. Glucose is an essential food. From this basic substance, plants and animals build other substances including starches, fats and oils, proteins, and vitamins. These all contain the energy from photosynthesis and are related directly to the activity of green plant tissues.

The *cell membrane*, which is composed of protein and fat substances, surrounds the cell and gives it form. It is present in both plant and animal cells. Under the microscope the cell membrane appears merely as the outer surface of the cytoplasm. In plants, this cell membrane is surrounded by a *non-living cell wall* made up of cellulose and lignin. *Cellulose* is the substance mainly responsible for the tough elastic nature of the cell wall. Following the maturity of the cell, another layer of cellulose is deposited. Generally this outer wall is thicker than the other layers. Cellulose will not dissolve in water, though it will absorb water in large quantities and allow it to pass freely into and out of the cell. *Lignin* gives rigidity and hardness to the cell wall, and is deposited between units of the cellulose. Cellulose is softened by cooking the plant in a moist atmosphere; lignin is not softened by cooking. You are probably familiar with mature asparagus, carrots, and parsnips which have become tough and "woody." This is due to the presence of the lignin.

The *nonliving inclusions* in animal and plant cells are found in the cytoplasm and nucleus. Certain of these inclusions are variously sized cavities—small in animal cells but large in plant cells—called vacuoles.

The *vacuoles* gather food material at the cell membrane to transport it into the interior of the cell. The process by which food material passes through this semi-permeable membrane from an area of greater concentration to an area of lesser concentration is called *osmosis*. *Cell sap* is a watery material also located in the vacuoles. This sap contains sugar, acids, tannins, and often pigments. The water-soluble pigments, anthocyanins, give certain red plants their characteristic red color.

The plant cell begins its existence in the tip (apical region) of the stem. Around the solid mass of protoplasm is a thin membrane which separates it from its neighbors. This layer, which is common to two cells, is the *middle lamella* and exists as a cementing layer when the cells are more mature. Chemically, it is made up of a mixture of pectic compounds, one of which is calcium pectate.

The *pectic substances* vary in chemical properties; protopectins and calcium pectates are insoluble, whereas the soluble pectins produce a thick gelatinous material often referred to as a viscous gel. Pectic substances are present in cell walls in varying concentrations. As you will see later, the concentration of the soluble pectic substances is important in making jellies and jams. Many of the textural changes which occur in fruit during ripening are caused by the changes in the proportions of the various pectic substances.

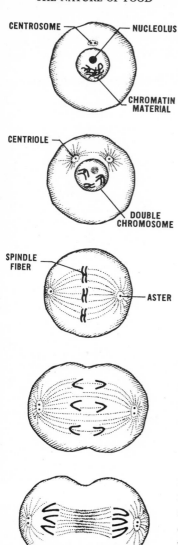

Cell division. As cells grow, their mass of protoplasm increases. The indefinite increase in the protoplasm of the cell is accomplished by *cell division*. Ordinary cell division starts with the division of the nucleus. The *chromatin*, carrying the hereditary traits of the organism, divides equally so that two new nuclei will have identical hereditary qualities. Following this, the cell is cut into two approximately equal parts by the formation of a membrane across the cell. In plant cells, this dividing structure is the middle lamella, against which both new cells add layers of a cellulose wall.

In single-celled organisms, cell division results in two complete organisms, while in many-celled organisms, cell division results in growth of the tissues.

Tissues

As cells divide some begin to perform special functions. A group of similar cells performing a similar activity is referred to as a *tissue*. For example, animal tissues are epidermis, muscle, bone, nerve, fat, and liquid (blood). In foods, the animal tissues are muscle, epidermis, fat, and nerve. Plants have epidermis, parenchyma, xylem, and phloem tissues.

Certain plant tissues are important to us, since they are associated with food. First is the *epidermis*, which is the covering tissue of a plant. The epidermis of plants functions chiefly in conserving the moisture supply of the inner tissues and in offering a certain amount of protection against parasites and other unfavorable external conditions. Second is the *parenchyma tissue* which is found in most fruits and vegetables, and is important for synthesis and storage of carbohydrates. Other tissues, cellulose and lignin, give support to the plant (page 123).

The most important animal tissues for our food study are connective tissue and muscle tissue. The *connective tissue* represents all the tissues lying between the nerve, gland, and muscle tissues. It serves as a "filter tissue" for the body of the animal and binds together many softer tissues, giving them

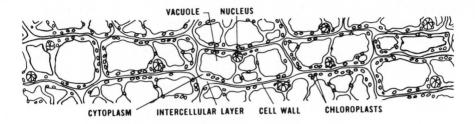

Above: Food-synthesizing cells of a green plant.
Below: Smooth and striated muscle fibers in meat.

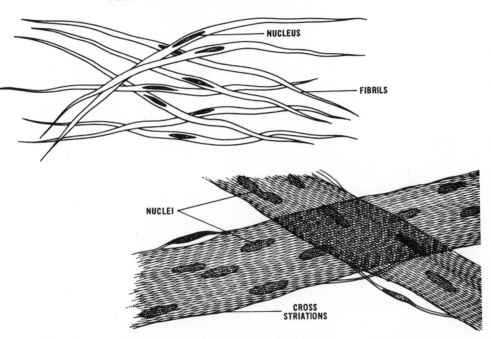

strength and firmness. Cartilage, tendons, and ligaments compose the connective tissue of animals. This tissue plays an important role in the tenderness of meat (Chapter 18). Connective tissue lies below the *epithelial tissue*, which includes the skin and linings of the digestive tract (stomach, intestine, etc.).

Muscle tissue supplies the force for either voluntary or involuntary movement. *The three classifications of muscle tissue are smooth, striated, and cardiac.* Tissues are grouped to form organs.

Organs

In plants and animals, even highly specialized tissues cannot perform a life activity to perfection. This requires a group of tissues working closely together;

heart, stomach, liver, brain, and kidney are all examples of related tissues, or organs. The stem of a plant is also an organ. It supports the leaves, flowers, and fruit, and moves food materials up and down between the roots and the leaves. In higher forms of life several organs often perform related tasks; a group of organs working together is called an *organ system*. For example, the digestive system in the human body performs functions related to the breaking down of food so that it can be assimilated by the body.

Plants and Animals as Food Sources

Plants. Vegetables, fruits, grains, and legumes are all plant foods eaten by man. They are consumed both raw and cooked. The grains which one might think of as seeds are actually the fruits of grasses such as wheat, barley, oats, and rye. They are not fleshy in nature as apples, pears, and peaches are. You have already found that plants are able to synthesize and store food substances by the process of photosynthesis. In this process they use carbon dioxide, water, and light energy, and eliminate oxygen. Man, on the contrary, uses oxygen

There are many varieties of plants which are consumed by man. These may be vegetables, fruits, grains, or seeds.

and discards carbon dioxide. He is able to eat plant foods, break them down into their component parts and use them in maintaining his life. There is an interdependency between plant and animal life.

In our study of foods derived from plants we will be primarily concerned with cell structure and its influence on the preparation of foods for human consumption. In the cooking of plant foods we shall be studying the effects of heat on plant pigments, on the cell wall, and on the permeable membranes of cells.

Animals. Meat, poultry, fish, eggs, and milk with all of its dairy products are foods from animal sources. These foods are eaten both raw and cooked. All are excellent sources of protein which is necessary for the growth and repair of tissues in the human body. Fat is also animal tissue and is a major source of energy.

In plant food cookery major attention is given to the role that individual cell structure plays. In protein cookery the tissues are the chief consideration.

Man eats many kinds of animals and animal products. High-quality protein, necessary for the growth and repair of body tissues, comes from these sources.

THE NATURE OF FOOD

The characteristics of the various proteins found in the foods listed on the previous page, their interactions, and their reactions to other food substances and to temperature are interesting to study because they have definite influence on the ways we prepare foods which are largely protein in content.

As you study the succeeding chapters in this book you will begin to understand more clearly why methods for food preparation and cookery have been developed as they have. You will also learn why the selection, care, and storage of all foods are so important if people are to have the full benefit of food and its nutritive value. You will be more appreciative of the fact that if this knowledge of the basic structure of foods and the principles of food cookery are applied, you can have foods that are more pleasing to see, taste, and eat. At the same time these foods will be beneficial to you nutritionally.

MAJOR IDEAS

The following statements give the main ideas within the chapter you have just studied. Be sure you know the words underscored in these statements and in the questions to follow.

1. All living matter is made up of very small but complex living cells. Each cell contains specialized parts responsible for the processes of living with the nucleus serving as the coordinating center.
2. Plants and animals are dependent upon each other. Plants are equipped to manufacture food and release oxygen from carbon dioxide and water in the presence of light and chlorophyll. Animals use oxygen and eliminate carbon dioxide in their processes of living; they use plants for food to supply some of their own food needs.
3. The whole animal or plant is a collection of organ systems, each of which is composed of individual organs, tissues, cells, parts of cells, molecules, and atoms.
4. The composition and structure of the plant cell and its parts determine what happens to plants when they are cooked in any given way. Similarly, the component parts of animal tissues control what happens to cuts of meat when they are cooked in any specific manner.
5. Usually, animal foods contribute high-quality protein and plant foods contribute vitamins, minerals, and carbohydrates needed by man.
6. Plants and animals are sources of fats.

QUESTIONS TO STUDY

CELL STRUCTURE

1. In what ways does cell structure influence cooking methods?
2. In what respects do animal and plant cells differ? Show how these differences affect the preparation of animal and plant foods.
3. Describe ways in which knowledge of DNA and RNA could influence foods in the future.
4. Explain the interdependence of plants and animals.
5. What changes occur in pectic substances during the ripening of fruit?

TISSUES

1. The more specialized a cell becomes, the more it must depend on other cells. Explain.
2. In what way does the amount of connective tissue in a meat cut affect its tenderness?
3. Give examples of plant and animal tissues.

ORGANS

1. Name two organ systems.
2. Name four organs.

PLANTS AS FOOD SOURCES

1. What nutrients do plant foods supply to man?
2. What determines the color of plant foods? Why are some green, yellow, red, or white?
3. Why is the preparation of fruits and vegetables influenced so greatly by the structure of individual plant cells?

ANIMALS AS FOOD SOURCES

1. Why is the preparation of animal foods more influenced by tissue and organ structure than by individual cell structure?
2. Why are animal foods rich sources of high-quality protein?

BIBLIOGRAPHY

Biological Science: Molecules to Man. Biological Science Curriculum Study, Boston, Houghton Mifflin Company, 1963.

GREGORY, WILLIAM H., and GOLDMAN, EDWARD H., *Biological Science for High School.* Boston, Ginn and Company, 1965.

12 STRUCTURE AND COMPOSITION OF FOODS

Foods have many properties which are directly related to the structural (physical) and chemical composition of living cells. To develop some understanding of what happens when foods are prepared to eat, you need a working knowledge of their physical and chemical characteristics. This chapter presents the major properties of foods which influence their eating quality, nutritive value, and acceptability.

Physical Properties

The physical properties of food include such characteristics as its appearance, freezing and boiling points, solubility, specific gravity, viscosity, fluidity, and plasticity.

Whether or not a food has attractive color, texture, and shape determines to a large extent one's acceptance of it.

Sensory impressions. Our first impression of food is usually visual, and a major part of our willingness to accept a food depends on its *color.* The extent to which each of us accepts the color of any particular food varies depending on our ideas of how that food should look. For instance, we accept grayishness in raw oysters but reject that color in poultry. The color blue, universally disliked in most foods, is accepted in various shades in certain cheeses and fruits. The color of any food serves as a guide for judging its quality and indicating any deterioration or spoilage.

Fruits and vegetables free from brown spots or other blemishes are considered to be higher in quality than those with scars or bruises, and are generally preferred. The color of meat products is indispensable to consumer acceptance. A bright red color, for example, is usually associated with fresh beef; a pink "cured" meat color, with cured meats. A dark brown color in fresh meat usually indicates spoilage to most consumers.

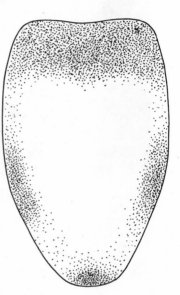

Flavor, another sensory impression of food, is considered the sum total of taste and odor; flavor together with feel, appearance, and even the sound of food determine its palatability. The four primary taste sensations are sweet, sour, salty, and bitter. Taste buds located on your tongue transmit these sensations to your brain. Thus, some foods may taste sweet to one person and bland or flat or sour to someone else. Taste buds may react to more than one type of taste; those reacting strongly to similar tastes are clustered together on the tongue. Substances must be in solution to stimulate the taste buds.

Aroma is a sensation closely related to taste. It is detected through tiny, sensitive receivers in the upper part of the nose. Many people are able to detect aromas of very low concentrations and it would seem that the sense of smell is more delicate than the sense of taste. Since substances must first exist as gases to be smelled, the perception of various odors is influenced by temperature. Hot foods, for example, have stronger odors than cold foods.

The great variety of textures in foods, such as crispness, crunchiness, smoothness, chewiness, oiliness, greasiness, hardness, and elasticity, add to the pleasure of eating.

Texture, another characteristic of food, is closely related to flavor and aroma. It has been defined in many ways but most definitions point out two important elements: the physical structure of the food and the way the material handles and feels in the mouth. Texture has been recently classified in three categories: (1) mechanical characteristics, (2) geometrical characteristics, and (3) other characteristics.

Mechanical characteristics refer to the reactions of food to stress. These characteristics are measured by the amount of pressure exerted on the tongue, teeth, and the roof of the mouth as food is eaten. Geometrical characteristics refer to the sizes and shapes of foods and are usually sensed by sight. Other characteristics include "mouth-feel" qualities related to the moisture and the fat content of food.

A chart of the classification of textural characteristics is shown on the next page to help you describe the various foods with which you will be working as you study foods.

Table 8

Classification of Textural Characteristics

(Relations between textural parameters and popular terms)

MECHANICAL CHARACTERISTICS

Primary parameters	Secondary parameters	Popular terms
Hardness		Soft→Firm→Hard
Cohesiveness	Brittleness	Crumbly→Crunchy→ Brittle
	Chewiness	Tender→Chewy→Tough
	Gumminess	Short→Mealy→Pasty→ Gummy
Viscosity		Thin→Viscous
Elasticity		Plastic→Elastic
Adhesiveness		Sticky→Tacky→Gooey

GEOMETRICAL CHARACTERISTICS

Class	Examples
Particle size and shape	Gritty, Grainy, Coarse, Smooth, etc.
Particle shape and orientation	Fibrous, Cellular, Crystalline, etc.

OTHER CHARACTERISTICS

Primary parameters	Secondary parameters	Popular terms
Moisture content		Dry→Moist→Wet→ Watery
Fat content	Oiliness	Oily
	Greasiness	Greasy

Reprinted from JOURNAL OF FOOD SCIENCE, Volume 28, 1963, copyright © 1963 by Institute of Food Technologists. All views and opinions are solely those of the author.

Foods have definite color, flavor, and texture. They exist in three *states of matter* or combinations of these states called *liquids, solids,* and *gases.* Before we discuss the states of matter it is necessary that you have some understanding of the composition of matter. *All substances—or matter—are composed of minute particles called atoms; a number of atoms chemically bound together form a molecule.* For example, a molecule of water, represented by the chemical formula H_2O, consists of two atoms of hydrogen combined with one atom of oxygen.

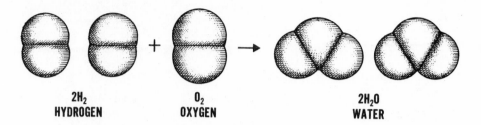

$2H_2$	O_2	$2H_2O$
HYDROGEN	OXYGEN	WATER

Above: Two molecules of hydrogen plus one molecule of oxygen produce two molecules of water.
Below: Matter exists in three states—solids, liquids, and gases. Temperature and pressure, which affect the closeness of the molecules, determine the state.

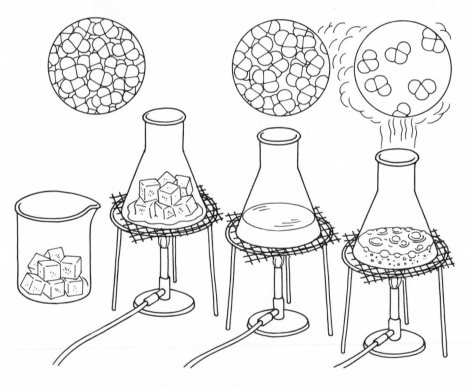

The closeness of the molecules in a substance determines the state of matter. *Molecules are closest together in a solid; in a liquid the molecules are relatively far apart; in a gas they are much farther apart than in a liquid.* A solid retains a definite shape, a liquid has a definite volume but its shape varies with that of its container, and a gas fills all available space.

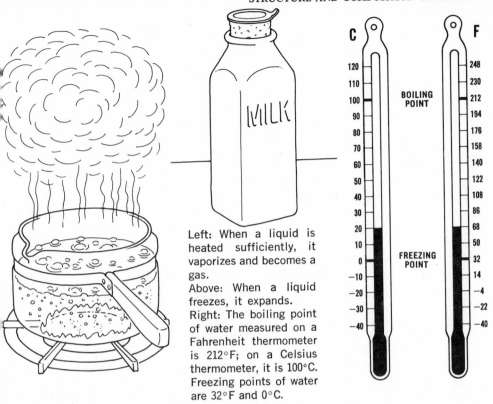

Left: When a liquid is heated sufficiently, it vaporizes and becomes a gas.
Above: When a liquid freezes, it expands.
Right: The boiling point of water measured on a Fahrenheit thermometer is 212°F; on a Celsius thermometer, it is 100°C. Freezing points of water are 32°F and 0°C.

Boiling and freezing points. The state of a substance may be changed by changing the temperature. For example, a gas that is cooled or compressed is changed to a liquid and, on further cooling, the liquid becomes a solid. A liquid begins to become a gas during the heating process at temperatures below the boiling point. The *boiling point* is reached, however, only when the vapor pressure of the liquid is equal to the atmospheric pressure. The temperature at which a liquid, when cooled, becomes a solid is known as the *freezing point*.

Quantitative scales are used for measuring temperatures. The two chief scales for measuring temperatures are the *Fahrenheit* and the *Celsius* (centigrade). On the Fahrenheit scale 32° is the freezing point of water and 212° is the boiling point at normal atmospheric pressure (760 mm. of mercury). The scale has one hundred and eighty equal divisions between the freezing and boiling points of water.

On the Celsius (centigrade) scale the freezing point of water is 0° and the boiling point is 100°, with 100 equal divisions between the two points. If you wish to change a Celsius (C) reading to a Fahrenheit (F) reading, multiply the number of Celsius degrees by 9, divide by 5 and then add 32.

$$°F = \tfrac{9}{5} °C + 32$$

The boiling point of a liquid depends upon atmospheric pressure. At sea level, water boils at 212°F; at higher altitudes, the boiling point is lower. The required cooking time for a food will be longer at higher altitudes.

If, however, the change is from Fahrenheit to Celsius (centigrade) one must subtract 32 from the Fahrenheit degrees, multiply by 5 and then divide by 9.

$$°C = (°F - 32) \times \tfrac{5}{9}$$

Because of the decreased pressure exerted on the surface of a liquid under a partial vacuum, evaporation is increased. This fact is used in the dehydration of foods. When barometric pressure is low, water evaporates faster than at normal atmospheric pressure, so foods tend to "boil dry" on a stormy day.

All that has been said about solids, liquids, and gases has been with reference to pure substances. In practice, however, we are continually dealing with mixtures of these substances.

Homogeneous mixtures. Gases, liquids, and solids may be mixed together in various combinations to form homogeneous (similar, or the same in nature throughout) mixtures called *true solutions*. Gaseous solutions are made by dissolving one gas in another. Since all gases mix in all proportions, any mixture of gases is homogeneous and a solution. Liquid solutions are made by dissolving a gas, a liquid, or a solid in a liquid. If the liquid is water, the solution is called an aqueous solution. Thus sugar dissolved in water would be an aqueous solution. Solid solutions are solids in which one solid is uniformly dispersed throughout another solid. Sterling silver, which has 92.5 percent silver and 7.5 percent copper, is one example of a solid solution.

Here we will consider true solutions. On page
138 we will discuss heterogeneous mixtures.

In discussing the properties of solutions, the terms
solvent and solute are used. The dissolving medium
is the solvent and the substance being dissolved,
the solute. A solution with a high percentage of
solute is said to be concentrated; one with a low
percentage of solute is said to be dilute.

The amount of solute that will dissolve in a given
amount of solvent determines the solubility of the
solute in that solvent. The solubility of a solute
depends upon (1) the nature of the solvent, (2) the
nature of the solute, (3) the temperature, and, to a
degree, (4) the pressure exerted on the mixture.

A *saturated solution* is one that has dissolved the
maximum amount of solute that it normally can,
under a given set of conditions. For example, if
sugar is added to water until the water cannot dissolve any more sugar, the resulting mixture is said
to be saturated at that temperature. However, if
this same mixture is heated, more sugar will be dissolved, and if then cooled to its previous temperature without the precipitation of any of the sugar,
the solution will be said to be *supersaturated*. With
a few exceptions (sodium chloride, or salt, for one),
the higher the temperature, the greater the solubility
of a solid in a liquid up to the point of saturation. In
the case of gases, their solubility in liquids decreases
with an increase in temperature. For instance, the
tiny bubbles which form when water is heated are
due to dissolved air becoming less soluble as the
temperature of the water increases. Another example is evident in a carbonated beverage. In this
case, more carbon dioxide is held in solution when
the beverage is cold than when it is warm. For this
reason, a chilled carbonated beverage is more flavorful than a warm one.

The concentration of a solution affects its boiling
and freezing points. The boiling point of a solution
rises above that of the pure solvent in proportion to
the concentration of particles (molecules or ions) of
the solute. Volatile solutes are an exception. Water,
for instance, boils at 212° F at sea level. With

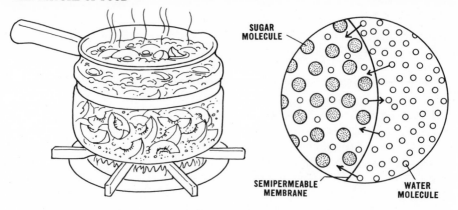

SUGAR
MOLECULE

SEMIPERMEABLE
MEMBRANE

WATER
MOLECULE

The movement of a pure solvent through a semipermeable membrane into a solution containing the same solvent is called osmosis.

the addition of sugar to the water, the boiling point will rise. The freezing point of a solvent is lowered by the addition of a solute. Water freezes at 32° F, but if a substance such as salt (sodium chloride) is added to the water the freezing point of the solution is lowered.

The solubility of all gases is increased as the pressure is increased. In a carbonated beverage, for example, before the bottle is opened, the gas is in solution under pressure. As soon as the cap is removed, however, the pressure drops and bubbles of carbon dioxide form and are able to escape from the beverage.

When a solution of sugar and water is separated by a membrane such as is found in fruit and vegetable tissues—as when cooking peaches in sugar and water solution—the water molecules pass freely through this membrane, but the sugar cannot pass through it. This action continues until a state of equilibrium (equal amounts of water passing back and forth) is reached. This process is called *osmosis* (page 123). The concentration of the sugar sirup will influence the extent to which water is drawn from the fruit to dilute the sugar sirup. The force with which the liquid is drawn from the more concentrated into the less concentrated solution is referred to as the *osmotic pressure*.

Heterogeneous mixtures. *Colloids* are mixtures which are not clearly homogeneous or heterogeneous. They contain particles that are too small to be seen under a microscope and that do not settle out on standing but are too large to be in true solution. These may be large molecules or aggregates. Colloidal particles are called the *dispersed phase* and the material in which they are held is the *continuous phase*. Since there are three states of matter—gases, liquids, and solids—we would think there are nine possible types of colloids. However, there are only eight because mixtures of gases, you will recall, are solutions and therefore they do not form colloidal mixtures.

The eight possible types of colloidal mixtures are listed below:

	Solid (S)	Liquid (L)	Gas (G)
Solid (S)	S in S	S in L	S in G
Liquid (L)	L in S	L in L	L in G
Gas (G)	G in S	G in L	

The colloids which are important in the study of foods are the solid-in-liquid, known as a sol; liquid-in-solid, called a gel; liquid-in-liquid, known as an emulsion; gas-in-liquid or gas-in-solid, called a foam.

Kinds of colloids. The first colloidal system is a *sol* which is a solid dispersed through a liquid. The liquid forms the continuous phase and solid particles form the dispersed phase. Sols resemble liquids in their physical properties since they flow and do not show rigidity of form. However, if the dispersed solid interferes with the free movement of the liquid, a viscous (thick) sol results. Gelatin which is dissolved in water is an example of a sol.

As a gelatin solution is cooled, it first becomes viscous and then finally forms the second type of colloid, a gel.

Gels are colloids in which a liquid is distributed throughout a solid arranged in a fine network which extends throughout the mixture. The network has been defined as a "brush-heap" structure. In some gels, this structure can revert to a sol. You may observe this happening in a fruit jelly or in a gelatin salad or dessert if it becomes too warm. On the other hand, the rigidity of a gel usually increases as the temperature drops. If the solid network of a gel separates from the liquid, the matter which precipitates out is called a flocculant (curd) and the process is known as flocculation (curdling). The precipitant which coats the bottom of a pan in which milk has been heated is one result of floccuation.

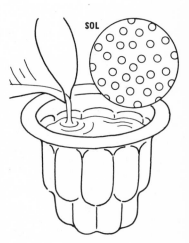

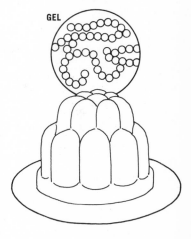

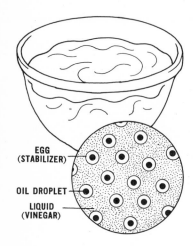

EGG
(STABILIZER)

OIL DROPLET

LIQUID
(VINEGAR)

Upon standing, many gel structures lose liquid and shrink. This condition is *syneresis* or "*weeping.*" The liquid which collects around a mold of gelatin in the refrigerator, the separation of whey during the souring of milk, and the separation of liquid from lean meat when that meat is cooked well-done are all typical examples of syneresis.

A third type of colloid is known as an *emulsion.* Emulsions are colloids in which a liquid is dispersed through another liquid in which it is not soluble. The most common type of emulsion in food preparation is oil dispersed in water. Another example of an emulsion is whole milk. In milk, butterfat globules are dispersed through an aqueous (water) solution. In the creaming process (when cream rises to the top of whole milk) the larger fat globules separate out. If the milk has been homogenized (page 244) the fat globules have been broken into small particles and will not rise to the top of the milk. Homogenization is, then, one means of preparing a stable emulsion. Substances such as proteins (pages 229–230), gums, and fatty acids may be added to emulsions to give them stability. These substances are called emulsifiers. They are used extensively in making salad dressings. Other emulsifiers will be discussed in Chapter 19.

Foams are a fourth group of colloids. In a foam, the air or gas represents the dispersed phase and the liquid or solid represents the continuous phase. A foam is created by the agitation of a liquid which results in incorporation of air in the liquid. The foaming properties of a substance depend upon its surface tension and the viscosity of the liquid or other characteristics that give stability to the structure of the foam.

Surface tension refers to the molecular forces which tend to pull the molecules to the interior of the liquid and away from the surface, thus causing the liquid to have a minimum surface area and to assume a spherical shape. A low air-liquid tension is necessary for foam formation. The foams of egg white, whipped cream, milk froth, and gelatin are important in foods.

Specific gravity. The specific gravity of any material is its weight in reference to the weight of an equal volume of water at a specified temperature. The specific gravity of water is 1.0 at 4° C. Since milk contains many components whose densities (mass per unit volume) are greater than that of water, its specific gravity will be greater than water. Milk normally has a specific gravity from 1.027 to 1.036, with an average of 1.032 at 60° F. As the fat content of the milk increases, the specific gravity of milk decreases, since fat has a specific gravity below 1.0. Skim milk has a higher specific gravity than whole milk and cream has a lower specific gravity than whole milk. Specific gravity is used in connection with the commercial purchase of such foods as jams, milk, and ice cream. It is also used as a measure of maturity of frozen peas, corn, and potatoes. Potatoes, tubers of high specific gravity, have been found to yield a more mealy cooked product than do tubers of low specific gravity.

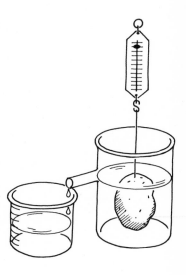

Fluidity, viscosity, and plasticity. All liquids have fluidity—the capacity to flow. Some do not flow as readily as others. This resistance to flowing is termed viscosity. The viscosity increases with the concentration and aggregation of the dispersed particles. For example, the higher the fat content in cream, the greater its viscosity. Whipping cream which has a greater percentage of fat than coffee cream will be more viscous. Protein sols become more viscous due to the coagulation of the protein. The pectin content of fruit juices and the sugar concentration of sirups are reflected in their viscosity.

The viscosity of a liquid can be measured by comparing the speed of its flow with that of water. While viscosity and fluidity determine the rate of flow of a liquid, plasticity is that property of certain nonfluid materials which enables them to hold their shape under a certain amount of applied pressure. These materials exhibit "plastic flow" after sufficient pressure is applied. Hydrogenated vegetable shortenings are usually described as plastic.

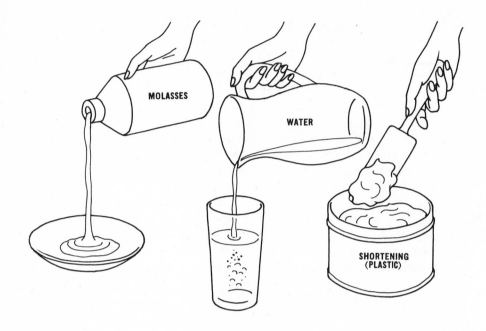

Chemical Properties

When you study food it is important to understand the chemical properties as well as the physical characteristics. In considering chemical properties we think of those qualities that describe a material's capacity to be changed into another material. The rancidity of fat, the hydrogenation of fat, and the souring of milk are examples of chemical changes which take place in food. Some of the chemical changes which occur are related to reactions with acid, hydrolysis, fermentation, browning reactions, and oxidation. The food nutrients—fats, proteins, carbohydrates—undergo change as a result of such chemical reactions.

Acidity. The degree of acidity of any food and of the medium in which it is cooked may affect the color, texture, flavor, and the retention of the nutritive value of that food. Acids are substances having in common a characteristic component, hydrogen, which in water solution exists as hydrogen ion. Litmus, a substance which changes color in the presence of an acid or a base (alkali), may be used to identify the presence of an acid (or base). Acids, which have a sour taste, turn blue litmus red; bases, which have a bitter taste, turn red litmus blue. Vinegar, lemons, limes, grapefruit, and oranges are examples of foods which contain acids. Baking soda is an alkaline (basic) compound sometimes used in baked products and other foods.

The degree of acidity in a food is indicated by its pH value. The lower the pH value, the more acidic the food. High pH values signify alkaline foods.

Acids in our study are considered in two aspects: the quantity and the intensity. *The quantity, or capacity, is the total or potential number of hydrogen ions that an acid could supply. The intensity is the actual hydrogen ion concentration of a solution and is expressed in terms of pH value.* The pH value is used to indicate the degree of acidity (or alkalinity) of any particular food or food product. The pH scale is numbered from 0 to 14; the number 7 is considered neutral (the pH of pure water), below 7 indicates acidity, and above 7 indicates alkalinity.

How is pH value related to food and food products? Unless fruit juices have a pH value below 3.55 they will not form jellies; if the pH is below 3.1 the jellies are stiff but will not hold as much liquid, so syneresis (page 140) may result. Lemons, limes, and grapefruit are foods with low pH values. The pH value is also related to the freshness of meat and eggs. Fresh egg whites have a pH value of 7.6 to 8.0 while older egg whites have a pH of 9.0 to 9.5. Fresh meat is slightly acid; decomposed or spoiled meat is distinctly alkaline. The handling of fruits and vegetables in the home is affected by pH values. Certain fruits will brown rapidly once their tissues are exposed to the air. This browning can be delayed, however, by adding high acid fruit juices to lower the pH value of the fruit that might otherwise turn brown. Cooking water with a low pH will cause green vegetables to become olive green in color while cooking

Table 9

The pH Values of Some Common Foods

Product	pH Value
Limes	1.8–2.0
Lemons	2.2–2.4
Gingerale	2.0–4.0
Vinegar	2.4–3.4
Gooseberries	2.8–3.1
Apples	2.9–3.3
Plums	2.8–3.0
Jellies	3.0–3.5
Grapefruit	3.0–3.3
Strawberries	3.1-3.5
Cherries	3.2–4.1
Raspberries	3.2–3.7
Sauerkraut	3.6
Apricots	3.6–4.0
Pears	3.9
Tomatoes	4.1–4.4
Beets	4.9–5.6
Carrots	4.9–5.6
Bread	5.0–6.0
Angel Food Cake	5.0–6.5
Cucumbers	5.1
Bananas	5.6
Egg Yolks	5.9–6.8
Chocolate (Dutch Processed)	6.0–7.8
Potatoes	6.1
Milk	6.3–6.8
Shrimp	6.8–7.0
Devil's Food Cake	7.5–8.4
Egg Whites	7.6–9.7

water with a high pH will preserve the green color, but may cause the vegetable to become mushy as a result of the breakdown of cellulose and the pectic substances (page 163). Some people practice adding a small amount of baking soda to green beans so that the green color is retained. High pH value will also accelerate the rate of destruction of thiamine in foods.

In the commercial manufacture of certain pastries which contain custard fillings, it is desirable that a pH of less than 4 to 4.5 be maintained in the custard in order to keep the bacterial count to a minimum since bacteria prefer to grow in weakly acid and slightly alkaline substances. The table on page 144 shows the pH values of some common foods.

Hydrolysis. When water unites with another substance to produce different substances we say hydrolysis has taken place. This is a chemical change. For example, water will, in the presence of certain enzymes or weak acids, unite with sugar (sucrose) to form the simple sugars, glucose and fructose. This hydrolysis of sucrose is often referred to as inversion and the mixture of simple sugars is called invert sugar. The process of inversion will be discussed in detail in Chapter 15.

Fermentation. Sugars are also changed chemically by fermentation. The chemical change from the action of bacteria or yeast on sugar will vary with the type of fermentation. For example, sugar is added to bread dough so that this action can take place. Through the action of the yeast on the sugar, carbon dioxide is released. The carbon dioxide, a gas, causes the bread to rise and become porous. Lactose (milk sugar) is not fermented by yeast but by certain bacteria. Lactic-acid-producing microorganisms (a type of bacteria) are used commercially in souring milk. Additional foods prepared by lactic fermentations are cucumber pickles, sauerkraut, and other lightly salted vegetables. Acid concentration is important in the fermentation of certain foods.

Onion pickles are prepared by the process of fermentation.

Bernard L. Lewis, Inc.

Wes Kemp

Enzymatic browning.

Browning. Browning of food occurs in at least three different ways. First, there is *nonenzymatic browning* which is the reaction between protein or amino acids and certain sugars. Second is *enzymatic browning* which involves the oxidative enzymatic changes which occur when cut fruit is exposed to air. *Caramelization* is a third type of browning. It is characterized by certain changes which occur when sugar is heated to a high temperature.

Nonenzymatic browning, or Maillard reaction* as it is sometimes called, is a chemical change which produces a brown color in dried foods such as milk, eggs, fruit, and meat. This same reaction produces some of the aroma, flavor, and color of cereals, toffees, coffee, and the crust of baked goods.

Enzymatic activity is responsible for the browning of cut fruit. It has been previously mentioned that this change can be prevented by lowering the pH value of the fruit with the addition of a high acid fruit juice such as lemon juice or by excluding air.

*This reaction was named for Dr. L. C. Maillard, who was the first to describe the development of brown color in mixtures containing amino acids and reducing sugar.

Nonenzymatic browning.

Wes Kemp

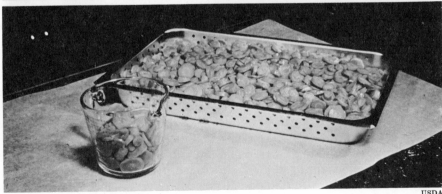

USDA

Caramelization, the third type of browning reaction, occurs in foods having a high sugar content, and explains why some vegetables—carrots, for example —brown during cooking. Caramelization is explained in Chapter 15.

Oxidation. The process by which chemical change occurs when food is exposed to oxygen (air) is oxidation. The rate at which oxidation takes place is increased with an increase in temperature and decreased with a decrease in temperature. This chemical process improves the baking quality of bread flour. Bread flour is usually matured when treated with certain oxidizing agents (chlorine dioxide) before being used in the baking of bread in order to produce a bread of good volume and soft texture.

Oxidative changes are also associated with the growth of microorganisms which produce undesirable tastes and odors in certain foods. For this reason many foods are packaged in tin containers under partial vacuum with an inert gas such as nitrogen, so that air will be excluded and oxidative changes in these foods will be prevented.

Chemical changes related to nutrients. Let us look at chemical changes which are related to specific food components. We shall be particularly concerned with those changes which occur in fats and proteins.

Fats may react with water and undergo *hydrolysis*. The products formed are glycerol and fatty acids. Fats are referred to chemically as esters (compounds formed by the reaction between an acid and an alcohol) of glycerol, an alcohol, and fatty acids.

Rancidity, hydrogenation, and reversion are changes resulting from chemical reactions which also occur in fats.

Rancidity. Rancidity is characterized by undesirable tastes and odors resulting from certain chemical changes in fats. There are at least three causes of rancidity: (1) the action of enzymes present in animal and fat tissues, (2) the action of microorganisms, and (3) atmospheric oxidation.

The absorption of odors produces off flavors but is not due to a chemical reaction. This occurs in packaging and also during the storage of fats or foods with high fat content. Milk, meat, eggs, and butter may absorb foreign odors. For example, if onions are left uncovered and are stored near milk, the milk is likely to absorb the onion flavor.

Lipase and lipoxidase, enzymes found in plant and animal tissues, accelerate chemical changes which cause undesirable flavor changes. Flavors of some fish, plants, and animal foods can be affected. These changes can be prevented by heating the food to a high enough temperature to destroy the enzyme.

Microorganisms do not grow in pure fat but in foods containing fat where moisture and other substances are also found. In their process of growing, these organisms cause deterioration of the food. The "fishiness" which occurs in butter is caused by this type of reaction.

Oxidative rancidity, previously discussed under oxidation, may be inhibited by the addition of certain substances called antioxidants. These will be discussed in detail in Chapter 19.

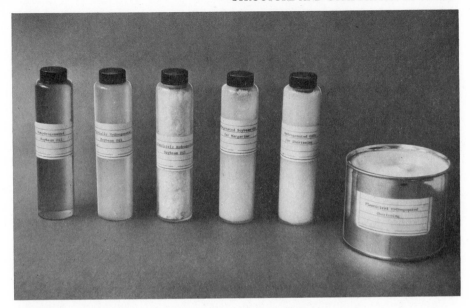

Through the process of hydrogenation, liquid fats assume varying degrees of hardness or plasticity.

Hydrogenation. The chemical process of hydrogenation is an important one in the food industry. In this process an oil or soft fat is reacted with hydrogen in the presence of a metal, nickel, and is thereby hardened. The nickel serves as a catalyst to speed up the chemical reaction. Fats produced by this process may have varying degrees of hardness or plasticity. The degree depends on the completeness of hydrogenation and whether some oil or soft fat is mixed with the final product.

There are also certain chemical reactions and physio-chemical changes common to proteins. The latter changes include denaturation, coagulation, and hydration.

Denaturation. In this process protein molecules are changed structurally through the application of heat, by the addition of acids or alkalies, by agitation, or by the application of pressure. Heat denaturation occurs when protein foods such as fish, meat, eggs, and milk are cooked. As the protein is denatured, that is, changed from its natural form, it becomes less soluble and may precipitate out of solution. If the solution is concentrated, the protein may aggregate to form a gel structure (coagulate). The addition of an acid or an alkali can cause the protein to coagulate or be precipitated from the solution. Agitation and application of pressure also cause denaturation of some proteins. For example, when egg whites are beaten to a foam, the protein in solution has a tendency to denature at the surface of the dispersed air bubbles. This surface is also known as *interface*.

Coagulation. The coagulation of protein involves two steps: denaturation and aggregation or flocculation. Coagulation is particularly important in the processing of foods. Most protein foods are heat-coagulated when they are prepared for eating. However, in some instances precautions are taken to prevent coagulation from occurring. In the processing of milk, for example, it is desirable that the protein, casein, in the milk retain its natural properties and not coagulate.

Proteins have a temperature of coagulation that is specific for each protein but these temperatures can be varied by the addition of acids, alkalies, salts, or sugar. Proteins have a certain pH range in which they are most stable. Outside this range denaturation may occur more readily. For example, deteriorated egg white (pH 9.0–9.5) requires a higher temperature than does fresh egg white for coagulation. Sugar raises the temperature of coagulation for egg protein, as is evident in the preparation of egg custards. This is also true in the beating of egg whites. An egg white foam is more difficult to form when sugar is added at the beginning of the beating period rather than after beating to obtain the desired volume. The effect of salts on coagulation depends on the kind of salt, its concentration, and at what point in coagulation the salt is added. There are times when the addition of salt will even prevent coagulation. For example, egg white which has had some of its natural salt content removed will not coagulate when heated. However, if common table salt (sodium chloride) is added to water in which eggs are to be poached, coagulation will be encouraged. Denaturation and coagulation are more rapid at high temperatures than at low ones.

Hydration. Hydration involves the ability of a material to absorb water. *When the proteins of wheat flour are combined with water, gluten* (page 174) *is produced.* Gluten forms the structure for the retention of the gas needed to develop volume in a baked product such as a loaf of bread or a cake. The hydration of protein is affected by such factors as the pH value and the presence of water-attracting materials such as sugar and salt. A concentrated sugar solution draws the water from the protein. This principle is brought to bear in the process of sugar-curing meat.

Salt may help to tenderize meat since its effect is to increase the hydration of the protein within the meat, yet the amount of salt required for the tenderizing process will make the meat unpalatable.

Increasing or decreasing the pH from the pH value at which a protein is least soluble reduces the loss of moisture from a protein food. For example, beef has been shown to become progressively more tender by lowering or raising its pH level. Toughness is at a maximum at pH 5.0–6.0.

In this chapter we have considered some of the structural and chemical properties of living matter as they relate to foods and their preparation. You will find in the chapters to follow how these properties serve as guides in determining desirable methods for handling and preparing foods.

MAJOR IDEAS

The following statements give the main ideas within the chapter you have just studied. Be sure you know the words underscored in these statements and in the questions to follow.

1. The properties and characteristics of plant and animal foods are directly related to the properties of tissues.
2. Foods are acceptable to us when they appeal to our sight, sense of smell, and taste.
3. Foods can be changed both physically and chemically by the manner in which they are stored and prepared. These changes can be controlled to some degree.
4. Basic knowledge of colloids, true solutions, and heterogeneous mixtures is readily applicable to food cookery.

QUESTIONS TO STUDY

PHYSICAL PROPERTIES

1. Why is it important to know the physical properties of food?
2. In what ways do true solutions and colloids differ? How are these differences applied to food preparation?
3. Why does water evaporate more rapidly from pure water than from a sugar solution cooked under the same conditions?
4. What are emulsifiers?
5. What are the four most important colloids found in food cookery?
6. What causes syneresis to occur in a gel?
7. Explain boiling and freezing points. How are they measured?
8. What is specific gravity? What importance does it have in foods?
9. What is meant by viscosity? Fluidity? Plasticity?
10. Why do you think egg whites fail to form a foam when beaten in a greased bowl?

CHEMICAL PROPERTIES

1. How does the degree of <u>acidity</u> within green beans or within the liquid in which they are cooked affect the cooked product?
2. Why is sugar used as one of the ingredients in bread dough?
3. What causes some cut fresh fruits to turn brown? How can this be prevented?
4. Give an example of <u>hydrolysis</u>.
5. Why do certain foods turn brown during cooking?
6. Why do dried milk and eggs sometimes turn brown after a period of storage?
7. Name a <u>catalyst</u>.
8. Give an example of <u>fermentation</u>.
9. What are some causes of <u>rancidity</u>?
10. How can an oil or soft fat be converted to a solid fat?
11. What is meant when we say that protein has been <u>denatured</u>?
12. What purpose does an <u>antioxidant</u> serve in food?
13. In what ways can the <u>coagulation</u> temperature of protein be influenced?
14. What purpose does <u>hydration</u> have in cooking protein foods?

BIBLIOGRAPHY

BATES, R. G., *Electrometric pH Determinations.* New York, John Wiley & Sons, Inc., 1954.

BRITTON, H. T., *Hydrogen Ions*, 4th ed. Princeton, D. Van Nostrand Company, Inc., 1956.

CHRISTENSEN, HALVOR N., *pH and Dissociation.* Philadelphia, W. B. Saunders Co., 1963.

CRAFT, C. C., and HEINZE, P. H., "Association of Specific Gravity with Weight of Individual Tubers in Late Crop Potatoes." *American Potato Journal*, Vol. 28, 1951, p. 580.

HABERMANN, H. M., "Applejack Technique; New Application of an Old Approach to Solute Concentration." *Science*, Vol. 140, No. 1, April 19, 1963, p. 292.

HODGE, J. E., "Dehydrated Foods. Chemistry of Browning Reactions in Model Systems." *Journal of Agricultural Food Chemistry*, Vol. 1, 1953, pp. 928–943.

JACOBS, MORRIS B., *The Chemistry and Technology of Food and Food Products*, Vol. 1. New York, Interscience Publishers, Inc., 1951.

JULESZ, B., "Texture and Visual Perception." *Scientific American*, Vol. 212, February 1965, pp. 38–48.

KRAMER, A., "Definition of Texture and Its Measurement in Vegetable Products." *Food Technology*, Vol. 18, March 1964, p. 46.

MACINNES, D. A., "pH." *Scientific American*, Vol. 184, No. 1, January 1951, pp. 40–43.

SHARON, I. M., "Sensory Properties of Food and Their Function During Feeding." *Food Technology*, Vol. 19. January 1965, p. 35.

SIENKO, MITCHELL, and PLANE, ROBERT A., *Chemistry*. New York, McGraw-Hill Book Company, 1961.

SZCZESNIAK, ALIMA SURMACKA, "Classification of Textural Characteristics." *Journal of Food Science*, Vol. 28, 1963, pp. 385–389.

VANDERWERF, CALVIN A., *Acids, Bases, and the Chemistry of the Covalent Bond*. New York, Reinhold Publishing Corp., 1963.

WALTON, A. G., "Nucleation of Crystals from Solution." *Science*, Vol. 140, April 19, 1963, p. 292.

13 FRUITS AND VEGETABLES

Man has been principally carnivorous throughout his development. From about 4000 B.C. there is evidence that he ate some cereals but plant foods of other sorts were comparatively rare. Although a few crops of turnips, onions, and garlic were grown in Europe, and even though yams were available in parts of Europe and in the Orient, potatoes, for example, were unknown as food before the time of Christopher Columbus.

Man has depended upon fruits for food since the early days when he gathered his dinner from trees, vines, and bushes. As man began to build civilizations, he also began to cultivate orchards and to develop juicier plums and sweeter oranges.

Citrus fruits such as lemons, grapefruit, oranges, and tangerines were first introduced to the Western world by traders from southeastern Asia. These fruits are now produced in large quantities in the tropic and subtropical areas of the world. California and Florida produce most of the citrus fruits used in the United States. Other fruits such as apples, cherries, peaches, and plums can withstand colder temperatures; thus they can be produced in areas of the United States which have a more seasonal change of climate.

Both fruits and vegetables of many varieties are now widely accepted and taken almost for granted. Modern storage, processing, and transportation methods have made it rather easy for us to have a good selection of these foods at any season of the year. This availability is important to us because fruits and vegetables are excellent sources of minerals and vitamins which are vital to our health and well-being.

In Chapters 11 and 12 you learned of the general structure of the cells which compose plant and animal tissues and how these cells function. In this chapter you will see how plant structures influence the quality, nutritive value, and choice of preparation method when certain plants and their several parts are used as food.

Plant Structure

Parts of a plant. Plants have roots, stems and tubers, leaves, flowers, and fruits. You will find that each part has a specific function in the life of a plant. What purpose each part serves affects its value as a source of food for man.

The *roots* anchor the plant in the ground and are the means by which the

154

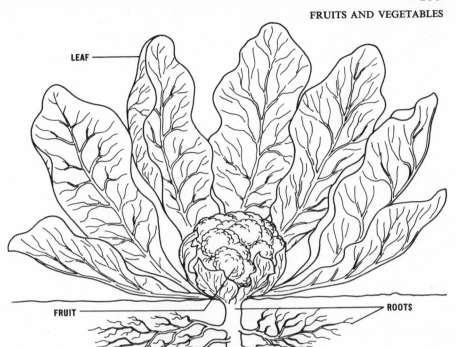

LEAF

FRUIT

ROOTS

Man uses the fruit from the cauliflower (illustrated above) for food. In other plants he may choose to eat the leaves (such as in lettuce, cabbage, and beet greens), stems (such as asparagus, celery, and rhubarb), or roots (such as carrots, radishes, and turnips).

plant absorbs moisture and plant nutrients from the soil. They are also storage areas for food for the plant. For instance, sweet potatoes, beets, carrots, parsnips, and turnips are roots where food materials are stored. These roots are used by man as food.

Stems serve as the passageway for plant nutrients from the soil to the leaves. They produce the leaves and expose them to the light. In many plants, green stems aid the leaves in their function of food manufacture in the process of photosynthesis. The stem, as does the root, often serves as a place for food storage. Asparagus, celery, and rhubarb are examples of this type of plant. Some plants have rootlike stems called rhizomes which are thick, fleshy, and filled with food. Tubers—white potatoes, for example—are enlarged tips of rhizomes swollen with stored food. A tuber, like other stems, has nodes at which buds or eyes develop. Each of these buds may form an aerial shoot and produce a new plant.

Leaves are the food-making organs of plants. They are vitally important not only to plants but also to all members of the animal kingdom. Chlorophyll, the visible green coloring matter in leaves, has a most important function. Under the stimulus of light, chlorophyll is active in the manufacture of plant food, mainly starch, from carbon dioxide and water. Brussels sprouts, cabbage, kale, lettuce, parsley, and spinach are leaves used by people for food.

Some plant *flowers* or *flower clusters*—broccoli and cauliflower—are also food. The flower represents one phase in the reproductive life of a plant. After fertilization has taken place, the flower has served its purpose. Then the plant pours its full energy into the development of its *seeds* and *fruit*. The term "fruit" is used to designate that part of the plant which provides the place and food for the developing seeds. Fruit need not be an apple, peach, or orange but may be a kernel of corn, a bean pod filled with beans, a cucumber, or a pumpkin. Some fruits become dry when fully ripened. Beans and nuts are examples of this type of fruit.

Maturation and Ripening

The term maturation means to come to full development. Ripening has a similar meaning, with both terms implying bringing to fitness for use when used in reference to foods. Maturation is generally associated with vegetables while the term ripening is used with fruits.

As tomatoes ripen, they lose their green color and become firm, plump, and red. As bananas ripen, they change from green to yellow.

Wes Kemp

Changes during ripening. During the ripening or maturation period of fruits and vegetables, changes in the starch content, size, and color take place. Action by certain enzymes within the plant tissues is responsible for these various changes.

The starch content is gradually converted to sugar with a consequent increase of sweetness in flavor. In fleshy fruits, such as watermelons, and in leafy vegetables, like lettuce, there is a marked accumulation of water which causes increased weight and size. With the changes in food content (starch to sugar) and in water content, there is often a change in the color. In tomatoes, for example, the chlorophyll disappears and is replaced by a carotenoid as the tomatoes assume a red color.

Artificial ripening. Some years ago it was discovered that ethylene gas hastens the ripening of citrus fruit. This knowledge has been applied to the ripening of oranges, grapefruit, and tomatoes. Rather recently it was found that ripening fruits and vegetables normally produce ethylene in minute quantities. Thus, the "artificial ripening" is only an acceleration of a process that occurs normally.

Qualities and Grades

Quality has many meanings. People who live in areas too far north for peach production may have had no opportunity to learn how good a fully tree-ripened peach can be. Their idea of acceptable quality in peaches may be quite different from that of persons who have experienced the tree-ripened fruit. Circumstances often cause our standards of quality to change. Some fruits and vegetables shipped long distances to winter markets may seem acceptable although their quality is not as high as at the peak of maturity in season.

The stage at which a fruit or vegetable is harvested and the time elapsing between harvest and consumption affect quality. Sweet corn, for instance, is usually harvested when it is in its "milk stage." The kernels are filled with a white, milky substance made up of starch granules suspended in water. At this time the corn is synthesizing and storing starch. This is the time when corn is at the peak of flavor.

We tend to associate certain combinations of characteristics with whatever we have learned to like or dislike. Physical makeup desired in one fruit or vegetable may not be wanted in another. We apparently do not like crispness, juiciness, or buttery texture just for themselves; they must be associated with certain foods. We want crispness in apples and celery but not in avocados and cantaloupes. Texture and consistency are greatly affected by the stage of maturity. Generally vegetables tend to become more fibrous and tough as they mature. Asparagus that has grown too old is, we say, "woody." It is not as acceptable for food as when it was young, free from the fibrous condition, and

Fresh fruits and vegetables available to the consumer vary in quality, appearance, and maturity.

tender. Certain fruits, such as pears, tend to become mushy and less flavorful as they mature.

The flavors experienced in eating fruits and vegetables greatly influence the acceptability of these foods. Flavors vary widely. Some are very mild and bland while others are very distinctive. Potatoes, for instance, are mild in flavor while cabbage, broccoli, and Brussels sprouts have a characteristic strong flavor.

Standards of quality. The United States Department of Agriculture has established standards of quality for judging fruits and vegetables. These standards are expressed as grades. Grades are based on these characteristics: size, uniformity of size, maturity, shape, color, freedom from disease and decay, absence of cuts or bruises. The grades range from USA Fancy, which marks the choicest products, to Culls which are substandard products.

The quality of perishable fresh fruits and vegetables is influenced by the way they are handled and stored from the time they are picked to the time they are used. When choosing fruits and vegetables, consider quality and size.

Table 10
United States Department of Agriculture Grades
Standards of Quality

Vegetables	*Fruits*
USA— Fancy	USA— Fancy
USB— Extra Standard	USB— Choice
USC— Standard	USC— Standard
Culls— Substandard	Culls— Substandard

Whether one chooses to buy the top grade depends upon the use to which the fruit or vegetable is to be put, the price one wishes to pay, and the strength of the desire to have "the best." The USA Fancy grade will indicate that the fruit or vegetable is as near perfect as it can be in every respect. The next grade will mark products lacking some of these characteristics but which may still be entirely acceptable for certain purposes. For example, if you are buying peaches which you wish to serve whole as a dessert, it may be very important that the peaches be uniform in size. On the other hand, if you intend to cut the peaches into small pieces to use with other fruits or in a pie or pudding, the uniformity of shape and size is not important as long as the flavor is good. Therefore it is wise to consider grades in relation to the intended use of a fruit or vegetable.

Principles of Fruit and Vegetable Cookery

The goals in both vegetable and fruit cookery are the retention of original nutritive value in so far as possible and the maintenance of a high level of palatability. The nutritive value of fruits and vegetables has been mentioned previously, and you will recall that vegetables and fruits contain significant amounts of the vitamins and minerals necessary for the regulation of the human body functions. Thus, the cooking methods used for vegetables and fruits should be such that they retain these vitamins and minerals.

Palatability and acceptability. To benefit from the nutrients present in fruits and vegetables, they obviously must be eaten. Therefore, it is important that the food be acceptable in both appearance and flavor. The retention of color during cooking is advisable since much of the attractiveness of fresh fruits and vegetables is related to their various colors.

Plant pigments. Earlier it was mentioned that plant pigments are of four types: red—anthocyanins; yellow—carotenoids; green—chlorophyll; white —flavones. These pigments will be discussed in relation to the changes in color which occur when vegetables and fruits are cooked.

Red pigments are in the cell sap of the plant cell. This particular pigment is not only water-soluble but it is also affected by acids, alkalies, and heat. Cooking red cabbage in an acid medium or with an acid food—apples or lemons, for example—is necessary if a bright clear-colored red product is desired. Alkalies, which are found in most tap waters, cause red cabbage to turn bluish-purple. However, this reaction is reversible so that if the cabbage begins to turn bluish-purple during cooking, lemon juice or vinegar can be added and the cabbage will become bright red again. It is presently thought that anthocyanins are responsible for the color in beets. Recent studies, however, suggest that the pigment in beets is not an anthocyanin but is a complex chemical compound

USDA

USDA

Wes Kemp

called a pyrrole. The pigments are less sensitive to changes in pH value than are those in red cabbage. Since this scarlet color is soluble in water, beets which are peeled and then cooked in a large amount of water may lose a great deal of coloring matter.

Yellow and orange pigments (carotenoids) are much more stable than red pigments. The yellow pigments are soluble in fat but insoluble in water. They are stable and little affected by acids or alkaline substances and show no apparent color change in the presence of heat. The browning sometimes observed in certain yellow vegetables, carrots, for instance, is due to caramelization of sugar present in the vegetables, and not to a change in their yellow pigment. Due to the stability of the pigment, the cooking method for yellow vegetables creates no problem when color retention is the only consideration.

The green pigment, chlorophyll, is relatively insoluble in water. The color change observed in cooked green vegetables is due to a chemical change related to certain plant acids. The raw plant is so constructed that membrane-like tissues protect and prevent these acids from coming in contact with the pigment. When the vegetable is cooked, this membrane loses its semi-permeable properties and the green pigment becomes exposed to the plant acids. If the acids are volatile (go off as gas in evaporation), they may leave the vegetable in the steam during cooking and the color of the vegetable is not affected. However, if the plant acids are non-volatile and remain in the cooking water, the bright green color of the vegetable may change to olive green.

This color change may be prevented by shortening the cooking period, leaving the cover off the pan, especially at the beginning of the cooking period, and by using a large amount of cooking water, particularly if it is alkaline, as some tap waters are. Shortening the cooking period will avoid the amount of time necessary for the chemical change to take place. Additionally, leaving the cover off the pan will permit the volatile acids to escape in the steam. Finally, using a relatively large amount of water will dilute and perhaps neutralize the acids. This practice is usually not recommended, however, because there will be an increased loss of soluble nutrients, especially the vitamins.

The neutralization of plant acids by the cooking water depends on the amount of alkaline salt present in the water as well as the amount of water used. The addition of an alkaline substance, baking soda, intensifies the green color of vegetables due to a different chemical reaction. However, the use of soda for color retention is usually not recommended since it excessively softens the texture of the vegetable and lessens the natural flavor unless conditions are carefully controlled. It may also destroy some of the thiamine content and vitamin C.

The flavones, or anthoxanthins, are almost colorless, white, or pale yellow pigments which are related to the anthocyanins. These pigments are water-soluble. In cooking they may be changed to yellow or deeper yellow in the presence of an alkaline substance. Even some water is sufficiently alkaline to cause this color change. The white pigments are stable in an acid medium. The anthoxanthins may be present alone in light-colored vegetables such as potatoes and yellow-skinned onions, or with other pigments such as anthocyanins.

Flavor. Flavor, as well as color, can be affected by *tannins* in fruits and vegetables. Tannins are a group of soluble, bitter substances which can be oxidized to form dark-colored products. For example, foods such as peaches and sweet potatoes may turn brown after cutting. This darkening is due to the oxidation of the tannins and related compounds by certain enzymes which are present. If lemon juice or pineapple juice is used to coat the peeled fruit, there is a reaction between the acid and the tannins, and light-colored compounds are formed. The coating also prevents contact of the fruit with oxygen in the air and so prevents the brown discoloration. This same principle can be applied to new potatoes but is not usually done because of the flavor factor. Can you think of any instances in food preparation where it would be important to follow this procedure? Ascorbic acid and sulfur dioxide are commonly used commercially in processing fruit to prevent or to retard browning.

Texture. Texture or "mouth feel" is a reason often given for the dislike of certain vegetables. These same vegetables may be more readily acceptable if they retain their shape and form and are tender but not "mushy." On the other hand, most fruits are well-accepted in a soft form. Careful attention to cooking methods insures acceptable texture.

Effects of cooking on plant structure. It has been pointed out that *fruit and vegetable tissue consists of cellulose-walled cells bound together with pectic substances.* Cooking softens this structure and causes partial solution of the pectic substances. The cellulose is also changed. If baking soda is added, the vegetable structure softens in a shorter time.

Calcium chloride, a salt, is used commercially at present to increase the firmness of some foods such as apple slices, canned tomatoes, and various types of pickles. It combines with the pectic acid present in vegetables and fruits to form an insoluble substance—calcium pectate—which acts as a binding material between the cells and helps to prevent their structural breakdown.

The addition of sugar to the cooking water of any fruit helps to retain the fruit's shape since the sugar solution draws water from the cells through osmotic pressure, leaving a more dehydrated cell structure. In addition, as the tissues are softened by cooking, the semi-permeable properties of the membranes in the fruit are lost and the sugar is absorbed into the fruit. An example is found in the preparation of preserves or cooked fruit where maintenance of the natural shape of the fruit is important.

Changes in flavor. Both taste and odor are needed if one is to experience different food flavors. Most flavors are due mainly to aromatic substances that are detected by the sense of smell.

There are four primary components of taste: sweet, sour, salt, and bitter. As in texture and color, properties such as sweetness are not necessarily desirable in themselves, but become so when we associate them with particular foods. We do not want sweetness in potatoes but we do want it in corn. The flavor of onions and chives is delightful in certain cheese preparations but not in milk from which cheese is produced.

Many varieties of flavoring compounds occur in fruits and vegetables. As was mentioned earlier, tannins may affect the flavor as well as the color of some vegetables and fruits by giving the food an astringent, bitter flavor, as, for example, the flavor experienced in unripened bananas. Sugars are responsible in part for the characteristic flavors of freshly-harvested vegetables. For this reason some people add sugar to the water used in the cooking of vegetables or they add sugar at the end of the cooking period.

The ways in which vegetables are cooked usually are matters of personal preference. However, methods which will result in retaining most of the natural characteristics of fresh vegetables are generally preferred. The mild, sweet flavor of some vegetables is affected greatly by extensive cooking. For example, sulfur compounds are known to be important flavoring constituents in at least two groups of vegetables, the onion and cabbage families. The characteristic flavor of raw vegetables considered part of the cabbage family is due to a substance called sinigrin. Upon cooking, sinigrin is hydrolyzed to form a compound found in mustard oil. Large amounts of this substance are objectional to the taste. When cabbage, Brussels sprouts, broccoli, and kale are cooked for a long period of time, this decomposition occurs and substances of unpleasant odor and flavor develop.

Methods of Cooking

Methods using varying amounts of water in cooking vegetables. An important factor in retaining nutritive value in a cooked vegetable is the amount of water used. *Many vegetables are cooked by boiling in water.* All vegetables naturally contain large amounts of water. Some of them, such as leaves, contain as much as 95 percent. Leafy vegetables can be cooked without adding any appreciable amount of water but most other vegetables need some additional water. Some vegetables will be more acceptable in color and flavor if a moderate quantity of cooking water is used and we are willing to sacrifice some of the nutritive value in order to get more palatability. For example, in cooking cabbage, from a nutritional point of view, it is preferable to use as little water as possible. However, using a very small amount of water without having the vegetable burn requires that the cooking vegetable be watched carefully.

The vegetable may be cooked in a covered pan so that evaporation of water will be reduced and steam will be maintained to cook the vegetable that is not covered by the water. Even when a cover is used, however, some of the steam escapes, and the pan may still boil dry. Lowering the heat may help to prevent this from happening but rather than accept these inconveniences, often more water is used.

Whenever the water from a cooked vegetable is thrown away, some of the nutritive value is lost in the discarded water. The amount of this loss varies somewhat with the physical structure of the vegetable and with the details of the particular cooking method used. For example, if a water-soluble vitamin is present in the vegetable being cooked, it is probable that some of that vitamin will go into the cooking water. If the cooking water is discarded, the vitamin will be lost. If there is mineral content, more will probably be lost as the cooking period is extended. However, the amount of cooking water used and discarded is the most important single factor in the loss of vitamins and minerals in cooked vegetables. The cooking time appears to be less important in this respect.

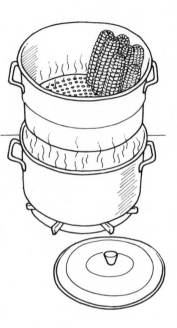

"Water-less" cooking is also a method used in cooking vegetables. In this case, vegetables are cooked in only the water which clings to them after they have been washed. Or just enough water is added to avoid scorching. The use of a heavy pan with a tight fitting lid is usually recommended when this method is employed.

Steaming of fruits and vegetables consists of cooking them in a perforated pan which is placed over a second pan containing rapidly boiling water. This method takes longer than boiling but conserves the soluble nutrients and better retains the shape of the fruit or vegetable. However, green vegetables cooked in this way tend to lose some of their bright color.

Pressure cooking involves the cooking of food in an airtight container at high temperatures under steam pressure. Since only a small amount of added water is required, this method retains the nutritive

value of vegetables. Mature beets and potatoes are quite successfully cooked in this way. Dried fruits and vegetables which normally require long cooking periods are cooked quickly by pressure cooking.

Baking offers a good method for retaining the nutritive value of fruits and vegetables. In this method the food is left whole and unpeeled and is cooked by oven heat. Much of the nutritive value is retained within the food because it is cooked with no moisture other than that within itself. This method prevents the loss of any food substance normally caused by solubility in water. White and sweet potatoes and apples are frequently prepared in this manner.

Microwave cooking. With the arrival of the electronic oven, microwave cooking became possible. Food is exposed to microwaves which penetrate it and produce fairly uniform heating throughout. This method seems to compare favorably with conventional ways of cooking fruits and vegetables in retaining color and nutritive content. In general, much less time is required than that needed for other methods.

Using a microwave oven reduces cooking time.

Raytheon Company

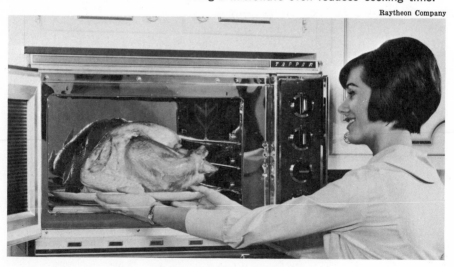

Generally speaking, any method of cooking which retains the color, texture, and flavor of the original fruit or vegetable may be recommended because the conditions that favor the retention of these qualities also favor the retention of nutrients.

In this chapter we have dealt with the importance of color, texture, and flavor retention in fruit and vegetable cookery. Although saving nutrients is important, the color, texture, and flavor of these foods must be appealing if many of these foods will be consumed in desirable amounts. In the next chapter we shall be studying plant food products which are produced from seeds and tubers.

MAJOR IDEAS

The following statements give the main ideas within the chapter you have just studied. Be sure you know the words underscored in these statements and in the questions to follow.

1. Food <u>synthesis</u> by plants is equally important to men and to plants.
2. <u>Palatability</u> and <u>acceptability</u> in cooked fruits and vegetables are directly related to the extent to which the natural flavors and <u>colors</u> are retained in the foods and desirable <u>texture</u> changes are produced during the cooking process.
3. Frequently the methods for cooking fruits and vegetables which produce an attractive, palatable product also retain significant amounts of the <u>nutritive</u> value.
4. The stage at which a fruit or vegetable is harvested and the time elapsing between harvest and actual <u>consumption</u> influence the quality of that product.

QUESTIONS TO STUDY

PLANT STRUCTURE

1. Why are fruits and vegetables classified as <u>roots</u>, <u>leaves</u>, <u>stems</u>, <u>tubers</u>, <u>flowers</u>, and <u>fruits</u>?
2. What is the major difference between a fruit and a vegetable?

MATURATION AND RIPENING

1. What takes place when vegetables <u>mature</u> and fruits <u>ripen</u>?
2. Why do fruits become sweeter when ripened?

QUALITIES AND GRADES

1. Why are color, texture, and flavor so closely related to quality?
2. Why is the <u>texture</u> referred to as <u>structural quality</u>?

PRINCIPLES OF FRUIT AND VEGETABLE COOKERY

1. Why does red cabbage "bleed" during cooking?
2. Which pigments are the most stable ones found in vegetables? Which are unstable?
3. Why is the use of soda not recommended in the cooking of green vegetables?
4. Why do some fruits turn brown when exposed to the air?
5. Why is chlorophyll stable in raw vegetables but unstable when heat is applied to the food?
6. What changes in cell structure take place when fruits and vegetables are cooked?
7. What can be done to retain the shape of fruit as it is being cooked?
8. How can the distinct flavor changes in cooked cabbage be explained?

METHODS OF COOKING

1. Explain the statement, "The amount of water used in cooking a vegetable is a major factor in the retention of nutritive value."
2. Why should the water used for cooking fruits and vegetables not be discarded?
3. Explain why foods cooked in a pressure cooker require shorter periods of cooking time.
4. What is microwave cooking?
5. What advantages are there in baking vegetables whole and unpeeled?

BIBLIOGRAPHY

DARAVINGAS, GEORGE, and CAIN, R. S., "Changes in Anthocyanin Pigment During Processing and Storage." *Journal of Food Science,* Vol. 30, 1965, pp. 400–405.

EHEART, MARY S., and GOTT, CLAIRE, "Conventional and Microwave Cooking of Vegetables. Ascorbic Acid and Carotene Retention and Palatability." *Journal of the American Dietetic Association,* Vol. 44, February 1964, pp. 116–119.

GRISWOLD, RUTH M., *The Experimental Study of Foods.* Boston, Houghton Mifflin Company, 1962.

HALLIDAY, E. G., and NOBLE, I. T., *Hows and Whys of Cooking,* 3rd ed. Chicago, University of Chicago Press, 1946.

NOBLE, ISABEL, and GORDON, JOAN, "Effect of Blanching Method on Ascorbic Acid and Color of Frozen Vegetables." *Journal of *the American Dietetic Association*, Vol. 44, February 1964, pp. 120–123.

NOBLE, ISABEL, and GORDON, JOAN, "Waterless versus Boiling Water cooking of Vegetables." *Journal of the American Dietic Association*, Vol. 44, May 1964, pp. 378–381.

PETERSON, R. G., and JOSLYN, M. A., "The Red Pigment of the Root of the Beet As a Pyrrole Compound." *Food Research*, Vol. 25, 1960, pp. 429–441.

SIMPSON, J., and HALLIDAY, E. G., "The Behavior of Sulfur Compounds in Cooking Vegetables." *Journal of Home Economics*, Vol. 20, 1928, pp. 121–126.

SWEENEY, J. P., and MARTEN, M. E., "Stability of Chlorophyll in Vegetables, As Affected by pH." *Food Technology*, Vol. 15, 1961, pp. 263–266.

14 STARCHES, FLOURS, AND FLOUR MIXTURES

Starches, as we have already learned, are classified as carbohydrates. Many plants store their energy as starch. Consequently, the main source of starch is found in the roots, seeds, and tubers of plants that are used for food. The plants producing the most starch on the United States mainland are those classified as cereals—corn, wheat, and rice. White and sweet potatoes also have large amounts of starch. In Hawaii and in some of the Central and South American countries, taro, cassava, and manioc are the principal sources of starches.

The milling of cereal grains for flour dates back to prehistoric times. There is evidence that wheat and corn were crushed and used as food at least 6,000

Sweet potatoes, wheat, bread, corn, potatoes, cereal, spaghetti, noodles, and other forms of pasta are some plants and plant foods which contain a large amount of starch.

An old grist mill.

years ago. The pounding stones used for this purpose have been found in archeological diggings in the British Isles, Switzerland, and elsewhere. The Romans used millstones for milling their grain.

In the United States, flour, unless otherwise named, is made from wheat. You will find that flours differ according to the varieties of wheat from which they are milled. These differences influence the ways in which flours are used in food preparation.

Starch Composition and Chemical Properties

Sources of starch. Starches alone or as a constituent of flour are used extensively in food preparation. Most starches used for food come from cereals —rice, barley, rye, corn, and wheat. They may also be obtained from tubers, such as potatoes and sweet potatoes. Tapioca from the cassava plant is used in food preparation, too.

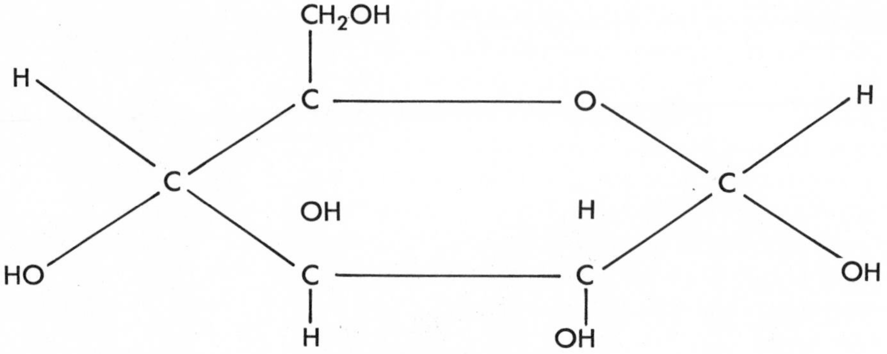

A STARCH MOLECULE

A starch molecule is composed of carbon, oxygen, and hydrogen linked in a certain pattern. When starch undergoes hydrolysis with acid, it yields the monosaccharide glucose.

Structure of starch. *Starches are synthesized by plants from the simple sugar glucose.* As the starch is built up from molecules of glucose, a molecule of water is eliminated for each molecule of glucose added. This process is repeated many times to form a starch molecule. Many molecules are contained in one starch granule. The size and shape of the starch granules in one plant will be different from those in another plant, although often starch granules are spherical or egg-shaped.

In addition to starch granules from various sources being characterized by different shapes and sizes, they also behave differently in food preparation. This variation in behavior is attributed in large part to the composition or relative proportions of amylose and amylopectin, two types of starch molecules. Some cereal starches, however, contain no amylose. These starches, known as waxy starches, are found in some of the corn, rice, and barley cereals.

Starch solubility. Starch granules are insoluble at room temperature, but when heated in water they swell, a starch paste is formed, and some of the amylose goes into solution.

Starch hydrolysis. When starch is boiled in acid, it is hydrolyzed (page 145) first to dextrins, then to maltose, and finally to glucose. This is a reversal of the process of starch formation in plants. Corn sirup is produced commercially in this way.

Principles of Starch Cookery

The effect of heat on starch. When starches or starch products are subjected to dry heat, substances called dextrins are produced. Dextrins can be formed from both amylose and amylopectin starches. Dextrins have less

thickening power in cooking than the original starch
from which they were formed. The toasting of
bread involves the process of dextrinization. Starch
changed to dextrin is considered easier to digest because the starch granules are broken down into a
simpler form. Starch granules are insoluble at room
temperature, but when they are subjected to moist
heat they swell and form a viscous sol. On cooling,
starch sols tend to increase in viscosity and many
set to gels. This entire process is called gelatinization.

Factors affecting gelatinization. The thickness of the paste and the firmness of the gel formed
varies with the concentration of the starch, the kind
of starch used, the temperature to which it is heated,
and the presence of other ingredients such as acids,
enzymes, or sugar.

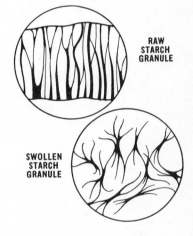

RAW
STARCH
GRANULE

SWOLLEN
STARCH
GRANULE

The concentration of starch is important in determining whether the hot paste will actually set to a
gel. The kind of starch also affects the gel structure.
For example, starches containing amylose (e.g.
wheat and cornstarch) form a rigid, nearly opaque
or cloudy gel, while amylopectin starches (e.g. waxy
maize) form a very viscous sol. These amylopectin
starches are used extensively by commercial firms
for fruit pies and sauces which are to be frozen.
Although starch may swell to a certain extent at low
temperatures, it does not reach its maximum viscosity until a higher temperature is reached. Probably a temperature of at least 194° F or 90° C is
needed for maximum thickening and good flavor.

In high acid concentration starch is hydrolyzed,
resulting in a lowered viscosity and reduction in
gel formation. The weak acids and mild heat treatment used in the home do not usually cause extensive hydrolysis. However, mixtures such as
lemon puddings and other acid-containing starch
mixtures are often prepared by cooking the starch
and liquid mixture until it is thickened before the
acid is added. This is probably done to retain the
fresh fruit flavor, rather than to make certain that
the mixture remains thickened.

Enzymes found in fresh pineapple tend to break down gel structures. For this reason canned or cooked pineapple is recommended rather than fresh pineapple for use in puddings and pie fillings since the enzymes have been inactivated by the heating.

Sugar used in a gel produces the most transparent gels; the pastes are less viscous and the gels are more tender. If excessive amounts of sugar are added, a viscous sirup is produced and there will be no firm gel.

Retrogradation. Retrogradation is the process which occurs when a starch gel ages; the starch becomes less soluble and appears to be reverting to its original insolubility in cold water. You have probably observed this happening in a cornstarch pudding which has been in the refrigerator for a few days. This process occurs more readily in amylose starches than in amylopectin starches.

Kinds and Composition of Flours

Flours are produced from the seeds of wheat, rice, corn, rye, barley, and oats.

Composition. Wheat flour contains in addition to carbohydrates, proteins, vitamins, fat, minerals, and pigments. *Gluten is a complex of chemically-related proteins that enables flour, when mixed with water, to form plastic elastic doughs.*

Left: The identity of flour is maintained by requirements concerning its fineness, moisture, and ash content. Enriched flours must contain thiamine, riboflavin, niacin, and iron.

Below: In the milling process the endosperm is separated from the bran and germ of the seeds.

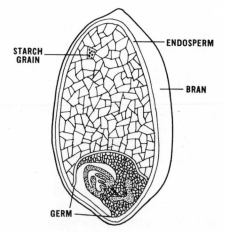

Among the enzymes found in flour are proteinases and diastases which are of protein composition. Proteinases are important in baking methods because they act to soften the dough and weaken the gluten in products such as crackers which are crisp and not highly leavened. Diastases produce maltose from starch. This is important in yeast breadmaking because the maltose provides food needed by the yeast to grow. The growing yeast produces carbon dioxide which causes the bread to rise. Whole wheat and enriched* flours are considered good sources of the B-vitamins: thiamine, riboflavin, and niacin.

The principal pigments (coloring agents) are the yellow pigments—the carotenoids. Flavones are also present. The color of flours is affected by the size of particles as well as by the pigments, and is changed by the use of bleaching agents.

The moisture content of flour is important in determining quality. By standards set by the United States Department of Agriculture, the moisture content of flour should not exceed 15 percent of the total weight involved.

The production of flour. The kind of flour produced is related to the purpose for which the flour is intended. The type also depends upon the classes of wheat from which the flour is milled and the milling process itself.

Flour is produced by milling, a process which separates the endosperm from the bran and germ of the seeds. The endosperm is the storehouse for the starch and for most of the protein of the plant. The bran is the outer covering of the seed. The germ is the small portion of the seed from which the new plant is formed.

Wheats are classified in five main groups: white, hard red spring, hard red winter, soft red winter, and durum. The major portions of the hard red spring wheat and durum are grown in the north central

---

*Products labeled "enriched" and sold in interstate commerce must meet the standard of identity set by the Federal Food and Drug Administration. These standards require that enriched flours contain thiamine, riboflavin, niacin, and iron. Calcium and vitamin D may also be added.

Wes Kemp

United States. The hard red winter wheat is found chiefly in the central and south central states. Soft red winter wheat is grown in Missouri and in the East. White wheat is produced in the Northeast and in Michigan.

Kinds of flour. The hard wheat varieties are used principally for the production of flour for breadmaking. The soft wheats are particularly suitable for flours for making cakes, pastries, and cookies. Durum wheats are used for macaroni and other paste products. There are many kinds of flour available for both commercial and home use. Those generally used in the home are classified as all-purpose, cake, and self-rising.

All-purpose flour is usually made from a blend of wheats. In the South, all-purpose flour is usually blended from soft wheats and in the northern part of the United States from hard wheats. This type of flour is satisfactory for all kinds of baking. Hard or strong wheat has a relatively high protein content that forms gluten with good gas-retaining properties, while doughs made from soft wheat flour have poor gas-retaining qualities.

Cake flour is ground from soft wheat. It is very fine in texture and the protein content is low. The gluten structure formed with cake flour is not as strong as that formed from all-purpose flour.

Self-rising flour was developed in the 19th century. It is flour with added leavening and salt. A "convenience mix" is created in this way which can be used to simplify the preparation of many chemically-leavened baked foods. Self-rising flour may be substituted in recipes which call for flour plus baking powder and salt, by omitting the latter two ingredients.

One company, which has researched the no-sift, or instantized, flour has found it to be satisfactory for baked products. This company has suggested the use of the dipping method in measuring. The diagrams below show how the dipping method is accomplished.*

Instantized flour has been produced by changing the form of the flour particles. In one process small particles are compelled to adhere together after milling so that they form clusters of flour particles which are nearly the same size. In a second process the desired characteristics are obtained during the milling process. Instantized flour pours like sugar or salt and disperses rapidly in cold liquids. It does not pack on standing so it does not have to be sifted. Its baking characteristics are similar to those of all-purpose flour. You will want to compare instantized flour with all-purpose flour.

Durum, or macaroni flour, is milled from durum wheat which has a high protein content.

DIP	LEVEL	POUR

Dip nested dry measuring cups into flour sack or canister.	Level off with spatula or straight-edged knife. (Do not tap cup or pack more flour into cup before leveling off.)	Pour flour into mixing bowl with other ingredients. When recipe calls for flour to be sifted with other dry ingredients, stir thoroughly to blend.

Flour Mixtures

Kinds. Flour mixtures are classified as batters and doughs. A batter, as its name indicates, is a mixture of such consistency that it can be beaten or stirred. Batters vary in stiffness and are designated as "pour" or "drop" batters, depending on the proportion of liquid to flour. Some examples of pour batters are ones for popovers and griddle cakes. Dropped cookies and biscuits are made from drop batters. A dough is a flour mixture of such consistency that it can be handled or kneaded. Rolled biscuits, pastry, yeast bread, and rolled cookies are made from doughs.

Yeast bread is one of the basic foods of the world. People eat bread in some form everywhere. Many of these breads are quite different from the plump, white enriched loaves familiar to people in the United States.

*Adapted from "How to Measure Wondra," THE GOLD MEDAL WONDRA WAY, General Mills, Inc., Minneapolis, Minnesota.

According to a study done by Standard Brands, Inc., yeast-baking women are of two types. There is the light baker and the heavy baker. The former bakes once a month while the latter bakes at least once every week. Both consider baking a creative process, demanding total involvement through mixing, kneading, punching, and shaping.

Table 11		
Classification of Basic Batters and Doughs		
Pour Batters	*Drop Batters*	*Doughs*
Popovers	Muffins	Biscuits
Griddle cakes	Drop cookies (variation	Pastry
Waffles	of cake)	Yeast breads
Cakes (containing fat)		Rolled cookies
		(variation of cake)

Ingredients for yeast bread. Ingredients for making bread are the same the world around. Proportions and flavorings may vary, but basic ingredients and ways of mixing are the same. *Flour is the chief ingredient.* In home baking usually all-purpose flour is used because bread flour is not often available. The gluten of the dough forms the framework that will undergo prolonged stretching during the rising of the dough. This framework sets as the protein coagulates during baking, helping to form the structure of the loaf.

The liquid may be milk, water, or water in which potatoes have been cooked. Fresh milk, evaporated milk, or dry milk all give good results. Fluid fresh milk is scalded first to bring about changes in the milk to avoid poor texture of the bread. Diluted, evaporated milk need not be heated. Why? Dried milk may be added to the other dry ingredients with an appropriate amount of water as the liquid. The amount of liquid used varies with the absorption capacity of the flour. The use of too much or too little liquid causes a decrease in the volume of the bread and a coarse or harsh crumb.

Commercial *yeast* can be purchased in two forms: compressed and dry granular. For household use the dry granular form may be preferred. Why might this be true? Active dry yeast works best with water at 110° to 115° F. If compressed yeast is used, the water should be lukewarm, 85° F. If you did not have a thermometer how might you judge the temperature?

With the added moisture and food available in bread dough, the yeast plants multiply rapidly and in so doing form a large quantity of carbon dioxide gas. This gas causes the bread dough to rise. Can you think of other food products in which carbon dioxide gas is important?

After the yeast is added to the bread, a period of time is allowed to elapse before the bread is baked. This is the fermentation period. Bakers call it "proofing" and homemakers call it "rising." *Sugar* provides the food for the yeast to grow. The sugar necessary for the growth of yeast comes from three sources: the flour, which contains about 1 percent sugar; simple sugars produced by the action of the amylase enzymes of the flour and the enzymes of yeast; the sugar added in the recipe. Breads that are sweet to the taste have more sugar than do plain breads and are more tender. The tenderness results from the effect of the sugar on the gluten structure. Too large an amount of sugar results in a decreased volume. This may be because the gluten structure cannot be maintained to permit further rising and because of a slower rate of gas production. Flavor, texture, and browning qualities are all related to the presence of sugar.

Salt adds flavor to yeast dough and prevents the yeast from growing too rapidly. If salt is not added to the dough, fermentation takes place very rapidly and the bread is coarse in texture. If too much salt is added, fermentation is much slower and the bread is firmer and more compact.

Shortening used in small amounts improves the volume of bread. The tenderness of both the crust and crumb and the improved volume of bread containing shortening are often attributed to the lubricating effect of the fat on the dough. Too much shortening results in a coarsely-grained product. Fat gives a velvety and softer crumb and finer grain.

Eggs are used in some breads to give them a "richer" quality and a shinier crust and crumb.

Methods of preparation of yeast breads. Yeast breads may be made by several different methods: the straight dough method, the sponge method, and the no-knead method.

In the *straight dough method* all the ingredients are mixed together at one time. The dough is then kneaded until it has a satiny appearance and is elastic.

Wheat and Flour Institute, Chicago

Step 1: The ingredients are measured. Note the active yeast in the small bowl.

Wheat and Flour Institute, Chicago

Step 2: The liquid and dry ingredients are mixed together to produce a dough.

Wheat and Flour Institute, Chicago

Step 3: The dough is kneaded to form a smooth mass.

Kneading is accomplished with a light folding motion using the palm of the hand and keeping the fingers curved. This process produces an elastic gluten in the dough. When the dough has been kneaded sufficiently, tiny bubbles can be seen beneath its surface and the dough is no longer sticky.

After kneading, the dough is placed in a bowl, covered, and set in a warm place (85° to 90° F) to rise. The time necessary for rising depends upon the temperature, the amount of yeast used, the richness of the dough, and the kind of flour. The dough is allowed to rise until it has doubled in bulk and the impression of a finger, lightly pressed on the surface, remains. Sometimes at this point the dough is punched down and then allowed to rise a second time. Light kneading after a period of fermentation is done to remove some of the excess carbon dioxide which prevents the over-stretching of the gluten strands. Kneading helps, too, to redistribute the yeast cells throughout the dough.

After punching, the dough is allowed to rest for 10 minutes. If it is to be made into rolls, the dough first is divided into balls. The rest period makes the dough more easily handled. The dough is then shaped and allowed to rise again until it has doubled in bulk. It is baked in a preheated oven. The heat of the oven makes the bread rise quickly during the first five to ten minutes of baking. This rising is called "oven spring." During baking, the carbon dioxide gas in the dough expands, the gluten in the bread sets, the growth of the yeast stops, and some of the flavor of the bread develops. The development of some of the flavor comes from the cooking of the starch in the flour, the evaporation of some of the yeast fermentation products, and the changing of the surface starch to dextrin. This last step forms the brown crust. Probably nonenzymatic browning and caramelization are also involved in crust browning.

Wheat and Flour Institute, Chicago

Step 4: The dough is punched down.

Plain or less sweet batters and doughs are baked at moderately hot temperatures (400° to 425° F). Richer doughs, that is, those with more fat and sugar, are baked at moderate temperatures (350° to 375° F).

The *sponge dough method* consists of mixing the liquid, the yeast, some of the sugar, and part of the flour to make a thick batter. The batter is set to rise in a warm place until it is light and full of gas bubbles. The fat (melted or liquid), salt, remaining flour, and sugar are added to this batter to form a dough. Then the dough is kneaded. The final steps are the same as those used in the straight dough method. Bread made by the sponge dough method has a slightly different flavor from that of bread made by the straight dough method. Look again at the illustrations on these two pages so that you will further understand the steps in breadmaking.

Wheat and Flour Institute, Chicago

Step 5: The dough is shaped after it has risen.

Batter breads, made by the *no-knead method*, are short-cut yeast breads and are considered easiest to make. They need neither kneading nor shaping. The dough can be dropped directly into the pan before rising or it can be chilled and shaped later. Bread made by this method results in a more open texture and uneven surface. This method seems to work best for sweet rolls and coffee cakes because of the soft rich doughs involved.

A new method for mixing bread was introduced in 1954. It will probably be used only by commercial bakers because it has few advantages for the home baker. This method, *the stable ferment* or *brew method*, is a modification of the sponge method. A stable ferment is prepared and used for many

Wheat and Flour Institute, Chicago

Step 6: The dough is placed in a baking pan and allowed to rise again.

batches of bread. The stable brew, after rising for 3 or 4 hours, can be stored for 24 hours at room temperature or for longer periods of time if it is refrigerated. The brew contains part or all of the yeast and water, part of the sugar, about one-half the salt, and a buffer ingredient, but no flour. The buffer ingredient keeps the mixture from becoming too acid. Ingredients used as buffers include nonfat dry milk, soy flour, and calcium carbonate. The quality of the bread seems to be comparable to bread made by the sponge method.

Deterioration of bread. Bread deterioration may be due to staling, drying, mold growth, and sometimes microbial growth. You are probably aware that as bread ages it becomes more firm, its crumb becomes more crumbly, and it may have evidence of mold. Even when the moisture content of bread is unchanged during storage, the bread becomes stale.

Because of its great commercial importance, the *staling of bread* has been extensively investigated. Formerly it was thought that staling was related to the transfer of moisture from the starch to the protein. Currently, changes in the starch fraction are thought to be the most important factors. Within limits, staling is a reversible process. Stale bread can be freshened by heating.

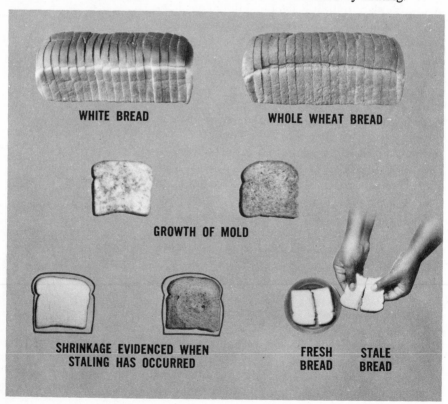

WHITE BREAD   WHOLE WHEAT BREAD

GROWTH OF MOLD

SHRINKAGE EVIDENCED WHEN   FRESH   STALE
STALING HAS OCCURRED   BREAD   BREAD

Moldiness is prevented in commercial bread by minimizing the mold in the areas where bread is sliced and wrapped. This means eliminating all the potential breeding places where slicing and wrapping are done. The area, with special attention to cracks and corners, is kept clean; any stale loaves and crumbs are discarded. Propionates (a kind of food additive) are commonly used commercially in doughs to retard the growth of molds and certain bacteria in breads.

Quick breads. Our hot breads are the descendants of the early crude hearth cakes. The famous "cakes" which King Alfred forgot to watch as he sat in a peasant hut were the "bannocks o' barley" that Robert Burns wrote about. Quick breads are so named because they are made with quick-acting chemical leavening agents—baking powder or soda and sour cream or sour milk, instead of yeast.

Quick breads include many different types: biscuits, muffins, nut loaves, and corn breads. Some, such as pancakes and waffles, are baked on a griddle. Others—dumplings and brown breads—are cooked by steam. And, of course, quick breads such as doughnuts and fritters are cooked in deep fat.

Popovers are made from the thinnest of all batters commonly baked as bread. This batter contains equal volumes of flour and liquid. Eggs are an essential ingredient in popovers to provide structure because the proportion of water is so great that gluten particles do not form a mass of sufficient continuity to expand under pressure. The batter needs to be baked at a fairly high temperature so that steam can be formed rapidly. The popovers must be baked until the exterior is very firm and the structure is set, otherwise they will collapse on removal from the oven. A variation of popovers is Yorkshire pudding, a popular accompaniment to roast beef in an English meal.

Griddle cakes, pancakes, or *hot cakes* are prepared from flour, liquid, salt, and a leavening agent. They may or may not contain eggs, fat, and sugar. If fat is included, the cakes become more tender. Sugar aids in browning. Why would this be true?

Waffles are often mentioned in poems written in the latter part of the twelfth century. During this period waffles were made and sold in the streets. On a religious feast day, the waffle seller would set up his stall in view of the public and bake his waffles. The Dutch colonists brought their cherished "waffle" irons to America. These irons were long-handled and very heavy to hold over an open fire. Waffles are a variation of griddle cakes. However, they contain more eggs and more fat than do the latter. Because of the air incorporated into the beaten eggs or egg whites, less baking powder is needed for waffles.

Muffins are prepared from a drop batter. They usually contain flour, leavening, salt, sugar, fat, egg, and liquid. If sugar and eggs are omitted, muffins will have a flavor and texture like that of drop biscuits. The liquid to flour ratio is usually 2 to 1 by volume, providing the flour used is an all-purpose one. The

batter or muffin method is used in making muffins. The dry ingredients are first sifted together. Next the liquid ingredients, milk, egg (beaten), and melted or liquid fat are mixed. The dry and liquid ingredients are then combined and the batter is stirred just enough to moisten the dry ingredients. The mixture will have a somewhat lumpy appearance. If mixing is continued beyond this point, the batter becomes smoother and the amount of gluten developed in the dough becomes greater. The muffins when baked will then brown less readily and will have sharp peaks and a smooth, dull crust. Volume will be smaller and the product will be less tender. Inside the muffins will be large holes or tunnels starting at the bottom of the muffin and going through to the top. They are due to the expansion of gas in the resistant dough. Tunnel formation may also be caused by too high a baking temperature or an incorrect proportion of ingredients. Too large a proportion of flour or too little liquid or a small proportion of fat or sugar also increases the tendency for tunnel formation in muffins.

Biscuits are the simplest of the leavened doughs. Success in making both biscuits and pastry for pies requires correct proportions of the ingredients and skill in handling the doughs. Biscuits require a different method of mixing from that used in preparing batters. The dry ingredients are sifted together and then a solid fat is cut into this dry mixture. A liquid is added and the mixture is stirred until the ingredients form a soft dough. This dough is kneaded briefly to develop the gluten structure and to distribute the ingredients in the mixture more evenly. If a liquid fat is used, the dry ingredients are combined and the fat is mixed with the liquid. Then these liquid ingredients are mixed with the dry ones. After a short period of kneading, the dough is rolled or patted to the appropriate thickness and cut into whatever shapes are desired. Biscuits may also be dropped if the proportion of liquid to flour is increased. Beaten biscuits are made from flour which provides for more gluten development. These biscuits tend to be less high than those made with soft flour. They also have a crusty exterior. Biscuits are baked at 425° F.

Pastry. The "pyes" of old England were baked in long, deep dishes called "coffins." The first American pie pans were round, flat, and shallow. They were designed to make more servings per pie possible. As fruits and other types of fillings became more plentiful, pies became larger and were more richly crusted.

Ingredients in pastry making. The ingredients used in pastry are flour, salt, fat, and liquid. All-purpose flour is usually used for a flaky plain pastry but a pastry flour will make a more tender pastry.

Any number of fats can be used in plain pastry. Each gives the pastry a different character. Fats which are the most plastic and which become soft while being mixed into a dough, seem to make a tender and desirably flaky pastry. Tenderness is a preferred characteristic in pastry. The shortening power of a fat (ability to produce a tender product) is increased according to the ability of that fat to cover a large surface area. Fats that cover the greatest surface area of the flour particles during mixing have the greatest shortening power.

Of the solid shortenings, when used in equal amounts, lard usually makes the most tender pastry because of its plasticity, a quality believed to be essential for tenderness. Hydrogenated vegetable shortenings are frequently used in pastry because of their uniformity in plasticity, good shortening power, and bland flavor. However, slightly more of such fat is needed in a pastry before comparable tenderness can be realized. Because of their water content and limited plasticity, butter and margarine tend to produce less tender pastry.

Oil is also used for making pastry. The oil and water may be added to the flour and then mixed. Oil usually produces an excessively tender pastry if mixed by the conventional method. Tenderness increases with the proportion of fat in the mixture and too much makes pastry difficult to handle.

Water is an important ingredient in pastry because it dampens the flour surfaces so that the particles of the fat-flour mixture will form a dough. Too much water will toughen pastry and too little water will cause pastry to be dry, be difficult to handle, and to crumble.

Methods of mixing pastry. The temperature of the ingredients in pastry is related to tenderness. More tender pastry usually results when the ingredients are warm (68° to 75° F) rather than cold.

There are several methods which may be used for combining pastry ingredients. In the *conventional method* the fat is cut into the flour with two knives, a fork, fingertips or a pastry blender until the largest pieces of fat are the size of peas. Water is sprinkled over the flour-fat mixture gradually and mixing is continued until all the flour is moistened. If the proportion of water to flour is correct, the danger of overmixing is not great. However, overmixing or handling can cause the overdevelopment of gluten and result in tough pastry.

As soon as the mixture is sufficiently moist to form a soft pliable ball of dough, it can be placed in the refrigerator for a short time before rolling out. Allowing the dough to stand a few minutes increases its elasticity and makes it easier to roll and handle.

In the *modified conventional method,* a portion of the flour is blended with the water to form a paste. The fat is cut into the remaining flour. Then the flour and water paste are added to the fat-flour mixture to form a dough.

In the *"hot water" method,* boiling water is poured over the fat and the two are beaten together to form an oil and water emulsion. This emulsion is added to the dry ingredients and mixing is continued until a ball of dough is formed. The dough is chilled and then rolled. Pastry made in this way tends to be crumbly but more tender than pastry made by the conventional method. A similar procedure is followed when making pastry with oil.

Types of cakes. Foam-type cakes—angel food and sponge cakes—will be discussed later. At present we will be concerned with only those cakes which contain fat.

Among many peoples cake is a symbol of birthdays, marriages, parties, and other times of celebration. The idea of the wedding cake as the centerpiece for the wedding reception table originated during the Roman Empire. This custom still exists today. The Romans also prepared cakes to offer Ceres, the goddess of the harvest. These special cakes were made of honey, flour, incense, milk, and wine. During the early 13th century a new kind of cake was developed by a nun. This cake was made by creaming butter, sugar, and eggs for two hours before adding the flour. It was baked in small round layers and served at christenings, weddings, funerals, and other events with religious significance. Spices and fruits were added to symbolize the gifts of the Wise Men at Christmas time. Today there is still a cake called the Nun's cake.

Ingredients in cakes containing fat. Cakes containing fat have as their basic ingredients flour, liquid, sugar, eggs, leavening, salt, flavorings, and some type of fat.

Cake flour which is low in protein content is often preferred for making cakes. The decrease in the pH value of heavily bleached flour improves the quality of cake. All-purpose flour can be used but it has been found that cake flour produces a cake of larger volume, more velvety texture, and more even crumb.

Whole milk, water, buttermilk, fruit juices, and reconstituted nonfat dry milk are liquids used in cakes. The liquid has several functions in shortened cakes. These functions include enabling gelatinization of the starch and the development of the gluten and serving as a solvent for the chemical leavening agents and other ingredients. The use of too small an amount of liquid causes the cake batter to be very stiff. Excessive liquid causes the batter to be too thin, thereby producing a heavy compact cake.

Eggs influence the structure of cake. They function as coagulants, emulsifiers, and foaming agents (Chapter 16). Eggs also add flavor and color.

Sugar is used in cake mixtures to increase tenderness and flavor, and to give a fine, uniform texture, and a brown crust. The sugar has a tendency to tenderize the gluten, egg protein, and the starch gels. With increased amounts of sugar to the optimum, tenderness of the cake increases. Sugar increases the mixing time because it competes with the gluten and other ingredients for the liquid and prevents the development of the gluten. Granulated sugar, brown sugar, sirups, and honey can all be used as sweetening agents in shortened cakes. However, the amounts vary according to each of these sugars. Because of the many functions of sugar other than sweetening, non-sugar sweeteners cannot be substituted directly for sugar in a cake recipe. Weight for weight, well-sifted or granulated brown sugar may be used in place of white granulated sugar, except in white shortened cakes. Cake volume seems to improve greatly as the granulation of the sugar becomes finer. In equal measure all sirups are heavier than sugar and so increase the specific gravity of a batter. Adjustments in liquid are required in batters made with sirup. This ingredient tends to make a cake heavy, although special mixing procedures may be used to help incorporate air into honey cake batters. These batters are used to make cakes that are to be stored for considerable time. Such cakes retain their moisture well during storage because honey contains the simple sugar, fructose, which is hygroscopic (water-attracting).

Leavening of cake batter may be accomplished by incorporating air into the egg whites, egg yolks, and fat and by the addition of a chemical leavening agent—baking powder or baking soda plus an acid ingredient. Steam also contributes to leavening. The amount of chemical leavening agent needed depends on the other ingredients in the mixture, the method used in combining these ingredients, the extent of mixing, and the atmospheric pressure. Cakes made with a high sugar ratio require more baking powder. Because of the gluten

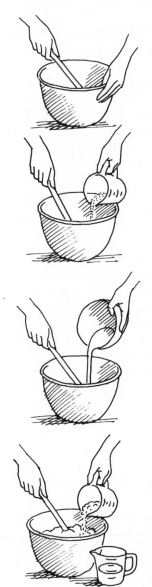

quality of all-purpose flour, more baking powder may be needed when all-purpose flour is substituted for cake flour. The amount and distribution of air in a batter affect both the texture and volume of the final product. Steam and carbon dioxide gas apparently do not produce new cells in a batter but merely enlarge the air cells. In fact, if air is removed from a cake batter under vacuum, the other leavening gases are relatively ineffective. It has been suggested that the baking powder be reduced by one-third for a one-egg cake at altitudes of 7200 feet where atmospheric pressure is low.

Baking soda is usually combined with an acid-containing food such as buttermilk, molasses, or fruit juice when used for leavening. The reaction of an acid with baking soda produces carbon dioxide gas. The variability of acidity in these foods makes it difficult to know just how much baking soda should be used. Excess baking soda gives the product a yellowish color and a soapy taste. It also weakens the gluten structure. Baking powder is a carefully balanced mixture of baking soda and an acid ingredient.

Salt contributes to the flavor of cake. The amount used depends on the kind of fat used. Why is this? Vanilla, other extracts, fruit juices, chocolate, and spices are also used as flavorings. The basic ingredients of the cake also contribute to its flavor.

Butter, margarine, hydrogenated fats and, with appropriate mixing methods, lard and oils can be used in cakes. Increased amounts of fat up to the optimum improve the tenderness and flavor. Cakes made with hydrogenated fat are usually large in volume. They have a fine, uniform cell structure which gives them high overall acceptability.

Butter has always been a favorite fat for cakes because of its flavor and color. It does have a limited temperature range within which it has good creaming quality when compared to that of hydrogenated shortenings.

Margarines vary greatly in the type of fat present in them and consequently vary somewhat in their suitability as cake shortening.

Lard is widely available but has not been readily accepted as a shortening for cakes. Cakes made with lard usually compare unfavorably with those made from several other fats because of lard's inability to hold air in the batter. However, cakes made with lard (and with oil) can be improved if the method of mixing is modified and whole eggs or egg whites beaten with sugar are added at the end of the mixing process.

Methods of cake mixing. Cakes can be prepared by a number of methods. Among these are the conventional method, muffin method, and variations of the quick mix method. Each type will produce a good product if the batter is thoroughly mixed and an "emulsion" is established. Several studies have shown that mixing a cake by the quick mix method will produce a superior cake if the mixing is done by machine or with a sturdy hand egg beater, rather than by hand. This is probably because this method requires vigorous beating in order to secure the best result, and hand beating may vary greatly.

Importance of temperature in cake baking. The objectives of baking are to (1) permit the cake to increase in volume, (2) gelatinize the starch, coagulate the protein of the flour and egg, and set the structure so that the cake will remain light, and (3) brown the crust. The temperature which can accomplish these goals depends on the kind of leavening, sugar content, thickness of the cake batter, and the other ingredients in the batter.

Since gas bubbles cause the cake to rise, the rate at which the batter is baked affects the volume and texture of the cake. If the temperature is low, the structure sets slowly, some gas is lost from the cells, the remaining cells coalesce (enlarge) and their walls become quite thick. Consequently, the volume is reduced. A very high temperature causes a crust to form on the cake before it has fully risen. The crust of the cake often cracks because the soft batter in the middle of the cake continues to rise after the crust forms and tunnels form in the crumb.

(1) Cake baked at too low a temperature. Note pitted surface, heavy coarse texture, and low volume.
(2) Cake baked at too high a temperature. Note dark crust, cracks, and uneven texture.
(3) If enamel or dark metal pans are used, the cake will be too brown and crusty.
(4) Correct pan size is important.
(5) Baked in correct pan at proper temperature, a butter cake will have a gently rounded top and light golden-brown crust.

Courtesy Betty Crocker of General Mills

The depth of the batter in the baking pan also affects the baking temperature required. A very deep batter, such as that of a loaf cake, requires a lower temperature for a longer period of time (325° F for 1 hour). Cup cakes and cakes baked in muffin pans or in layer pans require a higher temperature for a shorter time (350°–375° F for 20 to 30 minutes).

Since sugar delays protein coagulation and starch gelatinization, the cake batters made with a high ratio of sugar need a higher baking temperature. It has been suggested that 385° to 400° F may be the preferred temperature for cakes with a high sugar ratio. Regardless of what temperature is chosen for cake baking, it is important not to overbake the cake, since overbaking impairs the flavor. A cake should be allowed to cool until its internal temperature is 140° F before being removed from the pan. The time for this cooling varies, but it is usually 15 minutes or more. This cooling period allows the cake structure to become sufficiently firm.

Chocolate cakes. Chocolate cakes range in color from light brown to deep mahogany red. The color of chocolate cake seems to be related to the amount and type of chocolate used, the pH value of the batter, and the type of baking powder. Chocolate is slightly acid and will neutralize a small amount of soda, but excessive soda will give an alkaline reaction to the batter. The alkaline reaction gives the cake a reddish color, but lessens the distinctive chocolate

The color of chocolate cakes is influenced by the type of chocolate used, the acidity of the batter, and the type of baking powder used.

Photo Courtesy of Duncan Hines Cake Mix

flavor. Sweet milk and soda will give a deeper red color than will sour milk and soda, since the acidity of the sour milk neutralizes a part or all of the alkalinity of the soda. Any excess of soda always darkens the color of the cake. This darkening is probably due to a color change of the tannins and pigments of the chocolate or cocoa. A cake of lighter shade may be obtained by using baking powder as the leavening agent. If Dutch cocoa is used, the amount of soda may have to be reduced, since Dutch cocoas are subjected to high alkaline treatment during their processing. Probably because of their dextrin content, chocolate and cocoa increase the viscosity of cake batters.

Prepared Mixes

Whether a person chooses to use a mix is a personal matter. The decision usually depends on the time available for food preparation, personal preference, the person's skill in preparing foods, the intended use of the product, and the money one has available for food.

Commercial mixes. Mixes of all kinds have become a part of the American scene. Most homemakers use some kind of mix, whether it is a homemade or commercial one. The major advantage of mixes is that of saving time. The first cake mix was on the market in 1919 but was not widely accepted. Since World War II, mixes have been very well received. You have probably already used several mixes and found them to be satisfactory. As you used a commercial mix you may have wondered about its ingredients and the advantages involved in using such a mix. How much time does using a mix save? How do products made with mixes compare in quality and price with those made from the original ingredients? Do the same principles apply in preparing mixes as in making the same products from the original ingredients?

Since this chapter deals with flour mixtures, we will confine our discussion to prepared flour mixes. Although these mixes have various different ingredients, certain ingredients are common to all.

Flours with a low moisture content are desirable for mixes because there is less deterioration of the product during storage.

The leavening used depends on the product. A fast-acting leaven is necessary for doughnuts, while a slow-acting leaven is preferable for cakes. A slow-acting leavening agent is used in cake mixes to prevent premature reactions in the batter during its preparation or storage.

Fats which resist oxidation and which give high baking performance are usually chosen for mixes. Shortenings produced from lard (for pastry), and hydrogenated soybean, cotton-seed, and peanut oils are usually used in mixes. Fats used for cake mixes frequently have emulsifying agents added to improve the stability of the cake batter.

Wes Kemp

Many kinds of commercial mixes are available to the consumer.

To extend their shelf life, many commercial mixes contain antioxidants to limit oxidative rancidity of the fat (page 301).

Dry milk solids are the most common form of milk used in mixes. Spray-dried milk solids are more soluble than roller-dried milk solids and are generally used.

Dried egg yolks are found in doughnuts and sweet dough mixes. *Dried egg whites* are used in devil's food cakes, white layer cakes, and angel food cakes. Dried whole eggs have not been used extensively in mixes because they limit the storage life of the mix. For this reason it is necessary to add fresh eggs to some cake mixes, thus increasing the total cost of the final product.

Sucrose is the most widely used sugar in mixes. Granulated sugar is used in cake mixes; powdered sugar, in icing mixes. Dextrose or corn sugar is sometimes used in pancake mixes because it browns more quickly than does sucrose.

Biscuit mixes are prepared from flour, salt, soda, phosphate, dried nonfat milk solids, and shortening. The dry ingredients are mixed together first, then the shortening is added. The shortening may be added in the form of a plastic or a dry shortening. The shortening may be sprayed into the mix or cut in with high-speed cutters. Biscuits tend to be somewhat more moist if the mix is prepared with dry shortening rather than plastic shortening.

Muffin mixes vary greatly. There are muffin mixes similar to baking powder biscuits. Others resemble the cake mixes. Monoglyceride shortenings are used in the cake-type muffin mixes, while plastic shortenings are used in the biscuit-type mixes.

Pie crust mixes are prepared from either soft wheat or hard and soft wheat flour blends. The shortening is either sprayed on the flour mixture or it is added in a powdered form. If plastic shortening is used, it is added in flakes which give the crust a flaky texture.

These are only a few of the mixes available to the consumer, but the same basic ingredients will exist in other mixes with some minor variations.

Homemade mixes. The homemade mixes may not always save time but may be convenient because they can be made when the homemaker is not rushed. Quick breads, pastries, and cakes can be made from homemade mixes. In a homemade mix, flour, salt, baking powder, and sometimes sugar and dry milk solids are combined with a shortening. This mixture is stored in a cool place until needed. The final product is then made by combining the mix with the liquid ingredients—liquid, egg, and flavorings. What kind of shortening would be used in this type of mix?

In this chapter you have found information pertinent to the study of starches, flours, and flour mixtures. You have also read about prepared mixes and some of the factors which influence their uses and qualities. In the next chapter we shall consider another group of carbohydrates, the sugars.

MAJOR IDEAS

The following statements give the main ideas within the chapter you have just studied. Be sure you know the words underscored in these statements and in the questions to follow.

1. Starch is an insoluble substance produced and stored by plants. The size and shape of starch granules distinguish one starch from another.
2. The firmness of a starch gel varies with the concentration of the starch, the kind of starch, the temperature, and the presence of acids, enzymes, or sugar. The starch in an aging starch gel tends to revert to its original insolubility.

3. In the presence of dry heat, starch dextrinizes and loses some of its thickening power. When heated in liquid, starch granules swell and thicken the liquid.
4. The kind and quality of a flour depend upon the grain milled, the milling process used, and the purpose for which the flour is intended.
5. Because gluten is formed when wheat flour is mixed with water, a dough can be made. The more gluten formed, the stronger and more elastic the structure of the dough.
6. Flour mixtures are classified according to the proportion of flour to liquid.
7. The rate of growth of yeast in bread dough is controlled by temperature, the amount of sugar and salt, and the proportion of liquid to flour.
8. Bread deterioration occurs when there is staling, drying, or growth of microorganisms.
9. The degree of tenderness in pastry depends on the type of fat used, the proportion of fat to the other ingredients, the temperature, and the method of combining ingredients.
10. Sugar affects the tenderness, flavor, and texture of a cake; flour affects the volume, texture, and tenderness of the crumb; liquid influences the development of the gluten and consequently, volume and tenderness.
11. Cakes containing fat are leavened by air, chemical leavening agents, and steam.
12. Eggs are coagulating, emulsifying, and foaming agents in cakes.
13. Baking temperatures of a batter or dough are determined by the type of leavening agent, the sugar content, the thickness of the batter or dough in the baking pan, and the other ingredients present.
14. The rate at which a cake is baked affects its volume and texture.
15. Commercial ready-mixes will usually produce a satisfactory product if the manufacturer's directions are followed.

QUESTIONS TO STUDY

COMPOSITION AND CHEMICAL PROPERTIES

1. Why does each starch behave differently?
2. What are waxy starches? How do they differ from other starches?

3. Describe what happens when starch is mixed with water and then heated.
4. Of what is starch composed?

PRINCIPLES OF STARCH COOKERY

1. In what way does the kind of starch affect the gel structure of a starch mixture?
2. Why are amylopectin starches used in frozen pies and sauces?
3. Explain why fresh pineapple should not be used in puddings which are thickened with starch.
4. What is retrogradation? Give an example.

KINDS AND COMPOSITION OF FLOURS

1. What is gluten? What purpose does it have in flour mixtures?
2. Explain why the moisture content of flour has to be regulated.
3. Describe the differences between all-purpose flour, cake flour, and self-rising flour.
4. What are the advantages of using instantized flour? How do its properties differ from those of other flours?
5. Explain the differences between flour made from hard wheat and flour made from soft wheat.

FLOUR MIXTURES

1. Explain the differences between a batter and a dough.
2. Why must fresh milk be scalded before using in making yeast dough?
3. What reason is there for the variation in the amount of liquid required in yeast bread recipes?
4. Explain why yeast dough is kneaded.
5. Describe staling and its causes.
6. Explain why a muffin batter should be mixed only until the dry ingredients have been moistened.
7. Why must popovers be baked at high temperature?
8. Support the statement that lard makes the most tender pie crust.
9. Describe the functions of eggs in a cake batter.
10. Describe the characteristics of a cake made with honey.
11. Why do cakes made with a high proportion of sugar require more baking powder than do others?
12. Explain how the creaming quality of a fat affects a cake.
13. Why is the use of an electric mixer recommended for mixing a quick-mix cake?
14. Describe what happens when cake batters are baked.

15. Explain why some cakes crack open at the top surface. How can this be prevented?
16. How does the pH value affect the color of chocolate cake?

PREPARED MIXES

1. Antioxidants are often used in prepared cake mixes. Why?
2. Why must certain types of fats be used in commercial cake mixes?

BIBLIOGRAPHY

GRISWOLD, RUTH M., *The Experimental Study of Foods.* Boston, Houghton Mifflin Company, 1962.

LOWE, BELLE, *Experimental Cookery*, 4th ed. New York, John Wiley & Sons, 1955.

MATTHEWS, R. H., and BATCHER, O. M., "Sifted vs. Unsifted Flour." *Journal of Home Economics*, Vol. 55, February 1963, p. 123.

OSMAN, E. M., and MOOTSE, G., "Behavior of Starch During Food Preparation I. Some Properties of Starch-Water Systems." *Food Research*, Vol. 23, 1958, pp. 554–564.

SENTI, F. R., and DIMLER, R. J., "High Amylose Corn—Properties and Prospects." *Food Technology*, Vol. 13, 1959, pp. 663–667.

STANLEY, LOUISE, and CLINE, JESSIE A., *Foods—Their Selection and Preparation*, Boston, Ginn and Company, 1950.

WILDER, R. M., and WILLIAMS, R. R., *Enrichment of Flour and Bread. A History of the Movement.* National Academy of Science, National Research Council Publication No. 110, 1944, p. 130.

15 SUGARS

At one time sugar was sold only by apothecaries, or druggists, as we know them today. Sugar was considered an indispensable medicine, not a food, and honey was used as a sweetener. The Arabs introduced the cane sugar industry to Egypt. Here it was discovered that sugar cane sap could be made much clearer by the addition of lime and plant ashes. The Egyptians also learned how to produce large crystals in sugar cane sirup. The resulting product was called "rock candy." Much of the available sugar in Europe came by way of Italy, and on the North American continent the sugar industry came first to Santo Domingo in the West Indies.

The United States today consumes about 19 to 20 billion pounds of sugar yearly. This supply comes largely from sugar cane although sugar beets are also a source. Most of the sugar cane in the United States is grown in Hawaii, Florida, Louisiana, and the Commonwealth of Puerto Rico. Sugar beets are grown in various states on the mainland. Sugar refineries are usually located close to the areas where the cane and sugar beets are raised. Today sugar is produced in many different forms for a variety of purposes, as you will learn in this chapter.

Composition and Classification

Composition. Sugars, also known as carbohydrates, are composed of carbon, hydrogen, and oxygen. Carbohydrates are classified as monosaccharides or simple sugars (glucose, fructose, galactose), disaccharides or complex sugars (sucrose, maltose, lactose), and polysaccharides (starches, etc.). The general chemical formula for the simple sugars is $C_6H_{12}O_6$. This means that one molecule of glucose, for example, is composed of 6 carbon atoms, 12 hydrogen atoms and 6 oxygen atoms. Two molecules of simple sugars are linked together to form a molecule of the complex sugars; starch molecules are composed of many glucose units.

Boiled sugar crystallized in large masses on string is called rock candy.

Classification. For our purpose we will discuss the simple sugars, glucose, fructose, and galactose, and the complex sugar, sucrose. Starches have already been discussed in Chapter 14.

The simple sugars are monosaccharides. Glucose, also called *dextrose*, is the sugar from which plants build starch (page 172). It is abundant in fruits, especially grapes, and in vegetables such as sweet corn. It is not readily available in pure crystalline form. Glucose is also found in corn sirup together with maltose and dextrins. Glucose is less soluble in water than fructose or sucrose and crystallizes more easily than either one of those sugars. In addition, glucose is less sweet than either fructose or sucrose. *Fructose*, also known as levulose, occurs together with glucose in plants, particularly in their ripe fruits. It is also found in honey. Fructose is more soluble than most other sugars and crystallizes with difficulty. *Galactose* is a third simple sugar. It is produced when lactose, a disaccharide, is hydrolyzed (page 145).

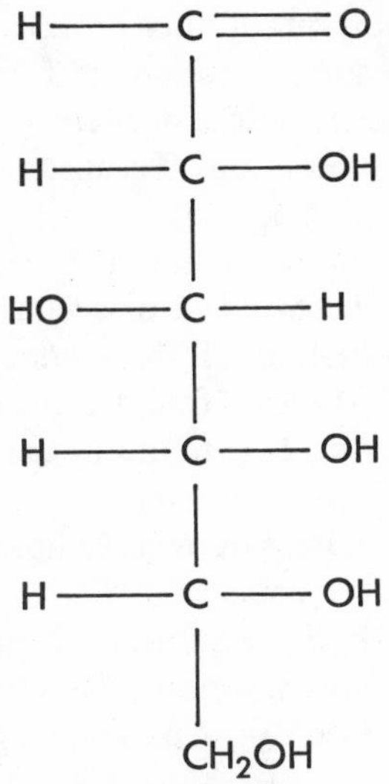

$$H - C = O$$
$$H - C - OH$$
$$HO - C - H$$
$$H - C - OH$$
$$H - C - OH$$
$$CH_2OH$$

d-GLUCOSE

The chemical structure of the monosaccharides glucose, galactose, and fructose.

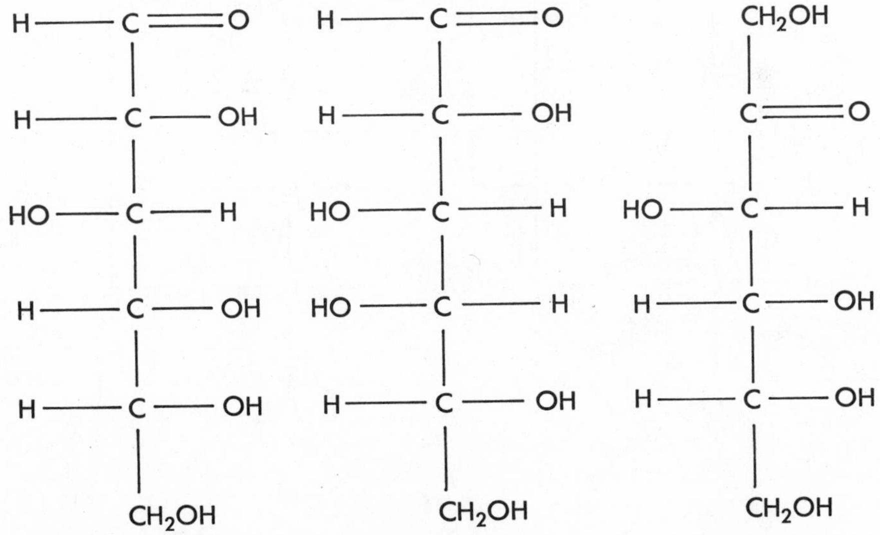

$$H - C = O$$
$$H - C - OH$$
$$HO - C - H$$
$$H - C - OH$$
$$H - C - OH$$
$$CH_2OH$$

d-GLUCOSE

$$H - C = O$$
$$H - C - OH$$
$$HO - C - H$$
$$HO - C - H$$
$$H - C - OH$$
$$CH_2OH$$

d-GALACTOSE

$$CH_2OH$$
$$C = O$$
$$HO - C - H$$
$$H - C - OH$$
$$H - C - OH$$
$$CH_2OH$$

d-FRUCTOSE

Certain complex sugars are known as disaccharides. Sucrose is the most important of this group. It is readily available, easily purified, and able to assume a variety of forms. Sugar cane, sugar beets, and maple sap are the chief sources of sucrose. It is easily obtained from plant sap by the process of evaporation. Because of its qualities, sucrose has wide commercial and home use. Sucrose is the most soluble of the disaccharides, will produce a supersaturated solution, and is easily crystallized.

Lactose is a disaccharide found in milk. It is the least sweet and the least soluble of all the sugars.

Maltose, found in cereals and in malt products, is rarely used in its pure form. It is found in the mixture formed during the hydrolysis of starch (page 172).

Later you will see how the characteristics of all these sugars are important in sugar cookery.

Polysaccharides are not sweet and many are insoluble in water. Polysaccharides include the substances *cellulose, pectins,* and *starch.* These are discussed in a separate chapter (pages 123, 172).

The chemical structure of lactose, a disaccharide.

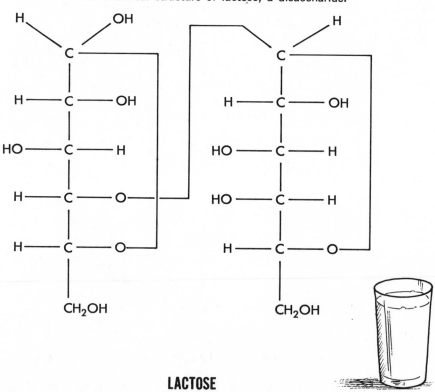

LACTOSE

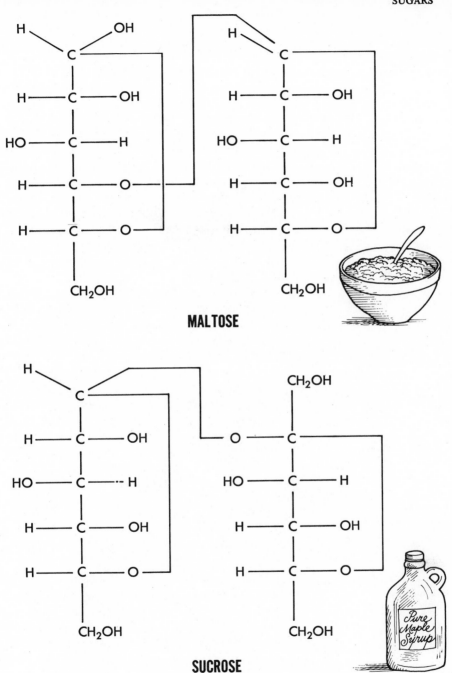

MALTOSE

SUCROSE

The chemical structure of the disaccharides maltose and sucrose.

Forms of Sugar

Granulated. When raw sugar (sucrose) undergoes a process called refinement, granulated white sugar is the final result. Brown sugar is produced by the partial refinement of raw sugar. All brown sugars have some molasses coating the sugar crystals. Brown sugars are classified by color as light, medium, and dark. These sugars differ from granulated white sugar in color and in the amount of moisture which they contain. Both color and moisture content are determined by the degree of refinement reached. Brown sugars, because of their greater moisture content, tend to pack more than white sugar does. However, it is now possible to produce a granular brown sugar which pours readily.

Powdered. Granulated white sugar, when pulverized, becomes powdered sugar. The crystals of this sugar are fine and tend to cling together. The degree of fineness is indicated by X's which range from 4X to 10X, the finest one.

Sirups. Cane and corn sirups are the sweet, thick liquids obtained in the process of manufacturing sucrose and glucose (corn sugar). They are sugar solutions. Since they are in liquid form, sirups are often preferred in the preparation of iced beverages. There is some advantage in the characteristic flavor, too. The sirups to be discussed here include corn sirup, molasses, maple sirup, and honey.

Corn sirup is a mixture of dextrins, maltose, and glucose produced by heating starch with an acid until the starch is hydrolyzed (page 172). This sirup contains about 25 percent moisture.

Molasses sirup is a by-product of the sugar industry. Molasses sirup contains sucrose and invert sugar (fructose and glucose) and small amounts of gums, calcium and other minerals, and additional materials used in the manufacture of sucrose. The standards for molasses are these: the total solids must be at least 75 percent; the minerals, not more than 5 percent.

Maple sirup is produced from the sap collected from sugar maple trees or by making an aqueous solution of maple sugar. In the former process, the sap is boiled and becomes concentrated as moisture is lost through evaporation. Continued evaporation produces maple sugar, a mixture of sucrose and a small amount of invert sugar.

Honey is made by bees from the nectar of flowers. It is available in three forms: comb, extracted, and strained. The color and the flavor of any honey depends on the kinds of flowers from which the honey has been produced. Some common flavors are clover, alfalfa, orange blossom, buckwheat, and Spanish needle. Orange blossom and clover honeys are light in color and have mild, pleasing flavors. Buckwheat honey is dark in color and has a characteristic strong flavor.

All honey contains about equal parts of glucose and fructose. The fructose shows little tendency to crystallize; any crystals that form during the storage of honey are crystals of glucose. Honey, because it contains fructose, has the ability to retain moisture (is hygroscopic, or water-attracting).

Principles of Sugar Cookery

Sugar is used extensively in food preparation because of these properties: the ability to sweeten, to crystallize, to change from a solid to a liquid of distinctive flavor and color when subjected to dry heat, and to inhibit the growth of microorganisms which cause food spoilage.

Sweetening ability. Very early you learned that sugar increases the sweetness of foods to the taste. In addition, it also affects other flavors. For example, the addition of a small amount of sugar to oversalted food counteracts the salty flavor. You may have tried this remedy if you have ever oversalted soup. The addition of sugar to fruit which is excessively acid offsets its sourness; for example, putting sugar on a tart grapefruit.

Earlier it was pointed out that some vegetables, through enzymatic action (page 157), begin to lose their natural sugar as soon as they are picked. If it is not possible to cook these vegetables shortly after picking, sugar is often added at the cooking time to help restore the "fresh, sweet" flavor. For example, sugar is frequently added to the cooking water of fresh corn on the cob, peas, cabbage, tomatoes, beets, carrots, onions, butternut and acorn squash, and sweet potatoes.

Crystallization. You will recall from page 137 that a solution may be unsaturated, saturated, or supersaturated. *In order for many crystals to form quickly in a sugar solution, the solution must be supersaturated.* This condition may be accomplished when a saturated sugar solution is cooled.

The first crystals which develop during crystallization form the nuclei (kernels) for the formation of larger crystals. To avoid the presence of crystals in

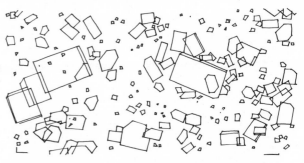

Microscopic view of the large sugar crystals in a cooked, saturated sugar solution.

a concentrated sugar mixture (e.g., candies) the mixture is stirred gently as it is heated until all the sugar crystals have been dissolved. If crystals form on the sides of the pan during heating, they must be removed. Otherwise such crystals may fall back into the mixture and form nuclei around which other crystals will cluster, thus producing large crystals rather than many small, fine ones.

This condition is prevented in two ways. The pan may be covered tightly and the mixture brought to boiling. As the sirup comes to a boil, the steam condenses and washes the crystals from the sides of the pan. Or, crystals can be wiped from the sides of the pan with a clean damp cloth. In either case, the important thing is that the crystals which may be clinging to the sides of the pan be removed.

The size of the crystals formed during crystallization is determined by the following conditions:

1. The degree of supersaturation of the solution which depends upon these factors:
    a. the final temperature to which the solution has been heated
    b. the extent of cooling before beating
2. Stirring during crystal formation
3. The presence of certain substances or agents which interfere with crystal growth: for example, a simple sugar (as found in corn sirup or honey), cream of tartar, lemon juice, and vinegar

Two factors which affect crystal formation in sugar solutions are the degree of saturation and the method of handling. If the mixture is cooled until it becomes supersaturated, beating causes many tiny crystals to form at the same time. Stirring as the crystals form keeps the small nuclear crystals separated from each other. It also helps surround the crystals with a viscous film of sirup and in this way prevents crystals from growing on one another and increasing in size. A creamy mass results. If, however, the sugar sirup is beaten without pre-cooling, when crystallization begins only a few nuclei will form and these will tend to grow. Because of the larger crystals, the product will be grainy in texture.

When noncrystalline candies—caramels, taffies, and brittles—are made, large amounts of corn sirup or invert sugar are often used to prevent crystallization. Fat—butter or cream—is often added to a sugar mixture to deter crystal formation.

Caramelization. When dry sugar is heated to a high temperature the sugar changes from a solid granular state to a liquid and undergoes chemical changes. Sugar so treated has a dark brown color and a distinctive flavor.

Preservation. Certain foods can be preserved by the use of a sufficiently high concentration of sugar. In the presence of a concentrated sugar solution water is drawn from the cells of yeast and bacteria by the process of osmosis (page 138). This withdrawal of water (dehydration) inactivates these organisms and stops their growth which would, if permitted to continue, produce spoilage in food. In jams, jellies, and preserves the sugar concentration is sufficient to prevent the growth of bacteria and yeast.

Sugar Mixtures

Sugar plays a significant role in the crystal formation in candies; in raising the boiling point in candies, jellies, and jams; and in lowering the freezing point in the preparation of frozen mixtures.

Candies. Candies are classified as crystalline and noncrystalline. *Crystalline candies are characterized by small, uniform crystals which make for a creamy, smooth texture.* Fondant, fudge, penuche, and divinity are examples of these candies. *Fondant* can be made with sucrose and water although corn sirup and invert sugars are often used too. As was mentioned previously, when sucrose is heated with water, some glucose and fructose are formed. This process, called inversion, is encouraged by the presence of an acid. The use of a catalyst (accelerating agent)—cream of tartar, lemon juice, or acid—also affects the amount of inversion. The amount of sucrose changed or inverted depends on the length of the cooking time and the temperature to which the mixture is cooked. The higher the temperature and the longer the cooking time for the fondant mixture the greater the amount of sugar (sucrose) inverted.

Cream of tartar is the acid salt commonly used in making fondant for these reasons: first, it produces a whiter fondant; second, it produces a less sweet fondant than one made with corn sirup; third, it has a constant composition. In other words, variation can occur in the degree of acidity of vinegar or lemon juice and in the composition of corn sirup, whereas the composition of cream of tartar is consistently the same. These factors control the color and production of invert sugar during the cooking time.

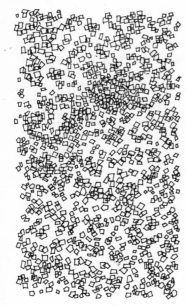

Fondant is beaten when it has cooled to about 104° F. At this temperature a desirable degree of supersaturation is reached. Beating the sirup causes many crystals to form simultaneously because of the instability of the highly supersaturated solution. If the sirup is not cooled enough before beating, only a few crystals will form at first. These will grow large, giving the candy a grainy texture. If cooled too much, the solution may form an amorphous solid.

Fudge, like fondant, is also crystalline. However, it contains, in addition to sugar and water, milk solids, often corn sirup, chocolate, and fat, which interfere with crystallization. These ingredients, also found in noncrystalline candies, are found in smaller amounts in fudge so that crystallization is possible. Fudge is cooked to a temperature of 236° F and beaten when cooled to control the size of crystals, thus encouraging a fine and even texture.

Penuche is similar to fudge but it is made from brown sugar. Since brown sugar already contains 2–6 percent invert sugar, a smaller measure of corn sirup is required to produce a candy of fine texture.

Divinity is a candy mixture prepared similar to fondant with the exception that the sirup, after being cooked to the proper temperature, is beaten into stiff egg whites to incorporate air into the mixture and give the candy a light, fluffy texture. Since egg whites contain water (85 percent) which will dilute the cooked sirup, it is necessary to cook the sirup until it reaches a highly concentrated state (254° F).

Noncrystalline candies contain more moisture than do crystalline ones. Crystallization in these candies is prevented by the presence of invert sugars and/or corn sirup, and by the addition of ingredients such as milk solids, egg whites, starch, and pectin.

Caramels are prepared from sugar, corn sirup, fat, and a large proportion of milk (evaporated, condensed, or nonfat dry milk). Because of this composition, great care must be taken during cooking to prevent scorching (page 146). The characteristic color and flavor of caramels comes from the browning reaction between lactose and the amino group in the milk protein and from sugar caramelization.

Brittles are another type of noncrystalline candy. They are made by caramelizing sucrose, heating it until a temperature of 294° F has been reached. Corn sirup or invert sugar may be added to the sucrose. After cooking, the candy is poured out and allowed to cool undisturbed. It has a glasslike texture when hardened. Crystallization is prevented by the rigidity which the mass assumes when it cools and by the presence of any corn sirup or invert sugar.

Taffies, also noncrystalline, are made by adding acid to the basic mixture of sugar and water (2 cups sugar to 1 cup water) used in fondant. Taffies are pulled as soon as they are cool enough to handle. Pulling the taffy incorporates air. The candy becomes opaque (does not reflect or emit light) due to small air bubbles and has a porous texture. Fondant is also opaque after stirring due to the fine crystals.

Tests in candymaking. There are two tests which are used in candymaking. These are the thermometer test and the cold water test.

The thermometer test is the most accurate method for determining the concentration of the sirup. The table on page 208 shows the temperatures for various sugar mixtures.

However, many cooks rely on the cold water test. This test consists of dropping $\frac{1}{2}$ teaspoon of the boiling candy mixture into 1 cup of cold water. The resulting cooled mass is tested with the fingers for firmness.

The two tests used in candymaking: a candy thermometer and the cold water test.

Temperatures and Tests for Sirup and Candies

Product	Temperature of Sirup at Sea Level* (Indicating Concentration Desired)		Test	Description of Test
	degrees F	degrees C		
Sirup	230 to 234	110 to 112	Thread	Sirup spins a 2-inch thread when dropped from fork or spoon.
Fondant Fudge Panocha	234 to 240	112 to 115	Soft ball	Sirup, when dropped into very cold water, forms a soft ball which flattens on removal from water.
Caramels	244 to 248	118 to 120	Firm ball	Sirup, when dropped into very cold water, forms a firm ball which does not flatten on removal from water.
Divinity Marshmallows Popcorn balls	250 to 266	121 to 130	Hard ball	Sirup, when dropped into very cold water, forms a ball which is hard enough to hold its shape, yet plastic.
Butterscotch Taffies	270 to 290	132 to 143	Soft crack	Sirup, when dropped into very cold water, separates into threads which are hard but not brittle.
Brittle Glacé	300 to 310	149 to 154	Hard crack	Sirup, when dropped into very cold water, separates into threads which are hard and brittle.
Barley sugar	320	160	Clear liquid	The sugar liquefies.
Caramel	338	170	Brown liquid	The liquid becomes brown.

HANDBOOK OF FOOD PREPARATION, © 1964, American Home Economics Association, Washington, D. C.
*Cook the sirup about 1 degree C lower than temperature at sea level for each increase of 900 feet in elevation, or 1 degree lower than temperature at sea level for each increase of 500 feet in elevation.

Altitude affects the cooking of candy. Most authorities suggest that the final temperature for cooking candies should be lowered 2.0° F for each 1000 feet of altitude for best results. For example, fondant is cooked to 236° F at sea level. At 1000 feet above sea level, the fondant would have to be cooked to 234° F. It is further suggested that the thermometer test be checked by using the cold water test as well.

Methods of freezing sugar mixtures. Sugar mixtures can be frozen in two ways: stirred while freezing and undisturbed while freezing.

Some mixtures are stirred while freezing. These mixtures may be prepared in a household freezer which consists of two containers designed to fit one into the other. The outside container, into which the freezing mixture (ice and salt) is placed, is preferably made of some nonconducting material such as wood or plastic. Into this container is fitted a second one made of metal such as aluminum which is a good conductor of heat. The metal container is provided with a dasher or paddle connected to a handle or electric motor, so that the mixture can be stirred as it freezes. This second container is filled with the mixture to be frozen. In the freezing process heat is absorbed from the mixture to be frozen. Heat is absorbed when the ice (solid) melts and becomes a liquid, and heat is given off when the water in the mixture to be frozen changes from a liquid state to a solid one. As the proportion of salt to ice (salt in solution) is increased, the rate of melting increases and the temperature of the brine becomes correspondingly lower.

The cold brine is in contact with the outside of the container in which the mixture to be frozen is placed. If undisturbed, the mixture will freeze around the sides of the container, where the temperature is coldest, and large crystals will form. The center of the mixture will remain unfrozen unless the dasher is turned to remove the crystals as they form on the sides of the container. This stirring process promotes more even freezing, incorporates air, and permits smoother texture by preventing crystal growth. After the mixture is frozen, the dasher is removed and the top of the container secured. The container is packed in a mixture of ice and salt and the frozen mixture is allowed to harden or ripen for several hours.

Mixtures can also be frozen without stirring. If this method is desired, however, some other way must be found to keep the crystal formation small and to incorporate air. Various interfering agents

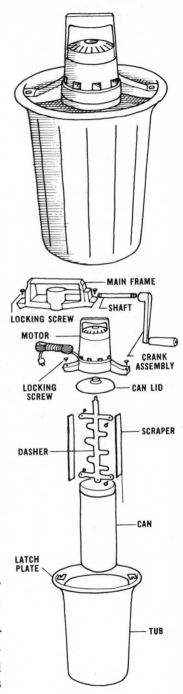

MAIN FRAME

SHAFT

LOCKING SCREW

MOTOR

CRANK ASSEMBLY

LOCKING SCREW

CAN LID

SCRAPER

DASHER

CAN

LATCH PLATE

TUB

can be used and the mixture is frozen rapidly. One of the best interfering agents is whipped cream. Beaten egg whites and gelatin can also be used to control crystallization and to incorporate air. The mixture can be removed from the refrigerator periodically and beaten before freezing is completed.

Frozen mixtures. Ice creams, sherbets, ices, and mousses are mixtures in which sugar plays an important role. In these mixtures sugar affects the freezing point and the texture.

More a perfection than a true invention, ice creams were developed from flavored ices. These ices were popular with members of the nobility at the time of Alexander the Great.

George Washington was also very fond of ice cream. Famous hostesses such as Dolly Madison and Mrs. Alexander Hamilton served ice cream on many state occasions. The popularity of ice cream in the United States today is self-evident. There are nearly 200 different flavors from which to choose. Chocolate is second in popularity and plain vanilla is the number one choice.

Ice creams are designated as Philadelphia, French, and American. Philadelphia ice cream is made from an uncooked mixture, whereas French and American ice creams are made from cooked mixtures. French ice cream contains cream, eggs, sugar, and flavoring. American ice cream is similar in composition but contains less cream and may also contain cornstarch, flour, or gelatin instead of eggs as thickening agents.

The basic ingredients of ice cream are sugar, milk, milk fat or cream, and flavoring. According to Federal government regulations, ice cream must contain not less than 10 percent milk fat and 20 percent total milk solids. The milk fat used is obtained from products of different fat content, such as dried cream, fluid or processed milk, and butter. Nonfat milk solids are also derived from concentrated forms of milk, such as condensed, evaporated, or dried milk.

Egg and milk solids (protein and fat) and gelatin (protein) will act as interfering agents, and some contribute to whipping properties. Palatability, body, and texture are influenced by these since they depend on flavors added by ingredients, air incorporated, and crystal size.

Sugar has the effect of lowering the freezing point of frozen mixtures. Sucrose is almost always used to sweeten ice cream because it lowers the freezing point less than simple sugars and most sirups. This, however, will depend on the composition of the sirup; dextrins of corn sirup have less effect on the freezing point than sucrose, maltose has the same effect, and glucose has a greater effect. If the freezing point is lowered too much, as might be the case if corn sugar were used, the ice cream is slower to freeze and a lower storage temperature is required to prevent melting.

Egg yolks improve the whipping quality of ice cream. It is thought that the presence of egg yolks brings about a finer dispersion (distribution) of fat in the ice cream mixture. Egg whites do not improve the quality of ice cream which

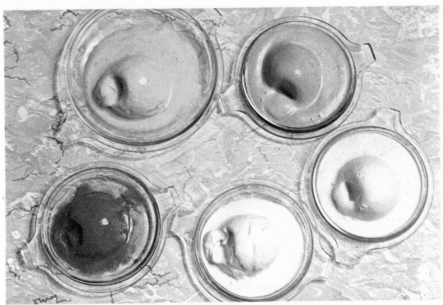

Wes Kemp

Frozen mixtures vary in the rate at which they melt. Those mixtures which have gel-forming substances will tend to hold their shapes even as they are melting.

is stirred during freezing. They may help to incorporate air into refrigerator-made ice cream, however, which is infrequently stirred during freezing, and thereby help to prevent formation of large ice crystals.

Fat prevents formation and growth of crystals. Although fat and gelatin do not increase whipping capacity, they do have a significant effect upon the size of crystals. The efficiency of fat is increased when the fat has been homogenized (page 244).

Gelatin has the ability to form a gel (page 139) in which the ice crystals tend to be small when formed and to remain small on standing. When gelatin or a gel-forming substance is absent from an ice cream mixture, a slight fluctuation in temperature will cause melting and refreezing. The new crystals will form on the ones already present and produce a coarse, crystalline product.

In commercial ice creams, sodium alginate (obtained from a certain type of algae) is used instead of gelatin because the gel will form immediately on cooling. You will recall that gelatin solutions require standing in order to reach maximum stiffness. Gel-forming substances are used in small quantities in ice creams because large amounts cause the ice cream to be spongy and to hold its shape even when melted.

Rennin, an enzyme which is found in the digestive juices, *causes milk to clot.* The rennin found in the digestive juices of calves is sold commercially and may be used in homemade ice cream to produce thickening of the milk protein.

Wes Kemp

Frozen mixtures include ice milk, fruit ice, ice cream, sherbet, and mousses.

Ices and sherbets. Sugar, water or milk, flavoring, and a stabilizer of some sort are the basic ingredients in ices and sherbets. The texture of sherbets is smoother than that of ices due to substances such as egg white or milk that hinder crystal growth. Because of their relatively high sugar content, fruit ices melt rapidly. Explain.

Mousses. Mousses are rich, frozen mixtures prepared from whipped cream and flavoring. Because of the high proportion of fat, which prevents crystal formation, mousses have an extremely smooth texture.

Preserved sugar mixtures. Certain types of microorganisms—bacteria and yeast—produce spoilage in foods. Sugar is used in some foods as a means of retarding or preventing the growth of these organisms. Jams, jellies, and preserves made of fruits or fruit pieces have high concentrations of sugar and are preserved in this way.

Jellies are clear, jelled products prepared from strained fruit juices. Jelly is said to be of high quality when it is beautifully colored and transparent and its mass quivers instead of flows when removed from its mold. *There are three major components in jelly: acid, pectin, and sugar.* The correct relationship between these three is necessary if the jelly is to be of high quality. The length of cooking time is also an important factor in securing the desired characteristics.

Acid is needed for making jelly since jelly formation is only possible in a fruit juice with a pH value below 3.5 (page 144). Below the optimum (2.5–3.4 pH), syneresis, or weeping, may occur. Some fruits may not have sufficient acid content needed for jelly-making. In these instances, lemon juice, vinegar, or lime juice can be added to supply the additional necessary acid.

Pectin (page 123) is the substance which gives structure to the fruit juice and sugar mixture as it becomes a colloidal system (page 139) called a gel. Pectin may be found naturally in some fruits in sufficient amount for making jelly. Tart apples, sour cherries, crabapples, cranberries, currants, grapefruits, lemons, limes, sour oranges, and sour plums have the necessary pectin and acid for jelly-making. In other fruits, such as strawberries and apricots, the pectin content is low. It is necessary, therefore, to add pectin extracted from orange or lemon peel, apple juice, or a commercial pectin if the fruit is to be used to make jelly. *Commercial pectin* is a product extracted from apples and citrus fruits. It is available in liquid or powdered form at most stores where foods are sold. Instructions are included with this product so that the correct proportions will be used. Commercial pectin is mixed with fruit juice and sugar and boiled for a short period of time. The shortened cooking time results in jelly that has a fresh fruit flavor.

The amount of sugar used in jelly depends on the amount and quality of the pectin. For fruit juices which are high in pectin, a ratio of 1 cup of sugar to each cup of juice is recommended. If the juice is moderately high in pectin, the ratio of $\frac{2}{3}$ to $\frac{3}{4}$ cup of sugar to one cup of juice is suggested. Usually more sugar is required when commercial pectin is used. For this reason, it is important to follow directions given by the manufacturer of the commercial pectin used. In a finished jelly, the concentration of sugar is approximately that of a saturated sugar solution.

Jelly doneness can be determined by the use of a thermometer or by the "sheeting-off" test. In the

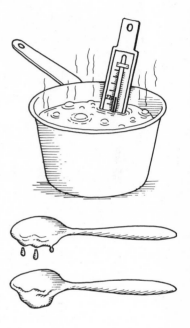

Wes Kemp

Excessive sugar or too little pectin causes jelly to be sirupy. Jelly is tough and stiff when the proportion of sugar to pectin and acid is too small or when the jelly is overcooked. Undercooked jelly will not hold a firm gel.

sheeting-off test the jelly mixture is allowed to drip from the side of a large cool spoon. When the sirup separates into two streams or drops which sheet off together, the jelly is done. The accuracy of this method of testing depends upon the experience of the tester. Use of a thermometer is the most accurate method for testing jelly. The finished jelly temperature at sea level should be 220°–221° F, or 8°–9° F above the boiling point of water (212° F) if it is necessary to make corrections for variations in atmospheric pressure.

Most jelly-making difficulties are due to (1) an unbalanced pectin-acid-sugar relationship, (2) the quality of the fruit juice, and (3) the length of time of boiling. Jelly is tough or stiff because too little sugar is used for the amount of pectin and acid in the fruit juice or too long a boiling period is maintained. Jelly may be sirupy because of excessive sugar, or because the fruit contains too little pectin. Crystals may form in jelly since undissolved sugar or other substances will produce nuclei for crystal growth.

Jams are made much the same as jellies except that jams are produced from the fruit itself rather than from the juice. Like jellies, jams must have the correct proportions of pectin, acid, and sugar. If liquid or powdered fruit pectin is added, manufacturers' instructions must be followed for best results. If commercial pectin or natural pectin in the form of apple juice, etc., is not added, $\frac{2}{3}$ to $\frac{3}{4}$ cup of sugar to each cup of prepared fruit is used. The jam is cooked until it will test in the same way as the jelly.

Preserves are prepared from whole fruits such as strawberries and cherries. The fruits are cooked in a sugar solution and the sweetness of the fruit determines the proportion of sugar to fruit. The main objective in making preserves is to keep the fruit plump and distributed throughout the sirup.

You can readily see that sugar in its various forms is extremely useful in the preparation and preservation of foods. Its special characteristics make it an important basic substance.

This chapter concludes the study of foods and food substances derived from plants. The following chapters involve foods which come from animal sources.

MAJOR IDEAS

The following statements give the main ideas within the chapter you have just studied. Be sure you know the words underscored in these statements and in the questions to follow.

1. Sugars range from the simple to the complex according to their molecular structure. Each sugar has its own degree of sweetness and solubility. The degree of solubility to some extent determines the best use for the sugar.
2. The source of a sugar and its degree of refinement determine the form of the sugar.
3. Sugars are used extensively in food preparation because of their ability to form crystals, to change from a solid to a liquid state, to sweeten other substances, and to inhibit bacterial growth.
4. The rate of crystallization and the size of crystals formed in a sugar solution can be controlled.

QUESTIONS TO STUDY

COMPOSITION AND CLASSIFICATION

1. What determines whether a sugar is classified as a monosaccharide or a disaccharide?
2. Why is glucose classified as a simple sugar?
3. What is the relationship of sugar solubility to sugar cookery?

FORMS OF SUGAR

1. What differences are there, other than color, between brown sugar and granulated white sugar?
2. How does the hygroscopic property of some sugars affect their use?
3. Why is the use of sirup preferable as a sweetening agent for cold beverages?

PRINCIPLES OF SUGAR COOKERY

1. Why must a solution be supersaturated for small crystals to form?
2. Why can sugar be used as a means of remedying overly-salted foods?
3. In candymaking, why are crystals removed from the sides of the pan during the cooking period?
4. How does stirring affect crystallization?
5. Why do large crystals form in sugar solutions beaten at high temperatures?
6. In what ways can crystal formation be prevented?
7. Why are cream and butter used in noncrystalline candies?
8. How does sugar function as a preservative in jellies and jams?

SUGAR MIXTURES

1. Why is ice cream considered a sugar mixture?
2. Why is fondant cooled before beating?
3. Why is taffy pulled after cooling?
4. What limits the use of corn sugar in making ice cream?
5. What effect does whipped cream have in a still-frozen mixture?
6. Why is a stirred-frozen mixture surrounded by a mixture of ice and salt during freezing?
7. Why is it recommended that apple juice, orange peel, or lemon peel be added to the fruit juice when making strawberry jelly?
8. What causes crystals to form in some jellies?
9. What conditions must exist before a fruit juice can be jellied?

BIBLIOGRAPHY

CARRICK, M. S., "Some Studies in Fondant Making." *Journal of Physical Chemistry*, Vol. 23, 1919, pp. 389–602.

DANIELS, A. L., and COOK, D. M., "Factors Influencing the Amount of Invert Sugar in Fondant." *Journal of Home Economics*, Vol. 11, 1919, pp. 65–69.

FRANDSEN, J. M., and ARBUCKLE, W. S., *Ice Cream and Related Products*. Westport, Connecticut, The AVI Publishing Company, 1961, pp. 31, 156.

MARTIN, L. F., "Application of Research to Problems of Candy Manufacture." *Advances in Food Research*, Vol. 6, 1955, pp. 1–65.

PANGBORN, R. M., and NICKERSON, H. A., "The Influence of Sugar in Ice Cream. Consumer Preference for Vanilla Ice Cream." *Food Technology*, Vol. 11, 1957, pp. 679–682.

STANLEY, LOUISE, and CLINE, JESSIE ALICE, *Foods—Their Selection and Preparation*. Boston, Ginn and Company, 1960.

16 EGGS

Wherever abundant, eggs have been used as food, both as a delicacy and as a staple. They have also been used as sacred symbols in religious rites and valued as gifts.

The egg has been perceived as a symbol of the world and its elements by some people. They believe that the perfectly formed shell represents the earth and the white and yolk symbolize water and fire. Additionally, the space immediately under the shell represents air. In Egypt, eggs have been found hanging

Ukrainian Easter Eggs were first created when Ukraine accepted Christianity in 998 A.D. These intricate and beautiful patterns are still being hand-done today.

Ukranian Youth League of North America, Inc.

in some temples of worship, and in Greece, eggs were glorified and used as symbols in paintings and sculptures.

The giving of highly decorated eggs as gifts originated in the pre-Christian era. Painted eggs were kept ready to present to friends and guests on special occasions. This custom is continued today at certain seasons of the year.

It is believed that chickens and eggs were brought to the Western Hemisphere at the time of Columbus's second voyage in 1493. Both eggs and chickens are important sources of food today. Eggs from geese, ducks, and other kinds of birds are eaten, too. However, for the purpose of discussing the structure and composition of eggs we will consider only the chicken egg.

Structure and Composition

A chicken egg has an oval shape and a hard porous covering, or shell, which varies in color from white to brown. The egg has a large yellow mass—the yolk—in the center of a clear, viscous material—the white or albumen. At each end of the yolk is a rope-like structure called the chalaza which attaches the yolk to the living membrane of the shell. The structural parts of the egg, then, are the shell and its membranes, the yolk, and the albumen.

The egg shell. The shell and its membranes serve as the protective barrier between the egg's contents and the outside environment. On the inside of the shell is a thin, semipermeable membrane made of an inner and an outer layer. Both these layers are important barriers to bacterial penetration of the egg.

The egg yolk. The yolk of an egg is essentially a concentrated source of food suspended in the center of the egg white. It serves as a protection for the developing chick (embryo) as well as a source of water and protein for it.

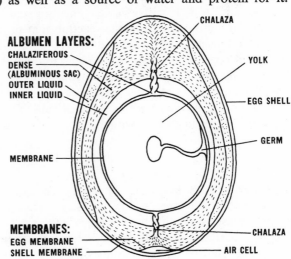

Structure of a chicken egg. In a fresh, high-quality egg, the yolk is held in the center of the albumen by the chalaza.

THE NATURE OF FOOD

The yolk differs from the white, or albumen, in that it contains large amounts of simple fats or fat-like substances known as *lipids*. Some of these lipids are combined with protein and are called lipoproteins.

The fat-soluble vitamins A, D, E, and K and the water-soluble vitamin B complex are present in generous amounts. The yellow color and the amount of vitamin A present in the yolk depend on the kind of feed which the chicken has received. The color of the yolk may vary from pale yellow to deeper yellow to deep orange. The amount of vitamin D depends on the content of the feed and the amount of sunshine to which the hen has been exposed.

The egg albumen. The egg white, albumen, is a clear viscous substance. It is made up principally of a solution of proteins and small amounts of salt and sugar. Riboflavin, one of the B vitamins found in eggs, acts as a pigment in giving the albumen its greenish-yellow tint. Most of the properties of egg white are related to individual proteins and the interactions of these proteins. There are five proteins of special note: *ovalbumin, conalbumin, ovomucin, avidin,* and *lysozyme*. The two major ones are ovalbumin and conalbumin.

The coagulability of egg white is primarily due to the relative ease with which the proteins, especially ovalbumin, can be denatured by heat. Conalbumin is an iron-binding protein and an antibacterial agent. It exerts a strong antibacterial action against organisms requiring iron and is, undoubtedly, of major importance in preventing contamination in the egg.

Ovomucin is responsible for the structure of the thick white and for the strength of the yolk membrane. Avidin is present in egg white in a relatively small amount. It is another agent in the antibacterial defense of the egg. The egg white protein, lysozyme (an enzyme), is also a bacterial defense agent.

Minerals are found in both the egg white and yolk. The iron in the yolk is important for its nutritive value. This iron and the sulfur of both the white and the yolk are involved in the reaction that produces a dark green deposit on the yolk surface of some hard cooked eggs. This discoloration is caused when hydrogen sulfide gas in the egg white comes in contact with the iron in the yolk and forms harmless ferrous sulfide. The heat of cooking and the alkaline reaction of lower quality eggs speed the formation of iron sulfide. The sulfur can also react with silver and cause the darkening of silver utensils when they come in contact with egg yolk.

Quality and Grade

Preserving the original quality of chicken eggs is of primary concern to the poultryman and to the poultry industry. Much effort has gone into finding ways to preserve quality and to increase the availability of eggs for food.

Egg grades are based on these factors: the condition of the shell, the size of the egg, and the interior quality of the egg.

Condition of egg shells. The proportion of shell to egg changes as the laying hen becomes older. Eggs from older hens are larger and have thinner shells. The shells may also be rough and unacceptable to the consumer.

Sizes of eggs. The size of an egg is also dependent on the age of the hen. During the first year of production for the hen, the eggs produced are small.

Eggs are graded according to weight. The sizes vary from Jumbo (30 ounces per dozen) to Peewee (15 ounces per dozen).

USDA Photo

JUMBO	EXTRA LARGE	LARGE
30 oz.	27 oz.	24 oz.
MEDIUM	SMALL	PEEWEE
21 oz.	18 oz.	15 oz.

THE NATURE OF FOOD

They are called pullet eggs. As the hen matures, the size of the eggs she produces increases. This factor becomes important in the price and selection of eggs. For example, if eggs are to be served individually—as poached eggs—you may choose to buy the top grade to obtain eggs of the desired size. If, on the other hand, you are buying eggs to be scrambled or to be hard cooked for a salad you may choose to purchase smaller, less uniformly-sized eggs, which will be perfectly suitable for your purpose.

The grading of eggs is based on standards determined and enforced by state departments of agriculture. Their guide is the set of standards developed by the Agricultural Marketing Service of the United States Department of Agriculture. The determination of the size of eggs is based on the total weight of one dozen eggs.

The six weight classes of U.S. graded eggs are Jumbo, Extra Large, Large, Medium, Small, and Peewee. In the following Table you will find the minimum weights authorized for each class.

Table 12

Weight Classes for U.S. Graded Eggs

Class	Weight per Dozen
Jumbo	30 ounces
Extra Large	27 ounces
Large	24 ounces
Medium	21 ounces
Small	18 ounces
Peewee	15 ounces

Interior quality of eggs. *Candling* is the process used in grading to check the interior quality of an egg. This process involves the rotation of the egg before a light so that the egg yolk and the air cell can be seen. The candler's opinion of the interior quality of the egg is based on the appearance of these two parts. It is a well-established fact that an egg is at its peak of quality when first laid and that this quality starts to deteriorate soon afterward. An egg of high quality has a small air cell, a large proportion of thick white (albumen), and a yolk that is upstanding and well-centered.

During deterioration, or loss of quality, the albumen becomes thinner; some of its water is transferred to the yolk and this causes the yolk to become enlarged and flattened out. As the egg ages, the shell becomes more porous and moisture is lost through the shell. As a result the air cell is enlarged. Carbon dioxide, responsible for the cloudy appearance of the fresh white, is normally present in the freshly-laid egg. The loss of carbon dioxide during storage is

INTERIOR QUALITY OF EGGS
(Recommended standards for scoring the quality of broken-out eggs)

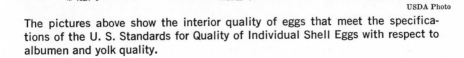

1. HIGH "AA" or "FRESH FANCY"	2. AVERAGE "AA" or "FRESH FANCY"	3. LOW "AA" or "FRESH FANCY"
4. HIGH "A"	5. AVERAGE "A"	6. LOW "A"
7. HIGH "B"	8. AVERAGE "B"	9. LOW "B"
10. HIGH "C"	11. AVERAGE "C"	12. LOW "C"

USDA Photo

The pictures above show the interior quality of eggs that meet the specifications of the U. S. Standards for Quality of Individual Shell Eggs with respect to albumen and yolk quality.

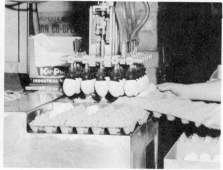

A rubber-type screw moves the eggs while they are brushed and washed.

Vacuum lifter takes eggs—one layer at a time—from case packed by producer.

Eggs are individually weighed and channeled into packaging units.

A carton of eggs ready for the consumer.

USDA Photos

associated with the increased alkalinity of an egg as it deteriorates and with the pronounced thinning of the egg white. This carbon dioxide loss is slowed by prompt and continued refrigeration.

The four U.S. quality grades for eggs, beginning with the highest, are **AA, A, B,** and **C**. These grades are based on the interior quality of the eggs so marked.

Preservation of Eggs

In preservation the goal is to minimize both the physical and chemical changes so that the egg, when broken out of its shell and used, will have the taste, odor, and functional properties associated with freshly-laid eggs.

Methods of preservation and storage. Refrigeration, oil dipping, thermostabilization, and overwrapping are methods which are used to preserve egg quality. *Refrigeration is the best method for egg storage.* However, it is not always possible to have proper refrigeration for this purpose, so other means must be used.

Oil dipping is not a new process. In fact, it was used as early as 1807 by Dutch farmers who immersed eggs in linseed oil for several hours before storing them for future use. Today aerosol oil spraying of eggs has become prominent. Eggs treated in this way are generally higher in quality and lower in weight loss than those that are oil-dipped or oil-emulsion-sprayed. Also, more protection is afforded by this method if the eggs are oiled within one hour or not more than six hours after they are laid.

Thermostabilization of eggs involves the immersion of the eggs for 15 minutes in 131° F water or 8 to 10 minutes in 136.4° F water. The thin outer film of albumen becomes coagulated during this process. The cooked albumen is highly impervious to carbon dioxide but not to moisture vapor. Therefore, there is a considerable weight loss in eggs which are treated in this manner.

Overwrapping of eggs has been used to maintain egg quality. Eggs stored in plastic bags retain higher quality than do oiled eggs or ones that have been thermostabilized. For example, a study of the packaging of eggs indicated that eggs stored in plastic bags for one week at 102° F were higher in quality than oil-emulsion-treated eggs, and the weight loss was lower than that of thermostabilized eggs held one week at 55° F.

Each of these techniques of preservation provides a means of minimizing egg quality deterioration. Since poultry and eggs have been shown to be an acceptable means of increasing protein levels of a substandard diet rapidly, any means by which eggs can be preserved and distributed successfully helps to make more eggs of acceptable quality available to more people. Any of the methods may be combined with refrigeration. However, in many less-developed countries where environmental temperatures are high and refrigeration facilities are nonexistent, refrigeration is not possible. For example, in the north central part of India the daily average temperature varies between 50° and 105° F with a relative humidity between 34 and 89 percent. Under these conditions preservation of eggs is difficult. However, any treatment used to protect the interior quality of eggs is better than using no treatment. The chances of the people benefiting from the protein and the other food nutrients available in eggs will be greater if the egg supply is readily available.

Freezing and drying are also methods by which eggs can be preserved. Eggs may be frozen (without shells) as egg whites, yolks, or whole eggs. Egg whites require no special treatment for freezing but yolks and, to a lesser degree, whole eggs, tend to thicken unless sugar, salt or glycerine has been added before freezing. Frozen eggs are used as a substitute for fresh eggs by bakers, candy manufacturers, and makers of ice cream.

This modern egg-breaking plant operates under the U. S. Department of Agriculture's Egg Products Inspection Program. To be eligible, a plant must first have equipment, facilities, and operating procedures that meet minimum requirements. Eggs enter this breaking room through chutes seen at right. Eggs will serve as breaking stock for the preparation of egg products.

USDA Photos

In this egg-breaking operation, shell eggs enter by conveyer, are mechanically opened, and then dropped onto a separator cup just large enough to hold the yolk. The white of the egg separates from the yolk and drops to the lower container. The operator of the machine checks each individual egg as it passes by for appearance and odor.

The U.S.D.A. resident egg products inspector checks the temperature of the liquid egg in a stainless steel coil vat. The temperature of liquid whole eggs must be reduced to 45°F or less within 1½ hours after breaking.

USDA Photos

The U.S.D.A. inspector checks the temperature of liquid salted yolk which is being prepared for export. Salt added to yolks acts as a preservative and improves the texture of the product.

USDA Photos

Scrambled eggs made from a dried egg mix that was sifted, measured, and then reconstituted.

Eggs can also be successfully dried. Dried egg solids (whole eggs) are used extensively in institutional food preparation while dried egg whites are used widely in packaged angel food cake mixes. Dried eggs are a protein food with no protection of the egg shell. They are subject to contamination by the same types of bacteria which infect any other protein foods. Salmonella* bacteria are able to grow in a wide range of protein foods—meat, dairy products, poultry, fish, and eggs. Foods which are made with dried egg solids may carry these organisms unless the eggs have been pasteurized before they are dried or are cooked quite thoroughly when used. Because some dried eggs may contain Salmonella organisms, the United States Department of Agriculture has recommended that dried eggs be used only in products that are thoroughly cooked. However, if the eggs have been dried under rigid bacteriological control, they are safe in any product. Dried eggs can be used successfully in scrambled eggs, baked custards, popovers, and plain butter cakes.

Functional Properties

Eggs are used in cooking because of their special functional properties: whipping and foaming properties of the egg white; emulsifying and thickening properties of the yolk; thickening, binding, and other properties of the whole egg.

Egg white used to produce foams. A foam is achieved by whipping egg whites. During this process, air is incorporated and surrounded by a film of the egg white protein to form many irregularly-shaped cells. Continued beating adds more air and the cells formed become smaller but more numerous. The protein film is spread more thinly but continues to surround the individual cells.

*Salmonella are a type of bacteria associated with acute inflammations in the intestines of animals.

Bernard L. Lewis, Inc.   USDA

Hard meringue shells.   Soft meringue for pie topping.

Underbeaten egg whites lose volume very rapidly and do not retain their rigidity; overbeaten egg whites lack elasticity, tend to break down into small curds, and lose volume rapidly. Usually egg whites produce a better product if the whites are beaten only until the peaks of the foam stand straight and bend slightly at the tip. However, the stage to which an egg white foam needs to be beaten depends upon the product being made. Top quality eggs at room temperature are usually recommended so that maximum foam volume and stability will be secured.

Foams are used to leaven products such as angel food cakes and to give light texture to whips, meringues, and other airy products. While the whipping technique is very important to the formation of a desirable egg white foam, each of the other ingredients used in a mixture will also affect the final product created.

Fat or fat-containing ingredients—egg yolk, whole milk, and oil—interfere with the formation of an egg white foam. For this reason, care must be taken that any equipment used in beating egg whites be free from fatty material of any sort.

Salt used in a small amount for flavoring has little effect on the quality of an egg white foam.

Acid is used to make an egg white foam more stable and to increase the whiteness of the product. For example, cream of tartar is used in making angel food cake. Lemon juice and vinegar may also be used but cream of tartar has been found to give the best result.

Sugar added to egg whites increases the stability of an egg white foam and also extends the beating time required. Sugar is, therefore, usually added to a foam after the desired volume has already been obtained and it is sufficiently stable so that peaks have begun to form.

Egg yolks used as emulsifiers. Emulsions, you recall, are prepared by mixing oil and water. The resulting mixture may be either of temporary or perma-

Some emulsions, such as mayonnaise and Hollandaise sauce, are made permanent by the inclusion of egg yolk. Other emulsions, such as French dressing, are temporary.

nent nature. Oil and water do not mix permanently unless a third agent is added which can keep one of the liquids suspended in the other. This agent is called an *emulsifier* or *emulsifying agent*. Egg yolk makes an excellent emulsifying agent because it surrounds the oil droplets and prevents them from joining to form larger droplets which can settle out. Mayonnaise and Hollandaise sauce are examples of emulsions in which egg yolks are used as emulsifying agents.

Egg yolks used as thickeners. Egg yolks are also important as thickening agents in sauces, custards, and pie fillings, and are, in fact, the sole thickening agent in some mixtures. In other mixtures they are used with starch. The thickening in the latter case is dependent on the gelatinization of the starch and the coagulation of the egg protein.

There are two methods suggested for cooking mixtures which have both starch and egg included. The first method involves the addition of the egg after the starch paste has been cooked until thickened. When the egg is added, the mixture is heated just enough to cook the egg. Failure to cook it sufficiently will result in a mixture that is thin. The second method involves mixing the egg with the other ingredients and cooking the mixture over direct heat until thickened. Constant stirring and careful control of the source of heat are essential to prevent sticking and lumping. Undercooking the egg is no problem.

Whole eggs used as thickening, binding, and "interfering" agents. Puddings and custards may be thickened by whole eggs; ingredients in croquettes are held together (bound) by coagulated egg protein. Beaten eggs act as interfering substances and help to produce small ice crystals in frozen mixtures such as sherbets and ice creams. Tiny bubbles of air trapped in the beaten eggs prevent ice crystals from coming together to form large masses of icy material. In the chapter on sugar we have already discussed the use of egg whites as interfering agents in the making of candies.

Principles of Egg Cookery

The temperature of coagulation, the time required for coagulation, and the factors that cause variations in coagulation temperature are of major importance in egg cookery.

Factors which affect coagulation temperature. *The coagulation temperature of egg whites varies with the rate of heating.* If the rate is very slow, the coagulation temperature is relatively low. Undiluted egg white coagulates to a jelly-like consistency at approximately 145°–148° F. As this temperature is increased, the egg white becomes firmer.

Egg yolks require a higher temperature for coagulation than do egg whites. Egg yolk begins to thicken into a gel as the temperature approaches 144° F. At 149° F it will not flow. At 158° F it is fairly firm but still jelly-like and tender. Thus, egg yolks thicken at 149° F and are firm at 158° F. An intermediate temperature between that used for egg white and egg yolk coagulation is adequate to coagulate egg yolk and white when they are together. In all instances these temperatures are well below the boiling point—212° F.

Egg white at 144°F.   Egg white at 158°F.

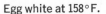
Wes Kemp Photos

Egg yolk at 149°F.   Egg yolk at 158°F.

The egg on the left shows shrinkage and toughness because it was cooked at a high temperature for a long period of time. The egg on the right was cooked at a lower temperature just long enough to coagulate the white and yolk. It shows no shrinkage or toughness.

Eggs can be successfully cooked by methods using relatively high temperatures provided the time is carefully controlled. High temperatures, however, plus long cooking tend to cause the egg protein to become more compact or dense. There is an accompanying loss of moisture and an evidence of shrinkage. Most directions for egg cookery suggest low to moderate temperatures because the timing factor is then not so critical.

Since eggs, hence their proteins, are often mixed with other foods during cooking, the coagulation of the egg proteins depends upon not only the amount of egg used but also on the other ingredients present. *Dilution of egg protein will raise the coagulation temperature; concentration of egg protein will lower it.* For example, in a custard mixture most of the heat-coagulable protein is furnished by the egg. As this mixture is heated, coagulation occurs. If the cooking temperature has been too high, or the cooking time too long, or both, the amount of liquid held within the coagulated protein framework is decreased and weeping or curdling results. If the proportion of eggs is increased in a custard, the coagulation temperature will be lower and a firmer custard will result at a given final temperature.

The addition of sugar to a mixture increases the temperature at which the egg protein will coagulate. The more sugar, the greater the heat required to bring about coagulation. Large amounts of sugar reduce the gel strength in mixtures such as egg custards. Excessive sugar—more than 30 percent in the mixture—may even prevent a custard from jelling at all.

The addition of an acid to an egg mixture (such as a custard) lowers the coagulation temperature and produces a firmer gel. When eggs are broken out of their shells and are cooked in water (poached), the addition of an acid—vinegar—to the cooking water lowers the coagulation temperature and helps to obtain a firmer gel.

When salt is added to an egg mixture, the coagulation temperature is lowered. For example, eggs poached in water which has been salted will coagulate more quickly. In an egg mixture, salt added at the beginning of the cooking time will have a similar effect. If the salt is added and stirred in at the end of the cooking period, curdling may occur.

In mixtures such as cooked pie fillings and cooked salad dressings the gelatinization of starch and the coagulation of egg protein cause the mixtures to thicken. In Chapter 14 you learned how starch gelatinization occurs and those substances which affect it. The coagulation of egg protein and the gelatinization of starch are different processes, as you have seen. Refer back to page 230 for two methods of handling mixtures in which both egg protein and starch occur as the thickening agents.

Ways to prepare eggs. The cooking methods used in preparing eggs are cooking in the shell, scrambling, frying, poaching, and baking.

Cooking eggs in the shell results in either a soft-cooked egg or a hard-cooked egg. The temperature used and the length of time the egg is cooked determine the stage of doneness. Soft-cooked eggs are simmered 5 to 8 minutes or boiled 3 to 5 minutes; hard-cooked eggs are simmered about 15 minutes or boiled about 8 minutes. Hard-cooked eggs should be cooled immediately to prevent overcooking and the formation of a green surface on the yolk (page 220). Best results in hard-cooked eggs can be obtained by using high-quality eggs, timing the cooking carefully, and cooling promptly.

The *scrambling* of eggs consists of breaking eggs into a dish, beating them enough to form a uniform mixture, then cooking in a skillet with occasional stirring until a fluffy, soft, smooth mass (coagulum) is formed. Milk, cream, or tomato juice are usually added to the beaten eggs. However, the amount of liquid added should not exceed the amount which the egg protein can thicken

The egg on the top was boiled for 8 minutes and then cooled immediately. The egg on the bottom was boiled for the same amount of time but was allowed to cool naturally.

Wes Kemp

(about 1 tablespoon per egg), otherwise the eggs will become watery and the coagulum (mass) will be smaller and firmer.

Frying requires the use of only enough fat to prevent the eggs from sticking (1 teaspoon fat per egg). After breaking the eggs into the moderately hot skillet, the skillet is covered and the eggs are allowed to cook for 3 to 5 minutes. The steam from the cooking eggs helps to promote uniform cooking and eliminates the need for basting the surface of the yolk. If necessary, a very small amount of water can be added to furnish additional steam.

Poaching involves dropping broken-out eggs into boiling water. It is desirable to have the water near the boiling point when the eggs are added so that the outer portion of the egg is coagulated in a short period of time. The cooking can then be completed at a lower temperature.

Baking or shirring is an easy way to prepare eggs. One or two eggs are broken into individual greased baking dishes and baked at 300° to 350° F for 12 to 20 minutes, depending upon the firmness desired.

There are two types of *omelets*: French and plain. Omelets are cooked in a skillet or omelet pan over direct heat. The ingredients of French and plain omelets are whole eggs, seasonings, and a small amount of liquid. The French omelet is prepared without separating the eggs. In a plain omelet the egg whites are beaten separately and then folded into the beaten yolks. Some omelets are made by combining flour, fat, and liquid to make a cream sauce, adding this sauce to the beaten egg yolks, and folding the mixture into the stiffly beaten whites. Omelets made in this way are more tender and not as expensive as egg omelets made only from eggs.

A *soufflé* is actually a baked omelet made with a cream sauce to which some kind of seasoning, flavoring, or other food has been added. Some soufflés have cheese, cooked meat, vegetables, chicken, or flaked fish added. Others are flavored with chocolate or fruit pulp.

Meringues are of two basic types: soft, used for toppings, and hard, used as foundations for or accompaniments to desserts. In making meringues one major concern is to make sure that the meringue does not shrink or lose moisture. The degree of coagulation of the egg protein in the meringue is an important factor in preventing this moisture loss or leakage. This same factor also affects beading (amber beads or droplets on the surface of the browned meringue). In the first instance, it has been found that liquid is most apt to collect under the meringue when the meringue has been placed on a cold, rather than on a hot, mixture. In the second case, beading is caused by over-coagulation of the egg protein at the meringue surface, thereby causing loss of liquid.

Hard meringues contain a larger proportion of sugar than do soft ones. They are dried in the oven with little or no browning. The oven must be operated at a low temperature during the entire baking period.

Custards are prepared from a liquid (usually milk), eggs, sugar, and flavoring. There are two types of custards, baked and stirred. In preparing cus-

USDA Photo   USDA Photo

USDA Photo   Poultry and Egg National Board

Higher-quality eggs—those in Grades AA and A—are particularly suited for serving poached or fried eggs where appearance is important. Proper temperature and correct cooking time are essential if the eggs are to look appealing. When scrambling eggs or making omelets, the temperature must be carefully controlled in order to insure tender products. Scrambled eggs can be prepared in a double boiler, as shown above, but more frequently they are cooked in a skillet.

tards the mixture must be cooked enough to coagulate the egg protein without decreasing its ability to bind the liquid in a gel or viscous sol (page 139). There must be no excessive heat.

Angel food cakes and *sponge cakes* are considered here because of their high proportion of egg used to give a foam structure. Angel food cakes contain the following basic ingredients: egg whites, sugar, cream of tartar, and flour. The remaining ingredients are flavoring and salt. High-quality egg whites are desirable for angel food cakes because they produce a cake with large volume and

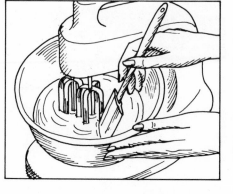

uniform texture. Sugar content is relatively high in these cakes. It serves as a tenderizer, stabilizes the foam, is a source of flavor, and produces a crust that is more crisp than that of a shortened cake.

Cream of tartar increases the stability of the egg-white foam and whitens the cake. The method of combining the ingredients affects the lightness of an angel food cake. There are several methods of preparing acceptable cakes, but the one method which appears to be the most consistent in producing an excellent product involves the beating of the egg whites until foamy; adding the salt, flavoring, and cream of tartar; then continuing beating until the egg whites form stiff peaks with slightly bending tips. Sugar is next folded in in small amounts. The flour is added last, also in small amounts. One fourth of the sugar may be mixed with the flour to insure smooth blending. Angel food cakes require an oven temperature of 375° to 400° F to produce a moist, high-volumed product. The crust will be heavy and dark. Manufacturers of commercial mixes recommend 375° F.

Sponge cakes are similar to angel food cakes except that in sponge cakes yolks are used as well as whites. Lemon juice, rather than cream of tartar, is the acid usually used. The major objectives when making a sponge cake are to beat the eggs thoroughly so as to form a stable foam and to reduce the toughening effect of coagulated egg protein by including a sufficient amount of sugar.

This chapter has discussed the structure and composition, quality, preservation, and functional properties of eggs, and the principles of egg cookery. Eggs are classified as protein foods. In the next chapter you will study another food which is also important for its protein content. This food, milk, like eggs, comes from an animal source.

MAJOR IDEAS

The following statements give the main ideas within the chapter you have just studied. Be sure you know the words underscored in these statements and in the questions to follow.

1. Because eggs can serve as emulsifying, foaming, thickening, and binding agents they can be used in many ways in food preparation.
2. Eggs are classified as protein foods and as such require the conditions in cooking which provide palatability and acceptability of other protein foods.
3. The grading of eggs makes it possible to have a reliable indication of the internal quality of the eggs marketed.
4. Retention of the fresh quality of an egg is directly related to proper care in handling and storage which provide for control of all conditions which might cause any loss in quality.
5. The rate and extent of coagulation of egg protein depend on the temperature and time of heating, the dilution of the protein, and the presence of sugar or acid. High temperature and long cooking will cause the protein to shrink, become more dense, and lose moisture.
6. Fats and fat-containing ingredients interfere with foam formation, while acids and sugar tend to stabilize foams.

QUESTIONS TO STUDY

STRUCTURE AND COMPOSITION

1. Explain why the understanding of the structure and composition of an egg is important in egg cookery.
2. What happens when egg quality deteriorates?
3. In what respects are egg yolks and egg whites different? Why are these differences important in egg cookery?

4. Give an example of differences in individual characteristics of the proteins found in eggs.

QUALITY AND GRADE

1. How are <u>alkalinity</u> and egg quality related?
2. What factors determine the quality of an egg?

PRESERVATION OF EGGS

1. Describe the various methods used for the <u>preservation</u> of eggs.
2. Why is the method of <u>thermostabilization</u> used or recommended for use in less-developed countries?
3. Why must rigid <u>bacteriological controls</u> be observed when preserving eggs by drying?

FUNCTIONAL PROPERTIES

1. Why is <u>cream of tartar</u> preferred to other acids in making angel food cake?
2. What purpose do eggs serve in salad dressings and mayonnaise?
3. What effect does a high level of sugar have on a <u>custard</u>?
4. What purpose do eggs serve when used in frozen mixtures?

PRINCIPLES OF EGG COOKERY

1. What factors affect the coagulation of egg protein? Give examples of the application of these factors in egg cookery.
2. Why is a low temperature recommended for cooking eggs?
3. What causes the discoloration of the egg yolk in a hard-cooked egg? How can this condition be prevented?
4. Why should the amount of liquid added to scrambled eggs be limited?
5. What causes amber beads to form on a <u>meringue</u>?

BIBLIOGRAPHY

BARTLETT, B. E., "Grading Eggs for Quality and Some Quality Comparisons." *Journal of Agriculture*, Vol. 62, 1944, pp. 365–371.

DAVIS, G. T., and BENKLER, A. F., "Plastic Packaging of Eggs." *Poultry Science*, Vol. 41, 1962, pp. 391–397.

GOODWIN, T. L., WILSON, M. L., and STADELMAN, W. J., "Effect of Oiling Time, Storage Position and Starage Time on the Condition of Shell Eggs." *Poultry Science*, Vol. 41, 1962, p. 840.

GRISWOLD, RUTH M., *The Experimental Study of Foods.* Boston, Houghton Mifflin Company, 1962.

KLINE, LEO, MEEHAN, J. J., and SUGIHARA, T. F., "Relation Between Layer Age and Egg-Product Yield and Quality." *Food Technology*, Vol. 19, August 1965, p. 116.

LOWE, BELLE, *Experimental Cookery*, 4th ed. New York, John Wiley & Sons, Inc., 1955.

MILLER, E. L., and VAIL, G. E., "Angel Food Cakes Made from Fresh and Frozen Egg Whites." *Cereal Chemistry*, Vol. 20, 1943, pp. 528–535.

MUKERJI, P. C., and FRY, JACK L., "Studies on Preserving Quality in Market Eggs." *Poultry Science*, Vol. 42, 1963, pp. 348–349.

SAUTER, E. A., and others, "Relationship of Candled Quality of Eggs to Other Quality Measurements." *Poultry Science*, Vol. 32, 1950, p. 850.

TOPP, ELEANOR B., and McDIVITT, MAXINE E., "Effect of Heat on Curd Tension of Baked Custard." *Journal of the American Dietetic Association*, Vol. 46, April 1965, pp. 298–301.

17 MILK

The story of milk goes back to the beginning of civilization itself. Mankind's earliest known writings mention milk as one of the most essential of all foods. Prehistoric drawings, unearthed in the Sahara Desert and dating back 8000 years or more, feature picture stories of cattle. A 5000-year-old mosaic frieze found in an ancient temple at Ur near Babylon depicts a dairy scene. Writings from the early Egyptian, Greek, and Roman civilizations describe the importance of milk, and even Marco Polo in his writings noted that the Tartars owed much of their strength and endurance to milk.

In the United States it was a customary practice for each family to have its own cow or cows for a source of milk. As towns and cities grew, this custom became impractical and was replaced by the establishment of dairies which served several families. Gradually the dairy industry grew. With the development of transportation, modern refrigeration, and greatly improved sanitary regulations, the milk supply for towns and cities now is obtained from dairies often located far from the metropolitan areas. Milk, produced and processed under carefully controlled conditions, is available in a variety of forms for drinking and for use in many food preparations.

Properties

Milk is generally defined as whole, fresh milk—meaning cow's milk. It has certain distinctive qualities of odor, taste, and appearance. You will see that it also exhibits certain special physical properties which make it important in food preparation.

Physical properties. The *odor* and *taste* of milk are directly related to the feed given the cow. The *appearance* of milk is related to the protein called casein. The reflection of light rays by the finely dispersed calcium caseinate and calcium phosphate produces the white appearance. A bluish tint in milk is due either to dilution with water or to the skimming off of the cream. The taste of milk, probably due in part to the presence of milk sugar (lactose), is characteristic but not pronounced.

The *creaming* of milk is not fully understood but it is known that the lipids (fats) in milk have a lower specific gravity (page 141) than the milk serum. Thus, the fat tends to rise. Fat globules present in fresh whole milk vary in size.

240

Milk of high fat content contains a greater number of large globules than milk of low fat content. The size of the fat globules varies with the breed of the animal and the stage of lactation. Jersey and Guernsey cows produce milk with larger fat globules than do the Ayrshire and Holstein breeds. Goat's milk also contains smaller fat globules than does cow's milk. As the lactation period continues, the size of fat globules becomes smaller. Cream which contains large globules whips more easily than cream with small globules.

Milk, like water, expands when heated and contracts when cooled. The maximum density of milk is probably close to that of water (approximately 40° F). When it freezes, milk expands. In filling milk containers, when milk is purchased on a volume basis, some authorities suggest that the milk be about 40° F so that when the milk is cooled there will be enough head space in the container to allow for variations in expansion and contraction.

Fresh milk will foam easily when agitated. The foam produced tends to show some permanence. This foaming makes it difficult to handle milk during pasteurization and during reconstitution of dried milk. The foaming of dried milk may be prevented by the addition of a small amount of oil.

The *whipping quality* of cream is affected by the fat content, the size of fat globules, the temperature, and the age of the cream. Thirty percent fat content is the minimum with which cream will whip with ease. An increase in fat content will improve the stability of the foam and decrease the time required for whipping cream but does not improve the volume of the whip. Large fat globules will clump more easily and result in more rapid whipping of cream. Homogenization impairs the whipping ability because it reduces the size of the fat globules in the cream. Cream at a temperature below 45° F is best for whipping. Aging of cream assists the clumping together of fat globules so that the whipability of cream increases with aging up to 72 hours.

The stability of whipped cream is due to the fine cell-like structure imparted by the air bubbles and the clumped fat globules in the surrounding film.

Physio-chemical properties. Milk has a pH value of 6.6 but it may vary from a pH of 6.3 to 6.7. The changing of the pH in milk, either to a more acid or more alkaline mixture, affects the solubility of the protein casein. Casein will coagulate when the pH has been reduced to approximately 5.2. It is least soluble at pH 4.6. If the casein precipitates out, curdling occurs.

Coagulation of milk occurs naturally by the action of the enzyme rennin on casein or by the growth of the lactose-fermenting microorganism which produces lactic acid. Heat also causes coagulation but casein is much more stable when heated than most proteins are. *In milk coagulation two factors are involved: the denaturation of the protein followed by the agglomeration (clumping together) of the protein molecules.* Some authorities think that dehydration may also be involved. Scum formation on the top of heated milk is an example of heat coagulation of whey (watery part of milk after removal of curd) proteins.

Composition

Milk, composed largely of water (87 percent in whole milk), contains lactose, fat, proteins, and mineral ash.

Lactose. Milk is the only known natural source of the carbohydrate lactose, or milk sugar. This sugar is a disaccharide (page 200) which yields glucose and galactose when digested in the body.

Although lactose is in true solution in milk, it is a relatively insoluble sugar. This insolubility creates a problem in the manufacture of condensed milk because the lactose may settle out from the milk and produce a granular texture in the finished product. Lactose may crystallize from ice cream since much of the water content is frozen. The souring of milk is also related to lactose. Bacterial action on lactose forms lactic acid.

Fat. The milk fat or butter fat is a mixture of the glycerides of various fatty acids, small amounts of phospholipids (phosphorus and fat), cholesterol, and the fat-soluble vitamins A, D, E, and K. The minimum fat content of whole milk is regulated by law. The Federal Government stipulates the fat content of 3.25 percent in whole milk. However, the amount actually required by various state governments may vary from 3.0 to 3.8 percent. Substitutions of other fats are made for milk fat in such products as filled milk, imitation ice cream, and margarine. To produce filled milk, dried skim milk is reliquefied in water, mixed with vegetable oils (usually coconut) and then the mixture is homogenized and pasteurized. In some cases water is evaporated from this milk until the concentration is about that of evaporated milk.

Proteins. The main proteins in milk are casein, lactalbumin, and lactoglobulin. *Casein* is the most important of the three and forms about 80 percent of the total. Casein exists in milk in colloidal dispersion (page 138) as a calcium salt, calcium caseinate. Casein is not readily precipitated by heat but

LACTOSE	5.0
FAT	4.0
PROTEIN	3.3
MINERALS [calcium, phosphorus, iron (trace), and others]	0.7
VITAMINS [A, riboflavin, niacin, thiamine]	+
WATER	87.0
	100.0

is coagulated by acid. In cheesemaking, the milk is usually coagulated by the action of the enzyme rennin; then the curd is separated from the whey.

Lactalbumin, the water-soluble albumin of milk, is not precipitated by acids or by rennin but by heat. Casein, as was noted above, is colloidally dispersed in milk. Lactalbumin molecules are also of colloidal size. You have probably noticed the material which settles on the sides and bottom of a container in which milk has been heated. This is called a flocculent precipitate and is formed from the albumin in the milk.

Lactoglobulin is insoluble in water but soluble in neutral salt solutions. Like lactalbumin it can be coagulated by heat but not by rennin. Both proteins are precipitated by the addition of certain salts.

Mineral ash. The mineral ash of milk contains calcium, phosphorus, magnesium, potassium, sodium, chlorine, and sulfur. The forms in which calcium, magnesium, and phosphorus are present greatly influence casein stability. Although these minerals occur in milk in relatively small amounts, they are important in the behavior of the protein in food preparation.

Processing of Milk

Milk is available fresh and preserved. It may be whole milk with fat or skim milk which has had the fat removed. Milk is marketed in fluid, dried, or frozen forms. Fresh or market milk represents almost half the milk produced and sold in the United States. Ninety percent of the milk is pasteurized.

Milk flows through this pasteurizer at the rate of 14,000 quarts per hour.

Photo Courtesy of H. P. Hood and Sons, Boston

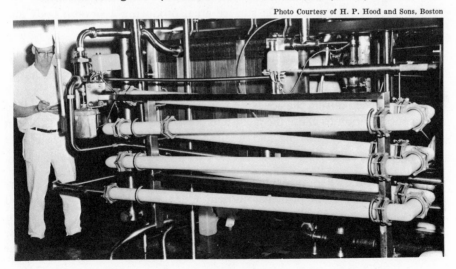

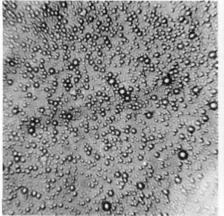 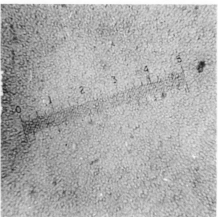

Fat globules before homogenization. Fat globules after homogenization.

Pasteurization. In pasteurization, milk is heated to 143° F and held at this temperature for 30 minutes, or heated to 161° F and held at this temperature for 15 seconds. After heating, the milk is cooled immediately to 50° F and kept at this temperature or a lower one. Since all milk contains both harmless and harmful bacteria, it is important that milk be pasteurized to destroy all pathogenic organisms (disease-causing bacteria). Most large cities will not permit the sale of unpasteurized milk.

Homogenization. This mechanical process alters the physical properties of milk by reducing the size of the fat globules to about one-tenth their original size, thereby emulsifying the fat so that it does not form a cream layer. The process greatly increases the fat surface area, producing a smooth body and rich flavor in the milk.

Concentration. Concentrated milk has two-thirds of its water content removed and is then pasteurized and homogenized. Even though perishable, the milk retains its sweetness under refrigeration for about 2 weeks. This milk can be sweetened during the concentration process. It must be carefully cooled after concentration to cause the lactose to crystallize into small crystals. Plain concentrated milk is generally sold in bulk to bakeries and other establishments which use large quantities of milk.

Fortification. When nutrients are added to milk, the milk is said to be fortified. Vitamin D is the principal nutrient added to whole milk. Usually 400 I.U. (International Units, page 95) are added per quart of milk. Since skim milk has had its fat removed, the fat-soluble vitamin A has also been lost. Therefore, 400 I.U. vitamin D and 2000 U.S.P. units of vitamin A are added

Cheeses of all types, ice cream, sour cream, and butter are some of the many products made from fresh, whole milk.

to each quart of fortified skim milk. Fortification is used as a means of restoring this vitamin content.

Certification. The sanitary standards for the production of certified milk are very high. The maximum bacteria count is low and the milk fat content is held at 4 percent. Certified milk is used chiefly on a doctor's recommendation in special cases of infant and invalid feeding.

Special perishable milk products. These products are manufactured from fresh milk. They include a skim milk with or without vitamin supplements and a chocolate-flavored milk drink prepared by adding sugar and cocoa to whole or skim milk.

Fermented milks are those which have a sour flavor resulting from the breakdown of lactose to lactic acid brought about by bacterial action. One of the chief fermented milks in the United States is buttermilk, a product originally a by-product of buttermaking. Now, however, buttermilk is made chiefly from pasteurized skim milk or partially skim milk which has been treated with a culture of lactic-acid-producing bacteria. A second kind of fermented milk is yogurt, a product of custard-like consistency. It is made from homogenized, pasteurized milk to which a mixed culture is added. Acidophilus milk, another fermented milk, is produced by inoculating fresh milk with a culture of *acidophilus bacteria*, an acid-forming bacteria.

Preserving milk. Fluid milk is preserved for short periods by using refrigeration. To extend the storage period, milk is preserved by sterilization, the addition of sugar, dehydration, and freezing.

Evaporated milk is sterilized milk. In the production of evaporated milk about 60 percent of the water is removed. The U.S. Food and Drug Administration defines evaporated milk as "sweet whole cow's milk, evaporated so it contains not less than 7.9 percent by weight of milk fat and 25.9 percent of total milk solids." These amounts are about twice those found in fluid milk. Evaporated milk is sealed in a container and then processed by heat to prevent spoilage. To insure smoothness, stabilizers (disodium phosphate or sodium citrate or both) are added. Evaporated milk may become more viscous, darker in color, and may develop an off flavor during storage due in part to a reaction of the casein and the lactose (page 146).

Sweetened condensed milk has also had about one-half of its water removed. Sugar is added in sufficient amount to preserve the milk so that sterilization is not needed after the milk is sealed in its container.

Dried milk is available as dry whole milk but more widely accessible as nonfat dry milk. Milk is dried to reduce volume, to preserve it, and to provide a usable form for use in concentrated or dried foods. Nonfat dry milk has most

Evaporated milk, sweetened condensed milk, and dried milk are forms of preserved milk. Each should be used and stored according to label directions.

The Carnation Company

The Borden Company

of its butterfat removed along with its water content. For the retail market, milk is usually spray-dried and may be agglomerated to give "instant solubility." Dried whole milk deteriorates more rapidly during storage than do nonfat milk solids. Both the dried whole milk and the nonfat dry milk solids are subject to a browning reaction between milk protein and lactose.

Frozen milk is available for special uses, but technological problems limit its production for general use.

Principles of Milk Cookery

Coagulation of milk protein. Since the coagulation of protein in relation to milk has been discussed previously, we shall be concerned here with milk coagulation as it occurs when milk is combined with other foods. Principles of milk cookery relating to the various forms of milk will be considered.

Fresh milk is seldom coagulated when heated in home use. *The addition of other foods to milk, however, may cause coagulation or curdling to occur rather rapidly.* Cooking asparagus, string beans, peas, and carrots in milk may cause milk to curdle, since vegetables such as these have some acid content. They also contain tannins and salts which may cause curdling.

Meats may be cooked or baked in milk or in milk products, as in the case of beef stroganoff. Curdling in such mixtures may occur because of the salt content of the meat, the temperature of heating, and the acidity developed. Curdling is more likely to occur if salted or cured meat or acid ingredients such as prepared mustard or apples are added. If evaporated milk is used, it has less tendency to curdle than does fresh milk because of the addition of stabilizers during processing. Curdling may be prevented if a portion of the milk is added to the meat when cooking is first started and the rest of the cold milk is added gradually during the cooking period.

The University of Utah

Above: Skim milk prior to coagulation on the surface of a glass bottle. Below: The same sample at the point of coagulation.

Wes Kemp

Curdling of tomato soup.

Tomatoes are another vegetable that may cause curdling. This happens sometimes in the making of tomato soup. The tomato, as you will recall from Chapter 12, has a pH value of 4.4 to 4.6. If the amount of tomato added to the milk is great enough to lower the pH of the milk and tomato mixture to about pH 4.6, the casein—milk protein—is precipitated out without heating. This curdling may be prevented in these ways: (1) by adding the tomato gradually to the milk, (2) by adding warm tomato to warm milk, (3) by heating the tomato and milk together for as short a time as possible.

The addition of fruit also affects the coagulation of milk. Fruits may cause the clotting or coagulation of milk because of their acidity or certain enzymes present in the fruit. For example, raw pineapple contains an enzyme, bromelin, that causes milk to clot or coagulate.

The effects of cooking on various forms of milk. Each form of milk produces somewhat different results when cooked. Products such as cornstarch pudding, white sauce, and hot cocoa tend to be somewhat thicker when prepared with homogenized milk rather than fluid fresh milk. The increased amount of protein on the surface of the small fat globules (characteristic of homogenized milk) may account for the increased thickness in some products.

Nonfat dry milk increases the viscosity of pastes made of flour, dry milk, and water. This increase in viscosity may be offset by reducing the amount of flour. Nonfat dry milk also tends to increase the thickness of such mixtures as white sauce, eggnog, custard, and chocolate pudding.

Wes Kemp

Curdling in scalloped potatoes.

Dairy Products

Milk is used in the production of dairy products such as butter, cheeses of all kinds, and sour cream. It is also an ingredient in ice cream and milk sherbets (page 245).

Butter. When cream is churned, its fat globules come together and form larger clusters of fat globules. These in turn break away from the surrounding liquid and form a semisolid or plastic material, butter. The chief components of butter are 80.9 percent fat, 16.1 percent moisture (water) and 2.3 percent salt. Butter is generally sold salted or unsalted in tub, cube, and print forms. Whipped butter may also be purchased.

Creams. Cream is classified as either coffee cream or whipping cream, depending on the fat content. *Whipping cream* has at least 30 percent fat while *coffee or light cream* has at least 18 percent fat as specified in the Federal minimum standard regulations. Feathering—coagulation of protein of cream added to hot coffee—is one of the problems with homogenized cream.

Whipping cream is now available in pressurized containers. This product, prepared from cream of 30 percent fat content, sugar, vanilla flavoring, and a stabilizer such as dried egg white, sodium caseinate, gelatin, or nonfat dry milk, is packaged with a gas (nitrous oxide or carbon dioxide) under pres-

sure. The foam formed when the cream is released is less stable than that of whipped cream produced by actual whipping. This is probably due to the way the foam is produced.

Sour cream is included in some of the old gourmet recipes dating back to the 17th century. Many a chef has built his reputation and career on the strength of a tasty beef stroganoff or a schnitzel—two popular dishes which owe their flavor appeal to sour cream. As much as early chefs valued the flavor-making quality of sour cream, however, they found it difficult to use. Before the days of pasteurization, sour cream was nothing more than its name implied—cream which was sour due to acid produced by bacteria. Now sour cream is produced under carefully controlled conditions so that its quality and taste are dependable and uniform.

Cheese. Cheese is made from the milk of goats, cows, sheep, llamas, reindeer, and buffaloes. Each source contributes special characteristics and flavors. There are so many different kinds of cheese that no list, however long, could possibly claim to be complete.

Cheese is truly an international food. Almost all countries, as well as many districts within countries, have their own special cheeses. Experts say that there are over 400 varieties of cheese ranging in taste from mild to very strong. Even though some cheeses differ only in name or geographic origin, there are many with different cheese flavors. The talent for the proper use of cheeses has come to be one of the marks of a fine cook.

History shows that cheese has long been a popular food. Olympic athletes of Greece were trained on a steady cheese diet. The Roman emperor Augustus was a cheese fancier as was Charlemagne of France. Thomas Jefferson was presented a gigantic wheel of Cheddar cheese on the occasion of his inauguration. A similar gift was made to President Jackson who allowed the cheese to stand in the hall of the White House where it was eaten by enthusiastic guests. Furthermore, a giant cheese

Wisconsin Cheese Foundation, Madison, Wisconsin

The world's largest cheese, 34,591 pounds of choice cheddar, took 43½ hours to produce.

weighing 1100 pounds was presented to Queen Victoria at the time of her marriage. This particular cheese required a day's yield of milk from 780 cows. It stood 20 inches high and was more than 9 feet in diameter. In 1964 at the New York World's Fair an even larger cheese was sent from Wisconsin.

Cheesemaking is an important industry in the United States. American cheesemakers are considered the equals of any anywhere in the world. Old World formulas plus American technology have made it possible to produce the finest of cheeses.

If you have looked at cheese in your community store or if you have ever visited a cheese factory in Wisconsin, New York, Missouri, Illinois, Iowa, Minnesota, Kentucky, or some other state, you are probably aware of how much cheeses differ. Cheeses can be almost white, white with bluish-green veins, deep yellow, hard, soft, firm and compact, full of holes, round, rectangular, or pie-shaped. Strong pungent odors are characteristic of certain cheeses while others have no odor at all. What are some of the reasons for all these differences? We will consider some of the factors which influence the kinds of cheese produced.

Since cheese is a milk product, its most important constituent is the milk protein casein. Two other components are fat and water. Soft cheeses contain more water, less fat, and less protein than hard cheeses.

The making of cheese. In the production of cheese the protein of the milk is first coagulated. The resulting curd is then stirred and heated to cause the whey, or watery part of the milk, to separate. Finally, the curd is collected and pressed. The coagulation is brought about by the addition of the enzyme rennin to the milk or by a bacterial development which produces acid in the milk. A combination of both these methods is also used. Rennin produces a more elastic curd than does the acid. The soft curd which is separated from the whey without further treatment is known as *unripened cheese*. Cottage cheese and cream cheese are typical examples.

The production of *ripened cheese* requires submitting the curd to varying degrees of heat and pressure and also adding special cultures of bacteria or mold. In ripened cheese the curd is formed into the shapes typical of the particular type of cheese being made. The cheese is permitted to cure or ripen under controlled conditions. During ripening, the cheese changes from a tough, rubbery mass to a soft and sometimes crumbly solid. Characteristic flavors are developed during this period.

Ripening is slower at low temperatures and more rapid at higher ones. Salting also affects the rate of ripening by controlling the bacterial growth. Cheeses owe their distinctive flavors, aromas, and textures to the types of microorganisms present. The *penicillium roqueforte* or *penicillium glaucum* molds produce the bluish-veined appearance of Roquefort, Gorgonzola, and Stilton cheeses. Limburger cheese owes its strong odor to putrefactive bacteria which are allowed to develop over a period of time.

In some cheeses, such as Swiss and Emmenthal, holes or "eyes" are formed by the bacteria which produce gas (principally carbon dioxide) during the early stages of ripening while the cheese is still soft and elastic. Mild cheeses are usually ripened for a shorter time than are sharp cheeses.

Processed cheese is a mixture of two or more cheeses with an emulsifying agent. These ingredients are all blended together with the aid of heat. Emulsifying agents or plasticizers are needed to produce a uniform product that has a pliable consistency and melts readily. The emulsifying agent is required to be no more than 3 percent of the weight of the processed cheese. The unqualified term "processed cheese" usually means processed Cheddar. As yet, no grades have been established for processed cheese and cheese foods.

Cheese food is a product which is made from a mixture of one or more varieties of cheese with added milk solids, salt, and an emulsifier (not more than 3 percent) which are comminuted (crushed or pulverized) and mixed together with the aid of heat. The moisture content of a pasteurized cheese food is somewhat higher and the milk fat content is lower than that permitted for processed cheese.

Cheese spreads are similar to cheese foods except that a stabilizer is used and the moisture content is lower. These foods are often flavored with pimiento, olives, pickles, and onions.

Excessive heat results in fat separation, stringing, and toughening of cheese. Cheese sauce which is heated excessively will curdle, then string and mat. Low temperatures and short cooking times are essential if the cheese is to remain smooth and soft.

Cheese is packaged in moisture-proof wrapping material. Such packaging protects the product from the loss of moisture and limits mold growth on the surface of the cheese. Machine packaging and vacuum sealing are special techniques which extend the keeping quality of the cheese.

Principles of cheese cookery. You know that cheese is a protein food. Ask yourself these questions: What kind of cheese is best for cooking? Why is cheese often combined with other ingredients in food preparation? Does ripening affect the cooking quality of cheese? Why does cheese sauce sometimes curdle?

Cheese cookery involves melting cheese when toasting a cheese sandwich, making a cheeseburger, making a sauce, or preparing any other products in which cheese is combined with other ingredients. It is most important to avoid long cooking and the use of excessive heat since these two conditions will cause fat separation and stringing and toughening of the cheese. Cheese can be combined with other ingredients which help to make the cheese less dense and less apt to become stringy.

Commercially, cooking qualities of cheese can be improved by the addition of emulsifying salts—disodium phosphate, trisodium phosphate, sodium citrate, or sodium bicarbonate. These salts prevent matting and stringing. However, sodium bicarbonate affects the flavor unfavorably even when the minimum amount necessary to prevent matting and stringing is used. These salts probably owe their effectiveness to the fact that they are alkaline in reaction or have the ability to remove calcium from its combination with casein. It seems that conditions which make casein more soluble lessen its tendency to form strings and to toughen during cooking.

Cheddar cheese with normal fat and high moisture content has been found to have the most satisfactory cooking qualities. Aged cheese has better cooking qualities than young cheese. This is probably due to hydrolysis of the protein during the aging process.

When the fresh milk from nearby dairy farms arrives at a cheese factory, the cheesemaker checks to see that it is sweet and pure. The milk is then pumped into large vats. Note the thermometer hanging over the side of this 15,000-pound vat. During the initial stages of cheesemaking, temperature control is very important.

A starter culture of lactic acid bacteria is added to the milk first, along with a small amount of pure vegetable coloring if desired. In this photograph the rennet (curdling agent) is being added. Paddles distribute the rennet evenly. After 30 minutes, the fluid milk is transformed into a jelly-like mass.

After the milk reaches a jelly-like consistency, the cheesemaker tests the firmness to determine if it is ready for cutting. If the curd breaks sharply along his finger, two cheesemakers, with special curd knives, cut the curd into small cubes. The cutting is to facilitate the expulsion of the whey from the curd.

The cutting operation leaves thousands of small cubes of curd (each ¼" square). Paddles keep the cubes floating, so matting will not occur. As the temperature is raised to 102°F, the whey is expelled from the curd. The cheesemaker now measures the exact acidity of the cheese.

Wisconsin Department of Agriculture

The whey drains out of the vat leaving the curd which is pushed to the side. Now the Cheddaring process begins. When the curd mats sufficiently, it is cut into large pieces which are stacked along the sides of the vat and turned at ten-minute intervals.

5

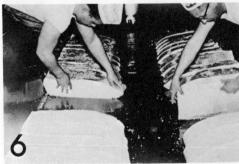

6

By stacking the slabs, any additional whey is expelled and the temperature can be kept more uniform. When the whey has drained and the correct degree of acidity has been reached, the slabs of curd are cut into pieces 2–3″ long and ½″ wide. Then the cheese is salted.

In making rindless cheese, the cheese is now placed in rectangular forms lined with a cheese bandage. It is later taken out of this hoop, the cloth is removed, and the cheese is wrapped in an air-moisture-proof wrapper in which it will be cured. In this photograph cheese hoops are being filled.

7

8

Horizontal presses are used to press the curd in the cheese hoop. Ten to fifty hoops are pressed at one time. These are held in the press under high pressure overnight. The next morning cheeses are removed and placed in aging rooms. After two months to a year or longer they are ready for the consumer.

Wisconsin Department of Agriculture

THE NATURE OF FOOD

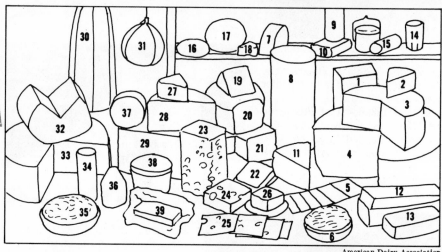

American Dairy Association

1) mild Cheddar, 2) random-cut aged Cheddar, 3) aged Cheddar, 4) white Cheddar, 5) sliced Cheddar, 6) shredded Cheddar, 7–8) Longhorn Colby, 9–10) Colby, 11) Monterey Jack, 12) processed cheese, 13) cheese food, 14) cheese spreads, 15) cold pack, 16) Baby Gouda, 17) Edam, 18) Camembert, 19) random cut Muenster, 20) Muenster, 21) Brick, 22) random cut Brick, 23) Swiss, 24) random cut Swiss, 25) sliced Swiss, 26) Limburger, 27) random cut Blue, 28) Blue, 29) Gorgonzola, 30) pear-shaped Provolone, 31) spherical Provolone, 32) Romano, 33) Parmesan, 34) grated Parmesan, 35) shredded Mozzarella, 36) Scamorze, 37) Italico, 38) cottage cheese, 39) cream cheese

POPULAR AMERICAN CHEESES*

CHEESE AND USE	COLOR, TEXTURE, FLAVOR, SHAPE
1–6. Cheddar—appetizers, sandwiches, salads, in cooked foods, desserts	Semi-hard cheese ranging from nearly white to yellow in color; firm to crumbly texture; mild to sharp in flavor depending upon aging. Generally circular; sold in weighed wedges, cylinders, slices, blocks, or shredded.
7–10. Colby 11. Monterey or Jack—sandwiches and appetizers	Somewhat softer than Cheddar. Mild in flavor. Same shapes as Cheddar.
12. Pasteurized Process Cheese 13. Cheese Foods 14. Cheese Spreads 15. Cold Pack Cheese Food or Club Cheese—same uses as Cheddar	Blend of natural cheeses which have been shredded, mixed. Semi-soft; smooth texture. Spreads easily, melts quickly. Slices, loaves, cut portions, rolls, jars, crocks.
16–17. Gouda and Edam—appetizers, salads, in cooked foods, desserts	Red wax outer surface; yellow interior. Semi-soft to firm; nut-like flavor. Spherical ball with flattened ends, loaf or cannonball-shape loaf.
18. Camembert—with crackers, fruits, for appetizers or deserts	Smooth creamy yellow, edible white crust. Soft, surface-ripened; mild to pungent flavor. Pie-wedge or circular.
19–20. Muenster—appetizers, sandwiches	Cream white, semi-soft with tiny holes. Mild to mellow flavor. Cylindrical, flat, loaf shape, wedge, slices.
21–22. Brick—appetizers, salads, sandwiches, desserts	Creamy yellow; semi-soft with small holes. Mild to sharp flavor. Loaf, brick, wedge, slices.
23–25. Swiss—appetizers, salads, sandwiches, in cooked foods	Light yellow, large holes; firm; nut-like sweet flavor. Slices, circular or loaf blocks.
26. Limburger—appetizers, desserts	Creamy white interior. Semi-soft surface-ripened cheese. Strong flavor and aroma. Cubical or rectangular.
27–28. Blue—appetizers, salads, dressings, in cooked foods, desserts	Blue veined, crumbly; semi-soft to firm. Sharp, salty flavor. Foil-wrapped wedges or 6-inch rounds.
29. Gorgonzola—same uses as Cheddar	Blue-green veined; semi-soft to firm. Less moisture than Blue. Sharp, salty flavor. Cylindrical and flat.
30–31. Provolone—appetizers, sandwiches, in cooked foods, desserts	Light yellow, semi-hard, smooth and somewhat plastic; mellow to sharp, smoky flavor. Pear-shape or salami-shape, ball-shape, wedges, slices, grated.
32. Romano—grated in soups, breads, on spaghetti, in cooked foods	Yellow-white; hard, granular (brittle). Sharp, piquant flavor. Cylindrical, wedges, or grated.
33–34. Parmesan—grated in soups, cooked foods, breads, spaghetti	Yellow-white; hard, granular. Sharp, piquant flavor. Grated, cylindrical wedges.
35–37. Mozzarella, Scamorze, and Italico—in cooked foods, on pizza, sandwiches	White stretchy cheese; unripened semi-soft cheese; delicate, mild flavor. Irregularly spherical in varying sizes or weights; loaf or small round; shredded or sliced.
38. Cottage Cheese—appetizers, casseroles, main dishes, cheese cakes, sandwich fillings, salads	White to creamy-white unripened cheese; soft, mild, may be small, medium or large curd. Creamed cottage cheese has added cream. Packaged in a variety of containers.
39. Cream Cheese—same uses as Cheddar	White unripened cheese; soft and smooth; mild, delicate flavor. Loaf or package.

*This listing is not a classification of cheeses but a reference to those shown in the picture.

American Dairy Association

In this chapter you have studied the properties, composition, forms, processing, and products of milk. You have also learned that there is a relationship between the principles of milk cookery and those of protein cookery. The chapter which follows will be concerned with perhaps the most complex protein food of all: meat.

MAJOR IDEAS

The following statements give the main ideas within the chapter you have just studied. Be sure you know the words underscored in these statements and in the questions to follow.

1. Milk, a complex food of high nutritive value, has both physical and chemical properties which make it extremely useful in food preparation.
2. Because milk is a protein food, it undergoes definite changes in the presence of heat, acid, and certain enzymes. These reactions influence the ways in which milk is used in the preparation of foods.
3. Milk can be treated in a number of ways to improve and insure its overall quality and to preserve it for future use.
4. Milk is obtainable in a variety of forms. Each brings specific qualities to food preparation.
5. Milk is the source of a wide range of dairy products.
6. Cheese is classified according to its source, the way in which the curd is produced, its texture, and its consistency. Its cooking quality is dependent on the moisture and fat content and the length of the ripening period.

QUESTIONS TO STUDY

PROPERTIES

1. Why are milk containers difficult to wash?
2. Why does cream in pasteurized milk rise to the top while it does not rise in homogenized milk?
3. What effect does fat have on the whipability and stability of cream?
4. How does a change in the pH of milk affect the use of milk in cooking?
5. By what means can milk be coagulated? How does this knowledge apply in using milk in cooking?
6. What factors influence the physical properties of milk?

COMPOSITION

1. What is casein? In what ways can casein be affected in milk cookery?
2. Why is fat content the principal factor used in pricing milk?
3. What is lactose? How does its degree of solubility influence the manufacture of milk products?
4. What is the relationship between the minerals and the casein in milk?

PROCESSING OF MILK

1. What is pasteurization?
2. In what way does homogenization alter the physical properties of milk?
3. What is the process of fortification of milk? Why is skim milk often fortified?
4. Why is sugar effective as a preservative in milk?
5. Why is the storage life of frozen milk limited?
6. What occasionally causes nonfat dry milk to turn brown during storage?
7. In what ways do condensed and evaporated milk differ?
8. In what ways can milk be treated so that it can be preserved for long periods of time?
9. What are the advantages of drying milk?
10. What difference in consistency can you expect if you substitute dried milk for fluid milk in making vanilla pudding?

PRINCIPLES OF MILK COOKERY

1. Why do certain vegetables cause milk to curdle?
2. Why do cured meats cause milk to curdle while fresh meats do not?
3. How does homogenized milk affect the beverage cocoa?

DAIRY PRODUCTS

1. How is butter produced?
2. Why is fermented milk sour to the taste?
3. What purpose do microorganisms serve in cheesemaking?
4. How is cheese made?
5. In what ways does the method for making a cheese affect its cooking quality?
6. Explain the differences between natural cheese, processed cheese, and cheese foods.

7. Why are emulsifying agents used in making processed cheese?
8. Distinguish between whipping cream, coffee cream, and sour cream.
9. What is meant by the feathering of cream?
10. Why is aged cheese better for cooking than young cheese?

BIBLIOGRAPHY

BABCOCK, C. J., *The Whipping Quality of Cream.* Bulletin No. 1075, U. S. Department of Agriculture, Washington, D. C., 1922.

GRISWOLD, RUTH M., *The Experimental Study of Foods.* Boston, Houghton Mifflin Company, 1962.

HOLLENDER, H., and WECKEL, K. G., "Stability of Homogenized Milk in Cookery Practice." *Food Research,* Vol. 6, 1941, pp. 335–343.

How to Use Whole and Nonfat Dry Milk. AIS–86, U. S. Department of Agriculture, Washington, D. C., 1949.

JACOBS, MORRIS, *The Chemistry and Technology of Food and Food Products,* Vol. I. New York, Interscience Publishers, Inc., 1951.

JORDAN, R., and others, "Nonhomogenized vs. Homogenized Milk in Baked Custards." *Journal of the American Dietetic Association,* Vol. 30, 1954, pp. 1126–1130.

LOWE, BELLE, *Experimental Cookery.* New York, John Wiley & Sons, Inc., 1955.

Milk and Its Products. Facts for Consumer Education. Agriculture Information Bulletin No. 125, U. S. Department of Agriculture, Washington, D. C., 1954.

MORSE, L., and others, "Use and Properties of Non-fat Dry Milk Solids in Food Preparation, II. Use in Typical Foods." *Food Research,* Vol. 15, 1950, pp. 216–222.

"Pacific A-tests blamed for hot iodine in milk." *Science News Letter,* Vol. 86, October 17, 1964, p. 247.

PERSONIUS, C., and others, "Some Factors Affecting the Behavior of Cheddar Cheese in Cooking." *Food Research,* Vol. 9, 1944, pp. 304–311.

"Quick Method Spots Insecticides in Milk." *Science News Letter,* Vol. 83, April 13, 1963, p. 237.

"Radioactive Milk Cleansed, Peril Eased." *Science News Letter,* Vol. 87, March 13, 1965, p. 168.

SCHROEDER, V. M., and HUSSEMANN, D. L., "Reconstituted Dried Whole Milk as a Beverage." *Journal of Home Economics,* Vol. 40, 1948, pp. 249–250.

VIRTANEN, A. I., "Milk Production of Cows on Protein-free Feed." *Science*, Vol. 153, September 30, 1966, pp. 1603–14.

"Vitamin A and D asked for nonfat dry milk." *Science News*, Vol. 90, October 8, 1966, p. 285.

WATT, B. K., and MERRILL, A. L., *Composition of Food—Raw, Processed, Prepared.* Agriculture Handbook No. 8, U. S. Department of Agriculture, Washington, D. C.

WEGNER, E. S., and others, "Homogenized and Nonhomogenized Milk in the Preparation of Selected Food Products." *Journal of Home Economics*, Vol. 45, 1963, pp. 589–591.

18 MEAT

Cattle, pigs, sheep, and goats were first brought to the West Indies by Christopher Columbus on his second voyage in 1493. Cortez introduced cattle, sheep, and horses into Mexico in 1519. The English settlers who established themselves along the Virginia and New England coastlines also brought domesticated animals to insure a meat and milk supply for themselves. Our livestock today are the descendants of these immigrant animals.

As the settlers moved westward across what is now the United States they took their animals with them. There was a gradual development of herding and marketing. Operations of local slaughterhouses were expanded. This expansion led to the development of the modern meat packing industry.

With the development of the livestock industries and meat packing came increasing demands for improved breeding practices. The Texas longhorns were replaced by the prime steer. The Arkansas razorbacks were replaced by the improved meat-type hogs. The black, brown, and spotted sheep were re-

USDA Photo

In 1906 a typical packing house looked like this. Here hogs are being inspected by government inspectors. Note the two blinding light bulbs and the lack of intricate equipment.

262

In this modern factory, meats are being canned. Note the well-lighted room as well as the complex machinery.

Swift and Company

placed by today's mutton and wool-type animals. Today it is possible to tailor meat animals so that they will possess particular characteristics that will make them most acceptable to consumers.

Classes and Grades

Meat is the muscle tissue of animals, poultry, and fish. Organs—tongue, liver, kidney, heart, pancreas, brain, thymus, and spleen—of fish, poultry, and animals are also meats. These organ meats have high protein and vitamin content.

Meat animals are most frequently used as food, while poultry and fish are eaten less frequently in the United States. The first part of this chapter is concerned with meat animals and the latter section with poultry and fish. Meat animals are divided into groups based on age; classes based on sex; grades based on quality. Each animal species is classified differently. Here we will consider the groups, classes, and grades of beef, pork, veal, and lamb.

Beef. Just as certain cattle have been developed to produce milk in both quantity and quality, beef animals have been bred for the production of meat.

The most widely produced pure breeds for meat purposes are the Shorthorn, Hereford, Aberdeen Angus, Brahman, and Santa Gertrudis. These animals have been developed not only as meat animals but also as meat animals with certain specific characteristics. For example, the Aberdeen Angus does not

Swift and Company

This prize Holstein-Friesian cow gave 23,980 pounds of milk in 1 year.

USDA Photo

A Hereford cow, bred for beef, is short, firm, and stocky.

thrive on desert range. Instead, this breed requires good pasture land like that in the Midwest and Pacific Northwest of the United States. It fattens well and matures early. The Brahman, however, can withstand intense heat. It thrives in the humid coastal areas and the southwestern portion of the United States. The Brahman's resistance to insect pests makes it an important breed in locations where such insects are a serious problem. Careful tailoring of breeds to fit existing conditions of climate, pasture, and humidity makes it possible to promote herds of beef animals in locations once considered unsuitable for raising cattle.

Steer, stag, heifer, bull, and cow are the *beef classes*. The bulk of our beef comes from steers raised especially for high grade beef. A dressed steer carcass (body) will range from about 550 to 1000 pounds in weight. A stag is a male animal which has stronger sex characteristics and coarser muscle tissue than those of a steer. Heifers are female and are marketed as 1- to 2-year-old animals. They are equal in quality to steers although the heifer carcass is generally smaller than the steer carcass. Bulls and cows are saved for breeding purposes. At the end of their breeding lives they are slaughtered and used for meat.

The *grading* of the beef carcass is based on three general factors: conformation, finish, and quality. *Conformation* refers to the shape of the animal and is closely related to the breed. Top conformation of a beef animal is described in terms of a short, blocky, compact carcass with short shank, and plump, smooth rounding at the hips. The neck is short, the shoulders smooth, and the rib and loin area thickly fleshed. Conformation is of special concern to the meat packer or retail butcher because the number of popular and therefore higher-priced cuts that can be obtained from a carcass is determined by its conformation.

The *finish* of the animal tells much of the story of quality. It refers to the distribution and quality of exterior fat on the carcass. Good finish sometimes

These fresh-chilled beef carcasses are being roller-branded by a USDA grader in a meat-packing plant.

USDA Photo

leads to excessive fat. This condition, of course, changes the proportion of fat to lean and may cause the lean to be more expensive per pound of meat, since it is considered the edible portion. If top quality beef is desired, however, some fat will be present. The color of fat is not a factor in grading but often the consumer objects to meat with yellow fat because such fat is associated with older animals.

Quality is probably the most important factor as far as the consumer is concerned because quality is related to the factors that contribute to the eating quality: flavor, tenderness, and juiciness of meat. Quality is related to the age of the animal, the amount and kind of connective tissue, the firmness and texture of the flesh, marbling (distribution of intra-muscular fat), and the color of the lean. Marbling is one of the most sought characteristics of quality because it is closely related to the juiciness and flavor, and probably to tenderness of meat. The latter relationship has not been established by research, however.

As animals mature, the amount of connective tissue increases with a resulting decrease in tenderness. Firmness of the lean indicates the type and amount of feed the animal has had. The lean will vary to the touch from velvet-smooth to Turkish-towel coarse. Meat from animals fed in a feed lot (a limited area in which the amount and quality of the feed given to the animals a few weeks before they are slaughtered are controlled) will have firmer lean. Animals which are short-fed (permitted to roam the pasture, therefore being allowed to expend energy, eat a simple grass diet, and toughen muscles) will have less firm lean. The color of the beef lean will vary from light cherry to deep red. As a rule, the more youthful the animal the lighter the color of the lean.

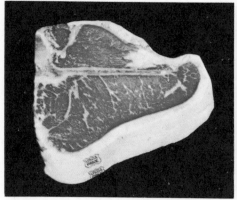

1

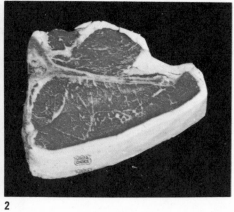

2

3

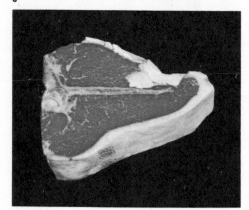

(1) USDA Prime
(2) USDA Choice
(3) USDA Good
(4) USDA Standard
(5) USDA Commercial

4

5

USDA Photos

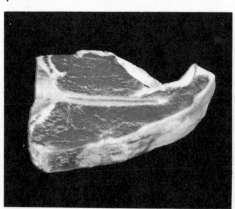

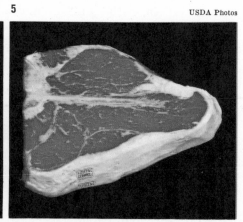

U.S. Government Grades. The grading of meat is based on the packers' grades or on Federal Government grades. Packers use special brand names to indicate their better grades of meat.

The seven U.S. Government Grades of beef are as follows:

1. **US Prime.** Only beef from young steers or heifers falls into this grade. These animals are the finest finished animals that come to market. Prime meat is available in limited quantity and is sold chiefly to hotels, restaurants, and clubs.

2. **US Choice.** The largest volume of fresh meat available to the consumer is in this grade. Choice grade meat has less fat than does Prime grade.

3. **US Good.** Meat so marked has less finish than that marked Choice. It has a high proportion of lean to fat and is relatively tender.

4. **US Commercial.** This grade is produced from older cattle and usually lacks the tenderness of the higher grades.

5. **US Utility.** This grade is produced from older cattle and is seldom sold as fresh meat.

6. **US Cutters.** Cows comprise most of the animals in this grade. The lean is very dark in color and is used in processed meat products.

7. **US Canners.** This is the lowest grade. It usually indicates old cows. This grade is also used in the production of processed meats.

Pork. Special attention has been given to the careful selection and breeding of meat-type hogs. Some of the English and American breeds are Berkshire, Hampshire, Yorkshire, Poland China, Chester White, and Duroc. In each of these breeds the intent has been to breed away from the fat-type hog to the meat-type hog which yields less lard and more lean muscle tissue. However, the development of meat-type hogs has been limited. The "meatiest" hog also requires a finishing period during which time the animal's diet must be restricted to increase the ratio of lean to fat.

Hogs are classified as barrow, stag, and boar (male animals); gilt and sow (female animals). Barrows and gilts are the chief classes used for meat and

Today, about 80 percent of commercial meat is Federally inspected in clean, modern coolers. Left: lamb carcass. Right: pork carcass.

are marketed between the ages of 7 and 12 months. The females are usually retained for breeding purposes.

In 1952 grade standards were established for barrows and gilts. These standards were based on yield and quality. The grades of pork are Choice, Medium, and Cull. The highest grade is described as having grayish-pink muscle with white fat and reddish tinged bone.

Sheep and lambs. Sheep and lambs serve as a source of meat and wool. The breeding of sheep for specific characteristics is just being developed. Most of the sheep marketed today for food are lambs. Widely known breeds are the Cheviot, Lincoln, Southdown, Merino, Oxford, Shropshire, and Rambouillet. The classes of sheep are lamb, yearling, and sheep. Lambs are usually 14 months old; yearlings, 1 to 2 years; sheep, 2 years and older.

Sheep are graded as lamb and mutton (older than 14 months). The grades are similar to those of beef with Prime being superior.

Structural and Physical Characteristics

Muscle, connective tissue, bone, and fat are the structural elements of meat.

Muscle or lean tissue. Muscle tissues—edible lean meat—are of two types: striated (voluntary or involuntary) and smooth (involuntary). The voluntary muscles are attached to the bony skeleton of the animal. They are composed of many muscle fibers which are bound together by connective tissue forming bundles. These muscle bundles vary in size, length, and thickness. The grain or texture of a piece of meat is determined by the size of the fibers and muscles. For example, small fibers and small bundles indicate meat of fine grain. Larger fibers and larger bundles indicate coarse grain or texture. The involuntary smooth muscles include such structures as the muscle tissues of the stomach, intestinal wall, and blood vessels.

Connective tissue. The connective tissue in meat forms the walls of the muscle fibers, binds them together into bundles, and surrounds the muscle as a membrane. It also makes up the tendons and ligaments which attach the muscles to the bone tissue. The amount and kind of connective tissue are important factors in determining the tenderness of meat. The activity or exercise of

Cross-section of cooked <u>longissimus dorsi</u>. Effect of cooking on animal tissues.

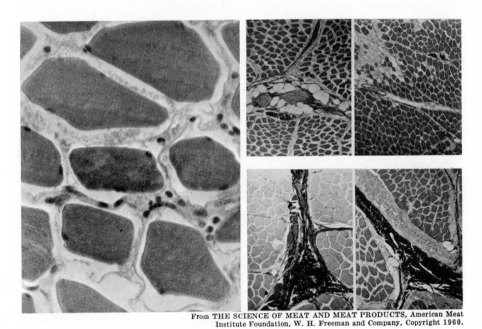

From THE SCIENCE OF MEAT AND MEAT PRODUCTS, American Meat Institute Foundation, W. H. Freeman and Company, Copyright 1960.

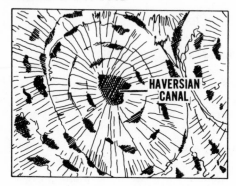

Cross section of bone. Blood vessels circulate nutrients to all parts of the bone via the Haversian canal.

muscle tissue and the age of the animal are controlling factors in the amount of connective tissue formed. For example, the shank or leg muscles have more connective tissue than does the tenderloin muscle and are therefore less tender. This would be less true in a young steer and would be more pronounced in an older animal.

Fat tissue. As was mentioned earlier, the exterior fat is called cover fat and serves both to protect against contamination by microorganisms and to retain the moisture of the muscle tissue. Other fat tissue, marbling, is located throughout the muscle tissue. This tissue is considered to be an important factor in both juiciness and flavor and probably in tenderness.

Bone tissue. The condition and appearance of bone tissue in a carcass is an indication of the age of the animal. Bones of young animals are soft, reddish in color, and spongy. In older animals the bones are white and flinty.

Chemical Composition

Structurally, the edible parts of meat are composed of muscle, connective tissue, and fat. Chemically, meat is composed of tissue proteins, fats, minerals, carbohydrates, extractives, enzymes, pigments, vitamins, and water. All of these substances play a role in the cooking of meat.

Proteins. Meat contains the proteins actin, myosin, collagen, and elastin. Actin and myosin are found in the muscle tissue. When they are combined, *actomyosin,* the contractile substance of the muscle, is formed.

Collagen is the principal part of the tendons and connective tissue, while *elastin* forms the major part of the ligaments. Both collagen and elastin are imbedded and held in place by a network called the "ground substance."

Muscles that are constantly used contain more collagen and larger, more elastic fibers than do muscles exercised less frequently. Collagen, and to a lesser extent elastin, is softened by heating in water. Collagen, when heated, softens and changes to gelatin. The softening process results in making the connective tissue—where collagen and elastin are found—more tender.

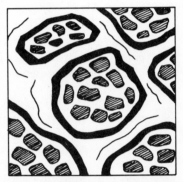

Fats. Fat occurs on the outside of the meat carcass and within the lean muscle tissue. Fat influences the juiciness of meat. When a cut of meat containing fat and lean tissues is cooked, the surface or cover fat melts and penetrates the lean. Fat scattered or marbled through the lean tissue also melts. This melting and penetration of the fat into the lean increases the juiciness of the meat.

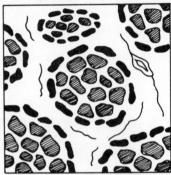

Minerals. Meat contains phosphorus, iron, calcium, and potassium in concentrated amounts in the muscle fibers. Sodium is more concentrated in the fluid of the meat. Meat owes its salt flavor to the presence of these minerals.

Carbohydrates. Glycogen and glucose are the carbohydrates in meat. Glycogen is in the muscle tissue; glucose, in the fluid (blood).

Extractives. Lactic acid and various extractives of nitrogenous content are present in meat. Lactic acid occurs in the muscle tissue and is found in increasing amounts after the slaughter of an animal. The nitrogenous extractives are also in the muscle tissue and are regarded by some authorities as the source of meat flavor.

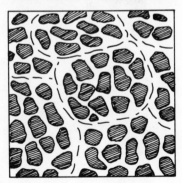

Enzymes. These substances are protein in composition. It is believed that they are responsible for increasing the tenderness of meat during the aging or ripening period. But recent studies also place emphasis upon the role of the salts (e.g. calcium, magnesium, sodium, and potassium) and their influence on the degree of hydration of the muscle proteins.

Pigments or coloring matter. Myoglobin and hemoglobin are the pigments in meat muscle. Hemoglobin transports oxygen in the blood stream while myoglobin holds the oxygen in the muscle tissue for contraction. When beef is first cut it is a dark color but it becomes bright red after exposure to the air. The oxygen of the air combines with myoglobin to produce oxymyoglobin. As the cut meat continues to be exposed to light and oxygen, slow oxidation of the oxymyoglobin results in the formation of metmyoglobin which is brown in color. This brown color is due to a change in the state of the iron of the myoglobin. In the presence of heat this oxidative change is speeded up.

Vitamins. Vitamin A occurs in the fat of most meats, and thiamine and riboflavin (a part of the vitamin B complex) occur in significant amounts in meat muscle. Liver, an organ meat, is an excellent source of these vitamins. Pork is particularly high in thiamine.

Water content. The water content of the lean muscle tissue of meat is proportionately large, about 74 percent. However, in many instances the percentage is somewhat lower.

When meat is left standing too long it begins to turn brown because of the formation of the brownish-red pigment metmyoglobin. Metmyoglobin is formed by the oxidation of the iron of the red pigment myoglobin. Although such meat may be satisfactory after cooking, its appearance before cooking is not appealing.

Wes Kemp

Cuts of Meat

We have considered groups, classes, and grades of meat animals; the structural and physical characteristics of animal carcasses; the chemical composition of the muscle, connective, and fat tissues of these carcasses. We have also seen how the quality of meat is affected by these various factors.

According to consumer studies, tenderness is the most important palatability factor in the acceptance of beef. This quality of tenderness is also important for pork, lamb, and veal. Because variations between beef and these meats is not great and cuts from each of them are similar, we will base our discussion of meat tenderness on beef cuts only. From the accompanying illustrations you will be able to make comparisons among the various carcasses showing positions of common cuts of meat.

The animal carcass which is to be used for meat is first cut into wholesale cuts and then into retail cuts. The latter are those which are most frequently offered to the consumer. On page 276 wholesale and retail cuts are illustrated to show the location of each cut in relation to its position in the original carcass.

Tenderness varies among these different retail cuts. However, a range in tenderness occurs among the muscle tissues found within each individual cut. In general, the muscles which contain the least amount of connective tissue are the most tender and those which contain the greatest amount are the least tender.

The major muscles in meat ranging from most tender to the least tender are the *psoas major, longissimus dorsi, biceps femoris,* and *romboideus.* The *psoas major,* which begins in the short loin and extends through the sirloin, is considered the most tender muscle of beef. Note the illustration below. The *longissimus dorsi* extends the length of the spine from the neck to the pelvis. It appears in the chuck, rib, short loin, and sirloin wholesale cuts. The *biceps*

PSOAS MAJOR

The tenderness of a cut of meat depends upon the muscles in it. Those cuts containing more tender muscles such as the psoas major and longissimus dorsi (as in sirloin steak) are most tender. Cuts with more connective tissues are least tender.

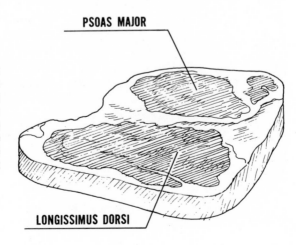

LONGISSIMUS DORSI

Names of Beef Cuts*

Names Commonly Used | *Other Names Used Regionally*

Names Commonly Used	Other Names Used Regionally
ROUND	Bucket Steak, Top Round, Bottom Round, Eye of Round (boneless), "Full Cut" Round, "Swiss" Steak
HEEL OF ROUND	Pike's Peak, Diamond, Wedge, Gooseneck, Horseshoe, Upper Round, Lower Round, Jew Daube, Denver Pot Roast
BOTTOM (OUTSIDE) ROUND	Silverside, Gooseneck, Silver Tip, "Swiss" Steak
SIRLOIN TIP (KNUCKLE)	Short Sirloin, Top Sirloin, Sirloin Butt, Crescent, Veiny, Bell of Knuckle, Face, Face Rump, Round, Boneless Sirloin, Round Tip, Ball Tip, Loin Tip, Family Steak, Sandwich Steak
BONELESS SIRLOIN STEAK	Top Loin Steak, Hip Steak, Rump Steak, "Top of Iowa" Steak, Top Sirloin Butt Steak, Bottom Sirloin Butt Steak
SIRLOIN (LOIN END)	Hip, Short Hip, Head Loin, Rump, K-Style Butt, Sirloin Butt Bone-in, Sirloin Butt, Sir Butt, Sirloin Butt (boneless), Family Steak
LOIN STRIP STEAK	Top Loin Steak, Sirloin Steak, Boneless Sirloin Steak, New York Steak, Kansas City Steak, Club Steak, Delmonico Steak, Shell Steak, Strip Steak, Boneless Top Sirloin Steak, Boneless Hotel Steak, Boneless Hip Steak, Minute Sirloin Steak, Key Strip Steak
PORTERHOUSE STEAK	T-Bone Steak, Large T-Bone Steak, Tenderloin Steak, King Steak
T-BONE STEAK	Porterhouse Steak, Small T-Bone Steak, Club Steak, Tenderloin Steak
CLUB STEAK	Sirloin Steak, Sirloin Strip Steak, Delmonico Steak, Market Steak, Individual Steak
FLANK STEAK	London Broil, Cube Steak, Minute Steak, Flank Steak Filet, "Swiss" Steak

Names Commonly Used	Other Names Used Regionally
RIB EYE STEAK	Market Steak, Spencer Steak, Beauty Steak, Delmonico Steak, "Boneless" Delmonico Steak, Center Cut Steak, Boneless Rib Steak, Club Steak, Boneless Club Steak, Boneless Rib Club Steak, Country Club Steak, Regular Roll Steak
TENDERLOIN	Filet Mignon, Petite Filet, Tenderloin Roast, Tenderloin Tips, "Tips"
SKIRT STEAK	Skirt Steak Filets
SHOULDER CLOD	Scalped Shoulder, Shoulder Roast, Boneless Shoulder, Cross Rib, Rolled Cross Rib, Clod "Roast," Boneless Clod "Roast," London Broil
ARM POT ROAST	Cross Rib Roast, Thick Rib Roast, Thick End Roast, Round Bone Roast, Shoulder Roast, Round Shoulder Roast
BLADE POT ROAST	Chuck Roast, Blade Cut Chuck Roast, Square Cut Chuck Roast, English Cut Roast, 7 Roast, 7 Bone Roast, Flat Bone Roast
ENGLISH CUT	Boston Cut, Bread and Butter, Boneless English Cut
CHUCK (SHORT RIBS)	Flanken, Brust Flanken
CHUCK TENDER	Scotch Tender, Jewish Tender, Kosher Filet, Round Muscle, Fish Muscle, Top Eye Pot Roast, "Cat Fish" Pot Roast
SHORT RIBS	Middle Ribs, English Short Ribs
BRISKET	Deckle, Boneless Brisket, Bone-In Brisket, Fresh Boneless Brisket, Beef Breast, Brisket Pot Roast, "Barbecue" Beef Brisket, Corned Beef
FORE SHANK	Shin, Fore Shin, Shank
MECHANICALLY TENDERIZED STEAKS	"Cubed," "Chicken," Minute, Quick Steak, Sandwich Steak

*Reprinted by permission, WHAT'S NEW IN HOME ECONOMICS.

BEEF CHART

RETAIL CUTS OF BEEF — WHERE THEY COME FROM AND HOW TO COOK THEM

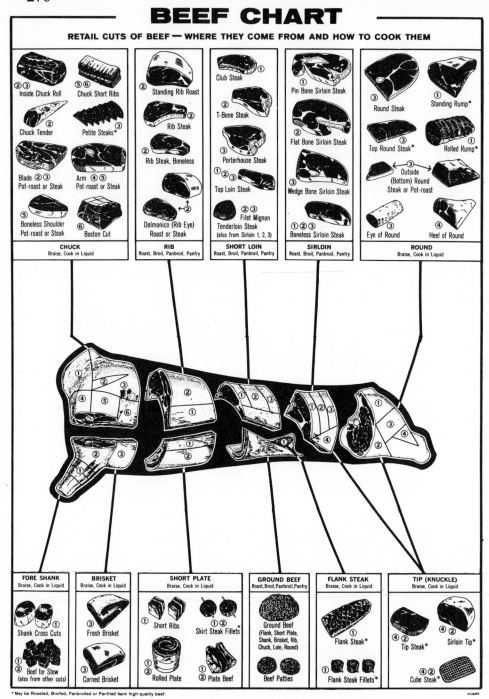

CHUCK
Braise, Cook in Liquid

Inside Chuck Roll ②③
Chuck Short Ribs ⑤⑥
Chuck Tender ②
Petite Steaks* ③
Blade Pot-roast or Steak ②③
Arm Pot-roast or Steak ④⑤
Boneless Shoulder Pot-roast or Steak ⑤
Boston Cut ⑥

RIB
Roast, Broil, Panbroil, Panfry

Standing Rib Roast ②
Rib Steak ②
Rib Steak, Boneless ②
Delmonico (Rib Eye) Roast or Steak ②→②

SHORT LOIN
Roast, Broil, Panbroil, Panfry

Club Steak ①
T-Bone Steak ②
Porterhouse Steak ③
Top Loin Steak ①②③
Filet Mignon Tenderloin Steak ②③
(also from Sirloin 1, 2, 3)

SIRLOIN
Roast, Broil, Panbroil, Panfry

Pin Bone Sirloin Steak ①
Flat Bone Sirloin Steak ②
Wedge Bone Sirloin Steak ③
Boneless Sirloin Steak ①②③

ROUND
Braise, Cook in Liquid

Round Steak ③
Standing Rump* ①
Top Round Steak* ③
Rolled Rump* ①
Outside (Bottom) Round Steak or Pot-roast ③
Eye of Round ③
Heel of Round ④

FORE SHANK
Braise, Cook in Liquid

Shank Cross Cuts ①
Beef for Stew ①② (also from other cuts)

BRISKET
Braise, Cook in Liquid

Fresh Brisket ①
Corned Brisket ③

SHORT PLATE
Braise, Cook in Liquid

Short Ribs ①
Skirt Steak Fillets* ①②
Rolled Plate ①②
Plate Beef ②

GROUND BEEF
Roast, Broil, Panbroil, Panfry

Ground Beef (Flank, Short Plate, Shank, Brisket, Rib, Chuck, Loin, Round)
Beef Patties

FLANK STEAK
Braise, Cook in Liquid

Flank Steak* ①
Flank Steak Fillets* ①

TIP (KNUCKLE)
Braise, Cook in Liquid

Tip Steak* ④②
Sirloin Tip* ④②
Cube Steak* ④②

* May be Roasted, Broiled, Panbroiled or Panfried from high-quality beef.

NLS&MB

National Live Stock and Meat Board

VEAL CHART

RETAIL CUTS OF VEAL — WHERE THEY COME FROM AND HOW TO COOK THEM

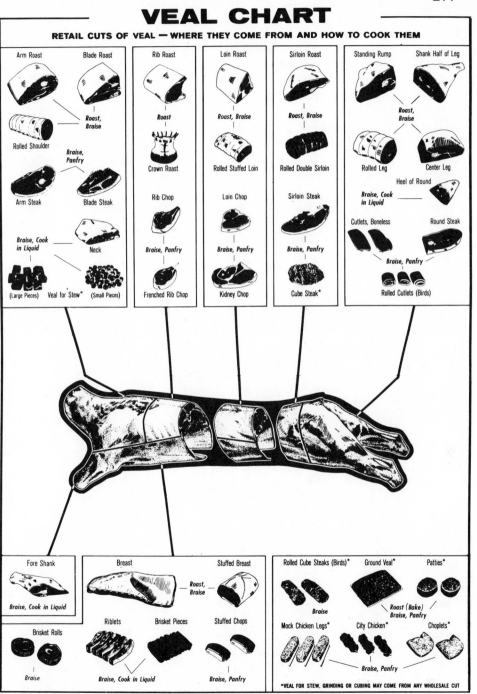

Arm Roast

Blade Roast

Roast, Braise

Rolled Shoulder

Braise, Panfry

Arm Steak

Blade Steak

Braise, Cook in Liquid

Neck

(Large Pieces) Veal for Stew* (Small Pieces)

Rib Roast

Roast

Crown Roast

Rib Chop

Braise, Panfry

Frenched Rib Chop

Loin Roast

Roast, Braise

Rolled Stuffed Loin

Loin Chop

Braise, Panfry

Kidney Chop

Sirloin Roast

Roast, Braise

Rolled Double Sirloin

Sirloin Steak

Braise, Panfry

Cube Steak*

Standing Rump

Shank Half of Leg

Roast, Braise

Rolled Leg

Center Leg

Heel of Round

Braise, Cook in Liquid

Cutlets, Boneless

Round Steak

Braise, Panfry

Rolled Cutlets (Birds)

Fore Shank

Braise, Cook in Liquid

Brisket Rolls

Braise

Breast

Roast, Braise

Stuffed Breast

Riblets

Brisket Pieces

Braise, Cook in Liquid

Stuffed Chops

Braise, Panfry

Rolled Cube Steaks (Birds)*

Ground Veal*

Patties*

Braise

Roast (Bake), Braise, Panfry

Mock Chicken Legs*

City Chicken*

Choplets*

Braise, Panfry

*VEAL FOR STEW, GRINDING OR CUBING MAY COME FROM ANY WHOLESALE CUT

National Live Stock and Meat Board

femoris extends from the round into the sirloin and makes up most of the lean meat of the rump. The toughest muscle has been found to be the *rhomboideus*. This is the muscle just outside the *longissimus dorsi* in the chuck cut. These tenderness variations between muscles and within muscles must be considered when meats are cut from the carcass.

In order to achieve maximum tenderness in any cut of meat, the appropriate cooking procedures must be used. For some time it has been commonly accepted that cooking methods for meats be selected on the basis of whether the particular cut of meat to be cooked is tender or tough. This state of tenderness or toughness was determined by the grade of the meat and the area of the carcass from which the cut came.

Here we will consider the cooking of meats from the standpoint of the relationship between time and temperature used in each cooking method, rather than whether the meat is a tender or tough cut.

Principles of Meat Cookery

When meat is cooked, the muscle fibers become less tender and the connective tissue becomes more tender. The softening of the connective tissue is the major concern when cooking cuts of meat with large amounts of this tissue.

Cross section of raw <u>biceps femoris</u> showing strand of connective tissue.

Longitudinal section of the same muscle after being heated for 30 seconds.

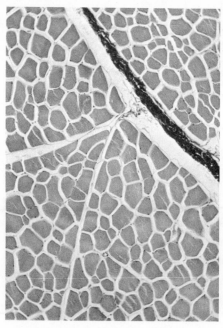 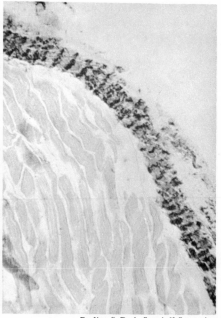

Pauline C. Paul. Campbell Symposium

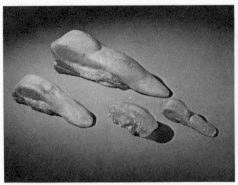

1

2

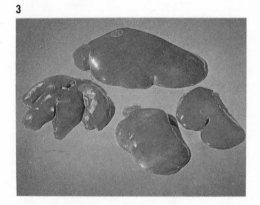

3

Variety meats include liver, brains, heart, kidneys, sweetbreads, tongue, and tripe.
(1) Tongues. In order of size they are beef, veal, pork, and lamb.
(2) Hearts. In order of size they are beef, veal, pork, and lamb.
(3) Livers. In order of size they are beef, pork, veal, and lamb.
(4) Brains and sweetbreads from beef.
(5) Kidneys. Starting with the largest and going clockwise they are beef, veal, lamb, and pork.

4

5

National Live Stock and Meat Board

PORK CHART

RETAIL CUTS OF PORK — WHERE THEY COME FROM AND HOW TO COOK THEM

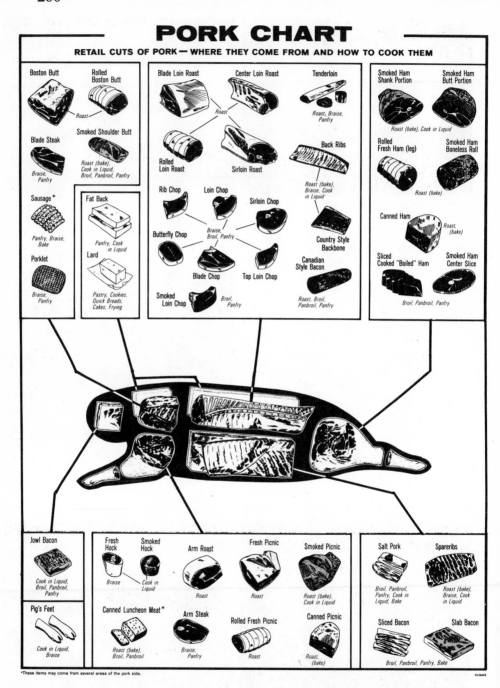

*These items may come from several areas of the pork side.

National Live Stock and Meat Board

LAMB CHART

RETAIL CUTS OF LAMB — WHERE THEY COME FROM AND HOW TO COOK THEM

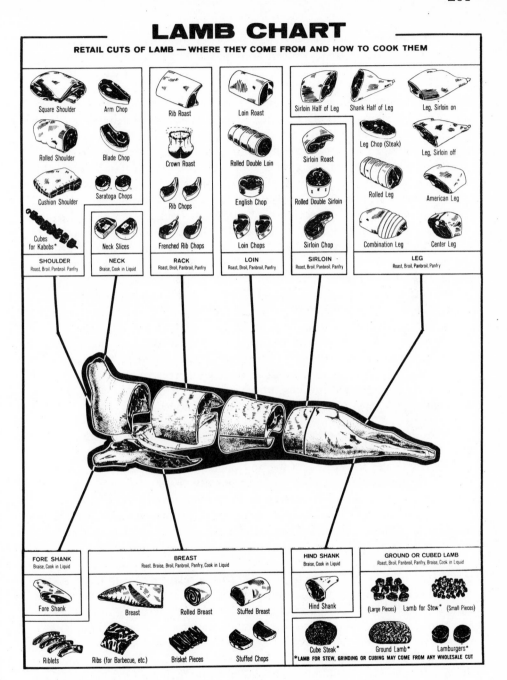

Square Shoulder
Arm Chop
Rib Roast
Loin Roast
Sirloin Half of Leg
Shank Half of Leg
Leg, Sirloin on

Rolled Shoulder
Blade Chop
Crown Roast
Rolled Double Loin
Sirloin Roast
Leg Chop (Steak)
Leg, Sirloin off

Cushion Shoulder
Saratoga Chops
Rib Chops
English Chop
Rolled Double Sirloin
Rolled Leg
American Leg

Cubes for Kabobs*
Neck Slices
Frenched Rib Chops
Loin Chops
Sirloin Chop
Combination Leg
Center Leg

SHOULDER	NECK	RACK	LOIN	SIRLOIN	LEG
Roast, Broil, Panbroil, Panfry	Braise, Cook in Liquid	Roast, Broil, Panbroil, Panfry	Roast, Broil, Panbroil, Panfry	Roast, Broil, Panbroil, Panfry	Roast, Broil, Panbroil, Panfry

FORE SHANK	BREAST	HIND SHANK	GROUND OR CUBED LAMB
Braise, Cook in Liquid	Roast, Braise, Broil, Panbroil, Panfry, Cook in Liquid	Braise, Cook in Liquid	Roast, Broil, Panbroil, Panfry, Braise, Cook in Liquid

Fore Shank
Breast
Rolled Breast
Stuffed Breast
Hind Shank
(Large Pieces) Lamb for Stew* (Small Pieces)

Riblets
Ribs (for Barbecue, etc.)
Brisket Pieces
Stuffed Chops
Cube Steak*
Ground Lamb*
Lamburgers*

*LAMB FOR STEW, GRINDING OR CUBING MAY COME FROM ANY WHOLESALE CUT

National Live Stock and Meat Board

The softening effect on connective tissues and the toughening effect on muscle fibers during cooking are dependent on both the length of time of the cooking period and the temperature. The time factor is more important for softening collagen in the connective tissue whereas the final internal temperature most influences muscle toughening. A cut of meat with much connective tissue requires a long heating period. For muscles or cuts of meat which contain small amounts of connective tissue, cooking methods involving the use of dry heat only for the time necessary to reach the doneness desired are recommended to minimize the toughening effect on the muscle fiber. Muscle composition differences explain why some muscles become more tender during cooking while others become less tender. For example, rib and loin steaks, which contain only small amounts of connective tissue, are less tender when broiled to the well-done stage (internal temperature of 170° F) than if broiled to the rare stage (internal temperature of 140° F). In this instance the rib and loin steaks do not require long cooking because there is little connective tissue to be softened. They should be heated only to the internal temperature desired for palatability in order to prevent the muscle fiber from becoming toughened.

Cooking procedures that involve long cooking times and low temperatures are suggested for cooking meats high in connective tissue, and other procedures that result in low internal temperatures are recommended for cooking meats low in connective tissue. Because of the water content of meat, the proteins of meat are always cooked in a moist environment, regardless of the cooking method. In roasting and broiling, however, the cooking conditions provide a dry heat. In stewing and braising, some liquid is added.

Methods of cooking meats. Broiling, pan broiling, frying, roasting, braising, and stewing are methods used in the cooking of meats.

Oven roasting (dry heat) is a method of meat cookery usually chosen for meat cuts that have small amounts of connective tissue. However, cuts with large amounts of connective tissue can also be oven roasted if they are roasted at a low temperature for a longer period of time than would otherwise be necessary. On the other hand, less tender cuts of the higher grades of meat can be roasted at 250° to 300° F for shorter periods of time.

Veal, pork, and lamb cuts may all be roasted. Veal, because of its connective tissue and lack of fat, has to be cooked for a relatively long time to soften the connective tissue. The lack of fat makes it desirable to bread veal chops and cutlets. With the exception of the neck and shank cuts, all lamb is tender and may be cooked by dry heat methods. Since pork is usually marketed at a young age, it has less connective tissue and all cuts can be successfully roasted. It is usually recommended that pork be cooked until it is well done to minimize the danger of any possible contamination from trichinae* which might be

---

*Trichinae larvae come from raw, untreated, poorly cooked pork. If the infected pork is eaten by man, the larvae develop into worms, are transported by the blood stream to the muscle tissues, and lodge there in the form of cysts.

Above: Meat ready for roasting.

Below: Meat ready for broiling.

National Live Stock and Meat Board

present. Pork loin roasted at 325° F to an internal temperature of 170° F is suggested. Pork may be roasted at an oven temperature of 350° F to shorten the time required to cook it to the well-done stage. For other meats a constant oven temperature of 300° to 325° F is commonly recommended for roasting. Since the degree of doneness of meat is related to internal temperature, a meat thermometer designed to measure this internal temperature will aid in determining the degree of doneness.

The suggested temperatures for various degrees of doneness are the following:

140° F	Rare	Meat is pink inside
160° F	Medium	Meat is slightly pink inside
170° F and above	Well-done	Meat is brown with a complete loss of pinkness

National Live Stock and Meat Board

Oxymyoglobin, the red pigment in raw meat, is the same pigment present in rare cooked meat. As meat is cooked to a higher internal temperature, the proportion of oxymyoglobin decreases. The pigment formed which is responsible for the tan to brown color of well-done meat is denatured globin hemichrome.

For many years it was believed that by searing (browning) meats at high temperatures prior to roasting, the juices and natural flavors were sealed in the meats. The fallacy of this theory has been proved many times since. Whether meat is seared or cooked at a constant oven temperature is a matter of personal preference. The use of a low temperature for the major portion of the roasting period is generally recommended.

Broiling, pan broiling, and frying are methods of cooking cuts of meat having little connective tissue. (T-bone, porterhouse, club, and sirloin steaks). *Broiling* is accomplished by placing a cut of meat on a rack and exposing it to some type of direct heat. The meat proteins coagulate, the extractives are retained if the meat is not cooked to the well-done stage, and the fat melts and is absorbed by the lean muscle tissue. Many experts favor exposing meat to temperatures of 350° to 400° F during broiling. This temperature range permits the meat to cook to the desired internal temperature without overcooking the surface and causes less smoking during cooking. Cooking the meat until rare rather than well-done makes for less shrinkage, more attractive appearance, and more tenderness and juiciness.

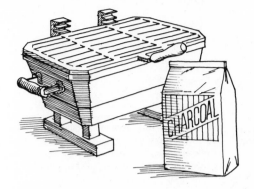

Left: A Japanese hibachi can be used to charcoal-broil meat.
Below: In braising meat, the meat is cooked in a covered pan or Dutch oven in a small amount of liquid. The cooking can be done either in the oven or on top of the stove. When meat is stewed, the meat is submerged in a greater amount of liquid and cooked until tender.

Pan broiling is similar to charcoal or grill broiling. Meat is placed in a moderately hot pan. No fat is added. Any fat that accumulates during cooking is poured off. The meat is turned several times to insure uniform cooking.

Pan frying or *sautéing* is a method which involves cooking meat in a small amount of fat. It is recommended for tender cuts of meat or for ones which have been tenderized by cubing, pounding, scoring, or grinding.

If meat is completely immersed in fat, it is said to be *deep fat fried*. Often the meats prepared in this fashion are coated with a batter which contributes to color, texture, and flavor.

Braising is one of two methods of cooking meat which add moisture in the cooking process. Braising is used for those cuts of meat which contain considerable connective tissue. For example, the flank, brisket, plate and chuck of beef; the breast, neck, and shank of lamb; spareribs, chops, and the shoulder of pork; as well as the breast, neck, and shoulder of veal can be braised successfully. When meat is braised it is cooked in a covered pan with a small amount of liquid. The meat may first be browned in a small amount of fat. The moist heat favors the gelatinization of the connective tissue and therefore makes a more tender product.

Stewing is another method using added moisture and slow cooking to cause softening of connective tissue. In this method the meat is submerged in a

Turkey is often roasted with a piece of aluminum foil loosely covering it to reflect the heat. Placing a steak on a rack in a pan lined with foil will also produce a satisfactory product.

Reynolds Metals Company

liquid and cooked until tender. Stewing is used principally for cuts of meat containing large amounts of connective tissue.

Other methods. In recent years a number of cooking methods, variations of the traditional ones discussed above, have been used. These include pressure cooking, cooking in aluminum foil, microwave oven cooking, and pre-brown-plus-oven.

Pressure cooking involves cooking with steam under pressure. This method produces results similar to cooking with moist heat. Meat cuts cooked in this way are similar to those braised or stewed. The advantage of pressure cooking is the shortened period of time required.

Meat can be *wrapped in aluminum foil* to prepare it for steaming. The foil holds in the steam as effectively as a covered pan. However, it has been found that beef roasts wrapped in foil and cooked well-done are less tender than roasts cooked by dry heat.

Microwave cooking of meat is still in the exploratory stage. However, it has been used to cook frozen products without defrosting and to reheat cooked foods. The advantage of microwave, or electronic, cooking is the short time required to cook the meat. There are disadvantages, however. For example, there is greater shrinkage in roasts cooked by microwave than in roasts cooked in the conventional manner. In addition, the cooking tends to be uneven because the microwave energy fails to penetrate very deeply. Beef roasts tend to be dry due to excessive loss of fat drippings.

Prebrown-plus-oven is a new method which has been introduced recently. Top round steaks cooked to the medium-rare stage have been prepared this way experimentally. This method requires the meat to be prebrowned slowly on a surface unit and then cooked in the oven at a temperature of 500° F. The prebrowning-plus-oven method was preferred over conventional broiling for this cut. The cooking losses are also less.

Cooking frozen meats. Frozen meat may be cooked from the frozen state or thawed state. Of course, extra time must be allowed if the meat is cooked from the frozen state. Trial and error procedures are sometimes needed to learn the length of time necessary to cook meat to a particular desired stage of doneness. The most common ways of defrosting are to transfer the meat from frozen storage into the refrigerator or to room temperature.

Refrigerator defrosting or thawing appears to be the preferred practice because with this method possible surface bacterial action is minimized. Room temperature provides an accelerated defrosting process. Meat thawed in this way may be held too long at a temperature which encourages an increase in the bacterial count on the surface of the meat.

The tenderness, juiciness, and flavor of meat is similar whether the meat is cooked from the frozen state or the thawed state.

Tenderization of meat. Cuts of meat can be made more tender by the use of both physical and chemical means.

For chemical treatment, commercial tenderizers in powder or liquid form are available for application to the surface of meat cuts. The enzymes papain, bromelin, or ficin are usually the active ingredients in such tenderizers. These products have been most effective in tenderizing steaks or thin cuts of meat. It is difficult for the enzymes to penetrate thicker cuts and secure uniform tenderizing.

Because of the inability of the enzymes to secure uniform tenderizing before the meat is cooked, a commercial process has been developed which makes it possible to add the tenderizing enzymes to meat before the animal is slaughtered. In this process the selected enzyme is injected into the jugular

vein of the animal before slaughter. The enzyme is distributed throughout the animal's body by the circulatory system. Beef is commercially tenderized by this antemortem enzyme process. The appearance and the keeping quality of this beef are the same as for regularly processed fresh beef. Cuts of chuck from beef so treated may be oven-roasted with dry heat to a medium or well-done stage and still be tender.

Less tender cuts of meat which contain large amounts of connective tissue and little marbling can be made more tender by physical treatments. These involve cutting or breaking muscle fibers and cutting or softening connective tissue, thereby changing the character of the cut of meat. Such cuts can be pounded, scored, ground, or cubed.

Poultry

Poultry is the term applied to all domesticated birds used as food. These include chickens, ducks, geese, turkeys, guinea fowls, squabs, and pigeons. The first four birds are the most commonly used in the United States.

Chickens. Chickens are birds hatched in the current year, and are not sexually mature. They are classified as broilers—under 3 pounds; fryers—3 pounds; roasters—over 3 pounds. Mature female chickens are hens; males are roosters and classified as cocks. Capons are male chickens which have been desexed. They are used primarily for roasting.

Control of the final animal product is important in the production of chickens as it is in the production of beef, pork, and other meats. Selective breeding to insure specific qualities is practiced. For example, by breeding for rapid growth to improve production efficiency, it is possible to market younger birds that are more tender than broilers produced under ordinary circumstances.

Chickens have been bred to produce fryers that are plump of breast and leg. At present this body conformation is not as important as formerly held because of the increasing sale of tray-packed cut-up fryers. Virtually all fryers grown for the market are both white feathered and rapid in feathering. For this reason they can be dressed more easily without the costly removal of pin feathers by hand.

Because it is assumed that consumers prefer yellow-skinned chickens, frying chickens are usually yellow-skinned. The degree of this yellowness is controlled by pigments in the feed of the chickens. Chicken has been genetically tailored to meet the desired qualities in the market.

Grading of poultry. There are Federal government standards for controlling the designated quality of poultry put on the market. These standards indicate market grades of dressed poultry. The grades are based on the proportion of edible meat and fat in the carcass. The United States Deparment of Agriculture has established these grades, which are AA, A, B, and C.

Swift and Company

Each kind of poultry has its own distinctive characteristics. Notice in the illustration above the differences in body contour and size. For example, duckling is readily distinguished from chicken by its rectangular structure and flatter breastbone. There are also differences in the type of meat of different birds. Ducklings have only dark meat whereas turkeys and chickens have both dark and light meat. Wild birds, for the most part, have only dark meat.

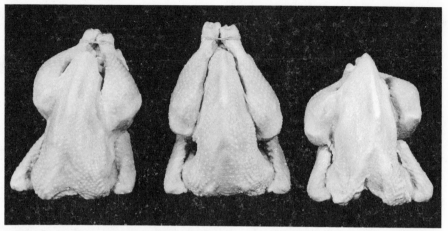

Above: These young chickens illustrate (left to right) U.S. Grade A, U.S. Grade B, and U.S. Grade C.
Below: U.S. Grade A (left) and U.S. Grade B (right) turkeys.

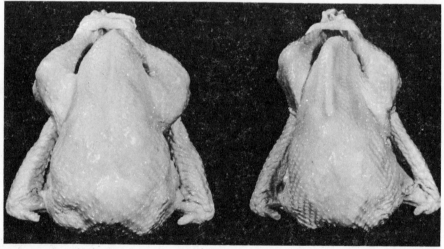

USDA Photos

U.S. Grade AA specifies a young, fine-grained, soft-meated bird with a broad, full-fleshed breast. The entire carcass is fully covered with fat and soft, glossy skin. AA Grade poultry must be bled, well-dressed, and free from pin feathers.

U.S. Grade A marks a young, soft-meated bird with a well fleshed breast. The entire carcass is well-covered with fat and a soft, glossy skin. This grade of bird must be bled, well-dressed, and practically free from pin feathers.

U.S. Grade B indicates a young, soft-meated bird with a fairly well fleshed breast. The carcass must be fairly-well covered with fat and fairly well bled and dressed. A few scattered pin feathers may show over the carcass.

U.S. Grade C designates a young bird with a poorly fleshed breast and a poor covering of fat. It may show evidence of poor bleeding and there may be numerous pin feathers over the carcass.

Grade names are printed on tags and attached to each bird by means of a seal which passes through the wing. These seals are designed so that they can be used only once.

Turkeys. These birds have also been bred with special genetic characteristics. For example, the Broad-Breasted White breed has been developed for more desirable carcass conformation. These turkeys have broad, full-fleshed breasts and white feathers. There is no problem of pin feathers.

A smaller or "apartment-size" turkey has also been developed. This bird is smaller, more compact, and has a broad, fleshy breast.

Turkeys are classified as fryer, a young bird weighing usually 4–6 pounds; roaster, a young bird weighing 8–16 pounds; hen, a female bird weighing 18–24 pounds; tom, a male bird weighing 18–24 pounds.

Ducks. Ducks are classified as duckling, a young bird weighing 4–5 pounds, and as duck, a young bird weighing more than 5 pounds.

Geese. Geese are also used as food. They are classified as gosling, a young bird weighing 6–8 pounds, and goose, an older bird weighing 10–22 pounds.

Nutritive value of poultry. Poultry, like meat, contains iron, thiamine, riboflavin, and protein of high nutritive value.

White meat is somewhat lower in fat, iron, thiamine, and riboflavin than dark meat. Dark meat is equivalent in fat content to beef with all visible fat removed. Chicken broilers and fryers have less fat than older chickens. Turkeys are usually marketed at a more mature age than chickens and have a higher fat content.

Cooking poultry. Tender turkeys, chickens, and ducks can be roasted by the same method as that used for tender cuts of beef, lamb, and pork. The percentage of drippings from roasting duck is exceptionally high—40 percent—compared to about 30 percent for roasting chicken and 25–30 percent for roasting turkey.

There is a preference for well-done poultry because of its fully developed flavor. However, cooking poultry to the well-done stage may result in a considerable loss of juice. The reliability of temperature as a guide to doneness continues to be studied. It is suggested that a meat thermometer be inserted in the center of the inside thigh muscle. When the thermometer reading reaches 185° F, the bird should be sufficiently roasted. It has been further suggested that cooking a stuffed turkey in a very slow oven (200°–250° F) may create a health hazard. In this instance heating occurs at such a slow rate that the food

When cooking poultry, a meat thermometer should be inserted in the thigh or breast. A turkey should be done when the thermometer reads 185°F.

Taylor Instrument Companies

may remain for a dangerously long time in a temperature range favorable to bacterial growth. It is recommended that turkeys be roasted in a moderately slow oven, 325° F.

Young poultry can be broiled, pan broiled, or fried. Braising and stewing are usually recommended for older poultry which requires a longer cooking time. Cooking in aluminum foil is also a way of cooking poultry.

Seafood

Each section of the country has its own seafood specialties. Lobsters and oysters come from the Atlantic seaboard; salmon, from the Pacific. The Great Lakes provide whitefish while the southern waters furnish pompano, Spanish mackerel, shrimp, and red snappers. Fish may be purchased in many forms: fresh, frosted, frozen, canned, mild-cured, pickled, dry-salted, and smoked. The first four listed make up the major part of the fish industry.

Seafood is divided into two groups: fish, or vertebrates; shellfish, or invertebrates. The former are covered with scales; the latter with some type of shell. Fish are classified as salt water, fresh water, fatty, and lean fish. Salt water fish have more distinctive flavor than do fresh water ones. Mollusks and crustaceans comprise the two classes of shellfish. Mollusks—oysters, clams, scallops, and mussels—are of soft structure and are wholly encased in a hard shell of mineral composition. Crustaceans—lobsters, crab, shrimp, and crayfish—have segmented bodies and are covered with a crustlike shell.

Nutritive value of seafood. Fish, like meat and poultry, contains protein of high nutritive quality. Fish also contains carbohydrates in the form of glycogen, in addition to vitamins and fat.

Varieties of shell fish: 1) Alaska king crab, 2) offshore lobster, 3) sea clams, 4) scallops, 5) rock crab, 6) blue crab, 7) squid, 8) sea turtle (terrapin), 9) frogs' legs, 10 Maine (northern) shrimp, 11) little neck clams, 12) quahogs, 13) gulf shrimp, 14) soft shell clams, 15) conch, 16) periwinkles, 17) mussels, 18) oysters, 19) cherrystone clams.

Wes Kemp

Varieties of fin fish: 1) gray sole, 2) dab (flounder), 3) lemon sole (flounder), 4) mackerel, 5) cusk, 6) wolffish (ocean catfish), 7) haddock, 8) pollock, 9) sea robin, 10) whitefish, 11) salmon, 12) buffalo carp, 13) tautog, 14) sea herring,

Wes Kemp

15) dover sole, 16) yellow pike, 17) ale wife, 18) pompano, 19) rainbow trout, 20) striped bass, 21) ocean perch, 22) smelts, 23) shad, 24) red snapper, 25) cod, 26) scup (porgy), 27) whiting, 28) butterfish.

The fat content differs with the kind of fish. Salmon, mackerel, shad, butterfish, turbot, lake trout, pompano, whitefish, bluefish, herring, catfish, eel, and halibut are all considered "fat" fish. Cod, haddock, flounder, pollock, pickerel, perch, and smelt are "lean" fish and contain very little fat. It is also well to remember that most fish contain a lower percentage of fat than does medium-fat beef.

Cooking fish. Since fish has only a small amount of connective tissue, mild heating is adequate for the cooking process. Long heating produces a dry and less tender product. The amount of fat also influences the cooking method of a particular fish. For example, since mackerel contains considerable fat, it is not necessary to add much fat during the cooking process. Baked haddock, on the other hand, would be very dry if fat were not added.

Overcooking is a common problem in fish cookery. Since fish has little connective tissue, it is tender before cooking and needs only sufficient cooking to coagulate the protein. There is no best temperature for cooking fish but there is a best length of time for each temperature that you choose. When done, the fish flakes readily when tested with a fork.

In this chapter we have dealt with the groups, classes, grades, structure, chemical composition, and cuts of meat, and principles of meat cookery. The principles have been approached from the point of view of the time-temperature relationship rather than from the traditional distinction between moist heat for tough cuts of meat, and dry heat for tender cuts of meat.

The following chapter will be concerned with some of the byproducts of meat which do not have the characteristics of this protein food. In addition, the techniques which are used to produce new products from the raw materials of plants will be discussed.

MAJOR IDEAS

The following statements give the main ideas within the chapter you have just studied. Be sure you know the words underscored in these statements and in the questions to follow.

1. Through improved breeding and production methods, meat animals and poultry have been developed with special characteristics which increase the availability of these products and improve their market quality.
2. Standards for grading meat and poultry established by the United States Government serve as guides in identifying quality in both wholesale and retail cuts of meat and poultry.
3. The appearance, texture, flavor, and tenderness of a meat cut depend upon its physical structure and chemical composition.

4. When meat is cooked, the <u>muscle tissue</u> becomes toughened at higher internal temperatures while the <u>connective tissue</u> becomes softened with long heating. Thus cuts with large amounts of connective tissue require a longer heating period. Cuts of meat with small amounts of connective tissue are most tender when cooked to low internal temperatures.

5. The method to be used in cooking meat depends upon the kind of meat, the cut and size, the time available for cooking, and the degree of doneness desired.

6. Tenderization of tough meat cuts may be brought about by changing the character of the meat through mechanical methods and chemical means such as <u>enzymatic action.</u>

7. Regardless of the method of cooking, tenderness may be achieved in a tough cut of meat if there is the correct relationship between time and temperature during the cooking process. Because of the water content of meat, the proteins of meat are always cooked in a moist environment, regardless of the cooking method used.

8. Similar changes can be obtained in tender muscle tissue by exposure to relatively high temperatures for a short time or to low temperatures for a longer time.

QUESTIONS TO STUDY

CLASSES AND GRADES

1. What special characteristics have been developed in chickens and turkeys to improve their market quality and to increase production?

2. What has been done to improve the distribution and production of beef cattle throughout the United States?

3. What are the problems that arise in producing hogs to meet consumer demand for lean pork?

4. Classify beef animals. From which classification does the major part of the beef come? What uses are made of the other beef animals? Distinguish between mutton and lamb. What are the chief classes of hogs used for meat?

5. When judging a beef carcass, what points does the grader consider in relation to <u>conformation,</u> <u>finish,</u> and <u>quality</u>?

6. Describe a beef carcass that would be considered <u>top grade</u> by the grader.

7. Give the characteristics of the top quality or grade of pork, veal, and lamb.

STRUCTURE AND PHYSICAL CHARACTERISTICS

1. Describe the physical structure of meat.
2. Account for the fact that one piece of meat or meat muscle may be coarse-grained in texture while another may be fine-grained.
3. What are the two kinds of connective tissue found in meat? Where are they located?
4. What is the relationship of tenderness to connective tissue?

CHEMICAL COMPOSITION

1. What two forms of fat are found in a cut of meat? Where are they located?
2. Why are moist heat methods used to soften the connective tissue in meat?

PRINCIPLES OF MEAT, POULTRY, AND FISH COOKERY

1. What is the effect of cooking on muscle tissue and connective tissue?
2. Illustrate what is meant by the time-temperature relationship in meat cookery by explaining the following statements:

   a. A porterhouse steak cooked at a low temperature to a well-done stage is more apt to be tough than one cooked at a high temperature to the rare stage.

   b. A beef plate, which is a tough cut of meat, may be made tender by oven roasting.
3. Describe methods of meat cookery.
4. What methods of meat cookery would you choose for cooking veal, pork, and lamb chops? Give reasons for your choices.
5. What methods of cooking are best suited for young poultry? For older poultry?
6. Indicate the advantages and disadvantages of the following methods of cooking meat:

   a. pressure cooking   c. wrapped in aluminum foil

   b. microwave cooking   d. searing meat first

   e. prebrown-plus-oven method
7. What precautions are necessary in cooking fish? Why?
8. How is enzymatic tenderization of meat accomplished? What are the advantages and disadvantages when compared with other methods of tenderizing meat?
9. How should frozen meat be prepared for cooking?

BIBLIOGRAPHY

COVER, S., and others, "Tenderness of Beef. I. The Connective-tissue, Components of Tenderness; II. Juiciness and Softness, Components of Tenderness; III. The Muscle-fiber, Component of Tenderness." *Journal of Food Science*, Vol. 27, September–October 1962, pp. 469, 476, 483.

COVER, S., and others, "Tenderness of Beef. IV. Relations of Shear Force and Fiber Extensibility to Juiciness and Six Components of Tenderness." *Journal of Food Science*, Vol. 27, November–December 1962, p. 527.

HINER, R. L., and others, "Comparative Tenderness of Representative Beef Muscles." *Food Research*, Vol. 10, 1945, pp. 497–509.

HOOD, M. P., "Effect of Cooking Method and Grade on Beef Roasts." *Journal of American Dietetics Association*, Vol. 37, 1960, p. 363.

KAHLENBERG, O. J., and NAUMAN, H. D., "Factors Influencing Beef Tenderness." *Journal of Animal Science*, Vol. 23, 1964, pp. 1027–1031.

LEVIE, ALBERT, *The Meat Handbook*. Westport, Conn., The AVI Publishing Company, Inc., 1963, p. 26.

PAUL, P. C., "Tenderness and Chemical Composition of Beef. I. Variations Among Animals Created Alike." *Food Technology*, Vol. 16, October 1962, p. 115.

PAUL, P. C., and others, "Eating Quality of Lamb I. Effect of Age; II. Effect of Preslaughter Nutrition; and III. Overall Comparisons and Interrelationships." *Food Technology*, Vol. 18, November 1964, pp. 121, 125, 127.

Proceedings—Meat Tenderness Symposium. Campbell Soup Company, Camden, New Jersey, 1963.

ROGER, CLETA, and others, "Comparison of Dry Heat Cooking Methods of Round Steak." *Food Technology*, Vol. 17, July 1963, p. 111.

The Science of Meat and Meat Products. American Meat Institute, W. H. Freeman and Company, San Francisco, 1960.

TUOMY, J. M., and others, "Effect of Cooking Temperature and Time on the Tenderness of Beef." *Food Technology*, Vol. 17, November 1963, p. 119.

19 FATS

Fats are concentrated food materials having more than twice the heat value of the same weight of carbohydrates or proteins. In addition, they serve as carriers of fat-soluble vitamins and they furnish the essential fatty acids without which the animal organism cannot thrive. Besides their direct nutritional value, they make many foods more appetizing. They are practically indispensable in cooking and baking.

In common usage, the noun "fat" refers to material which is insoluble in water, has an oily or greasy feel and consistency, and can be separated from plant and animal tissues. Plant fats reach the consumer in the form of salad oils, margarine, and shortenings while animal fats are marketed as butter, lard, suet, and chicken fat.

For reasons related to both history and climate, there are decided geographical divisions of fat- and oil-consuming peoples. The ancestors of the present inhabitants of central and northern Europe derived their edible fats almost wholly from domestic animals, such as pigs and cows, rather than from plants. Consequently the food and cooking habits of these people were developed around the use of solid fats—butter, lard, and more recently, shortenings and margarine.

In the older civilizations of southern Europe, northern Africa, the Near East, and the Orient, the pressure of population has made the extensive raising of livestock impractical and has required that the edible oils of these regions be derived principally from intensively cultivated vegetable crops. In the tropical regions of the world, conditions are relatively unfavorable for livestock production but are extremely well-suited to the cultivation of certain oil-bearing plants such as olive and palm trees.

In the Western World, plastic fats are the most widely used because of the predominantly northern European extraction of the earlier North American settlers and because large sections of both North and South America have adapted to the large-scale raising of domestic animals. Formerly, solid or plastic fats originally used for food were of animal sources. Today, however, vegetable sources are more frequently used since it is now possible to convert vegetable oils to solid fats (the process of hydrogenation).

Composition and Properties

Fats, like carbohydrates, are composed of carbon, hydrogen, and oxygen. Fats are built from combinations of a series of acids, called *"fatty acids,"* and

A molecule of glycerol.

$$H-\underset{\underset{H}{\overset{|}{O}}}{\overset{\overset{H}{|}}{C}}-\underset{\underset{H}{\overset{|}{O}}}{\overset{\overset{H}{|}}{C}}-\underset{\underset{H}{\overset{|}{O}}}{\overset{\overset{H}{|}}{C}}-H \text{ or } C_3H_8O_3$$

glycerine. This formula may help you understand the structure:

3 fatty acids + glycerine = fat + water

Chemically, fats may be defined as triglycerides since each glycerine molecule is combined with 3 molecules of fatty acids. (Monoglycerides are glycerides containing only one molecule of fatty acid. Diglycerides are glycerides having two molecules of fatty acids.)

If three fatty acids are identical, the product is a simple triglyceride; if they are different, it is a mixed triglyceride. Fats of plant or animal origin consist predominantly of triglycerides.

Both the chemical and physical properties of a fat are influenced by the kinds and proportions of fatty acids and their chemical arrangement in the glycerides. Fatty acids are called saturated when their chain of carbon atoms has united with all the hydrogen it possibly can. When there are less than 2 hydrogen atoms for each carbon atom in the fatty acid chain, there is a sharing between two carbon atoms. This sharing is called, chemically, a double bond. Fatty acids containing a double bond are unsaturated, and are polyunsaturated if there is more than one double bond in the fatty acid.

Natural fats usually contain free fatty acids, phosphatides, sterols, tocopherols, and fat-soluble vitamins. Free fatty acids are the uncombined fatty acids found in fat. Phosphatides consist of an alcohol (glycerol), fatty acid, and phosphoric acid combined with a nitrogen compound. Sterols are neutral, stable, crystalline alcohols, with melting points much higher than those of the fats. Tocopherols, such as vitamin E, are important minor constituents of vegetable oils. They serve as antioxidants to retard rancidity (Chapter 12). Vitamins A and D are found in large amounts in fish liver oils, are present in butterfat and egg yolk, and are frequently added to margarine and milk to ncrease their nutritive value.

Properties. The most important group of physical properties of fats consists of those associated with solid-liquid and liquid-solid changes, or the processes of melting and solidification. The words *fats* and *oils* are closely related to these physical changes. The term *fat* is ordinarily understood to refer to a mixture of triglycerides that is solid at room temperature. On the other hand, a fat that is liquid at room temperatures is called a salad or cooking oil.

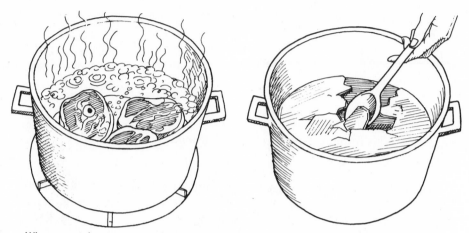

When meat is stewed and then cooled, the fat which melts separates from the liquid in the pot, rises to the top since it is lighter than water, and solidifies. When the meat is reheated, the fat melts again.

In many cases the use of fats in edible products is dependent upon such physical properties as oiliness, melting point, smoke point, and solubility. One of the most noticeable characteristics of oils and fats is their *oiliness* or ability to form a lubricant film. This characteristic is important in making certain baked products such as pie crust, certain other pastries, and cookies tender. The rolling process used in producing these products spreads an incorporated solid fat into thin parallel layers. In the finished product a "flaky" structure is evident.

Since fats are composed of mixtures of glycerides, their *melting points* are not sharp. In general, fats containing a high percentage of unsaturated fatty acids, the oils, have low melting points. Those fats with a high percentage of saturated fatty acids of low molecular weight, such as coconut oil, have intermediate melting points.

Fats with a high percentage of saturated fatty acids, such as beef suet and mutton tallow, have high melting points; an oil can be hydrogenated to a hard solid (page 149).

The smoke point of fat is the temperature at which decomposition products are evident in sufficient quantity to become visible. Some fats decompose at lower temperatures than others. The smoke point depends on the nature of the fat and the way in which it has been used. The smoke point is higher for fats that do not contain an emulsifier (mono- and diglycerides). Thus, the emulsifiers now used almost universally in shortenings to improve cake-making quality lower the smoke point. The absence of an emulsifier in vegetable oils may offer an advantage in frying. The smoke point for a particular fat is also lowered when the exposed surface of the fat is increased. This indicates the importance of using a deep pan of small diameter rather than a wider shallow pan for frying in deep fat. The presence of finely divided foreign particles lowers the smoking point. For this reason, fats which have been previously used should be strained before using again to remove as much of this material as possible.

Fats and oils at any temperature high enough to keep them in liquid form are completely soluble in any proportion in alcohol and many other organic liquids. The liquids which will mix in any proportion with most oils and melted fats are referred to as fat solvents. With water, however, fats are almost completely immiscible (will not mix).

Types

The kinds of fats marketed today include cooking and salad oils, plastic shortening agents, and spreads such as margarine or butter.

Cooking and salad oils. Oils are generally suitable for all types of cooking but special mixing procedures are needed for many baked products. Of course, they are not generally acceptable as spreads for bread or for the production of plastic products such as cream icings or fillings. In addition to their household uses, cooking oils are in considerable demand for commercial deep fat frying, particularly for products such as doughnuts. For frying potato chips, which must be able to withstand considerable periods of storage, plastic hydrogenated oil products are preferred because of their greater stability. However, vegetable oils are also commonly used. Cooking oils are also used extensively in the packing of certain canned meat and fish products such as sardines, anchovies, and sausages.

All cooking oils are vegetable products. The only liquid animal oils are whale and fish oils. These oils, because of their high degree of unsaturation, are not considered edible in natural form in most parts of the world. However, they are edible after they have been through the processes of hydrogenation and deodorization.

In the United States a distinction is made between cooking oils and salad oils. This distinction is particularly important for commercial uses. The term salad oil is applied to oils which will remain substantially liquid at refrigerator temperatures 40° to 45° F and will produce a mayonnaise emulsion (page 309) which is stable at low temperatures. The labeling of an oil as a cooking oil implies that it will not withstand low temperatures without some of the fats becoming solidified. In the household, however, cooking and salad oils are often used interchangeably.

Salad and cooking oils are of two different types: naturally-flavored oils and neutral, deodorized products.

The extent of flavor removal of vegetable oils depends on local tastes and customs. In the Orient, cooking oils such as soybean, peanut, sunflower, sesame, and rapeseed are consumed in their crude form. In the Occidental (Western

World) countries, however, it is a general practice to subject these oils to refining and deodorizing. The people of the latter countries are relatively unfamiliar with the natural flavors of these oils. Cottonseed oil, which is strongly and unpleasantly flavored, was one of the first vegetable oils consumed in the United States. Olive oil is one example of an oil which is marketed in the undeodorized form because the natural flavor of the product is an important asset. In the United States, however, deodorized oils are in particular demand. These are prepared from corn, cottonseed, peanut, rapeseed, sesame, soybean, and sunflower oils. All of these oils may be converted to bland, neutral products which do not readily deteriorate in flavor. Most of the neutral oils sold in the United States are actually salad oils, rather than cooking oils. They are usually stored at room temperature and are suitable for both frying and salad dressings. Some oils, such as cottonseed, must be subjected to "winterization," in order to remove higher melting glycerides, before they may be classified as salad oils.

Plastic shortenings. The term plastic shortening is applied to fats which are of a consistency that can be readily spread, mixed, or worked. This group of fats consists largely of lard or hog fat and the vegetable, or animal and vegetable, products of lard-like consistency which are known as hydrogenated shortenings.

The first fat products used by man undoubtedly were rendered from the carcasses of wild animals. As animals were domesticated, their body fat became an important article of commerce. In addition to being used as edible substances, animal fats served as illuminants, lubricants, and materials for making soap. As the various uses of fats became more highly specialized and standardized, the body fat of hogs—lard—came to be preferred.

The chief reason, however, for the favor enjoyed by lard as an edible fat was undoubtedly its particular consistency. At ordinary temperatures, lard has nearly the optimum consistency for incorporation into pastries and is satisfactory for yeast breads and many leavened baked products. For some time the production of lard has been far short of the demand for plastic shortening agents in the lard-consuming countries. This has stimulated the production and use of both vegetable and marine-oils (whole-fish oils). Since the people in these countries have been accustomed to the use of solid fats rather than oils, vegetable and marine oils have been converted to plastic products by a process known as hydrogenation. This process makes it possible to manufacture a plastic product entirely from a liquid oil and to produce shortenings and margarine.

Shortenings manufactured in the United States may be divided into two distinct classes: the compound or blended type and the all-hydrogenated type. Compound-type shortening may be divided further into animal and vegetable fat compounds and all vegetable fat compounds. All hydrogenated shortenings may be subdivided into regular or general purpose shortenings, high stability biscuit and cracker shortenings, and superglycerinated shortenings.

Animal and vegetable fat compounds at one time constituted the entire United States shortening production. At present, however, these compounds are exceeded in volume by vegetable shortenings. A considerable amount of the animal and vegetable fat compounds are made from vegetable oil and

Deodorized oils may be prepared from cottonseed, peanut, sunflower, sesame, corn, soybean, and rapeseed oils.

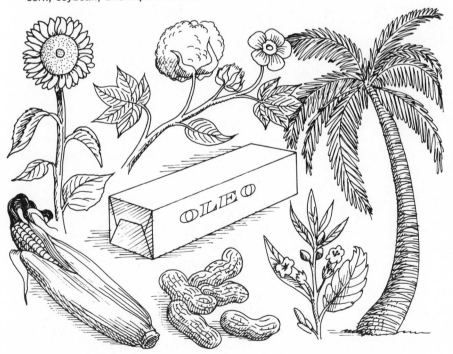

suet or tallow. The overall quality, and particularly the flavor stability of a blended animal and vegetable shortening, is greatly improved if the blend is subjected to slight hydrogenation.

In vegetable fat compounds highly hydrogenated vegetable oils are substituted for the hard animal fats used in the animal-vegetable products. Most of the all-vegetable fat shortening manufactured in the United States is prepared from cottonseed, soybean, and peanut oils. Corn, palm, sesame, or sunflower oils are entirely suitable materials, yet may not be readily available.

General purpose shortenings are produced by hydrogenation and blending of fats. These shortenings are sold to general bakeshops, restaurants, and hotels. They are also packed in one and three pound cans and sold for household use. These shortenings are designed to have a high stability and an extended range of plasticity. In general they will congeal or begin to solidify between 90.5° F and 92.3° F (32.5° C and 33.5° C) and the melting point will range between 105.8° F and 107.4° F (41° C and 43° C). A low free fatty acid content is characteristic of a good shortening in this class. In general, the manufacturers of all-hydrogenated shortenings achieve an excellent degree of uniformity in their products.

The manufacture of crackers and sweet biscuits presents a particular problem in fat stability since these products must withstand long periods of shipment and storage before final consumption. Therefore, shortenings with high stability are manufactured for biscuits and crackers. In these shortenings the plastic range of the fat is sacrificed in favor of having extremely high stability.

Superglycerinated shortenings are a special type of all-hydrogenated shortening with superior emulsifying properties. These shortenings contain a greater proportion of mono- and diglycerides than do ordinary shortenings. Mono- and diglycerides possess marked surface activity and are extremely effective in promoting dispersion of the shortening in batters and doughs, particularly those with high sugar content. Superglycerinated shortenings have become extremely popular for use in cakes and sweet yeast doughs. However, they are unsuitable for deep-fat frying because of their lower decomposition temperatures and consequent smoking.

Spreads. Butter, an animal fat, is widely used as a spread. Here, however, the discussion will be concerned with margarine. Margarine was invented during the Franco-Prussian War by a French scientist, Mége-Mouriés. Margarine resembles butter but the butter fat has been replaced by a different fat. Beef fat and lard were widely used in margarine until after World War I. After that date, nut oils became predominant and now cottonseed and soybean oils are also used. They are refined and hydrogenated so that the melting point and other properties of the final product are similar to those of butter.

In making margarine, the melted fat is agitated or churned with skim milk which has been pasteurized and cultured with a bacterial starter. Vitamins A and D, plus emulsifiers, a butter flavoring, and yellow coloring may all be added to margarine. The manufacturing standards of margarine have been established by legislation both by the Federal Government and by state governments. Margarine must be labeled plainly as oleomargarine or margarine.

Uses in Cookery

Fats are used extensively in baked products and confections, in salad dressings, for deep-fat frying, and as a flavoring agent for many dishes.

Baked products. In most classes of baked products, fat is a highly necessary ingredient, not only because it contributes to the flavor of the product, but also because it plays an essential role in the development of the physical structure. Such important considerations as the volume, texture, and tenderness of the finished product are all closely related to the amount of fat used, the method employed in incorporating it, and the characteristics of the fat itself.

If you examine a piece of cake, you will notice that it is cellular in structure and contains a large proportion of holes. The adequate development of this cellular structure leads to the lightness and tenderness of the product. Fat aids in forming a cellular structure in cakes because as the product is baked, the fatty walls of the air cells melt and are replaced by a structural framework of coagulated protein and gelatinized starch. Fat in other baked products prevents the formation of a firm, compact structure. The ability of a fat to lubricate and

Courtesy of Swans Down Cake Mixes

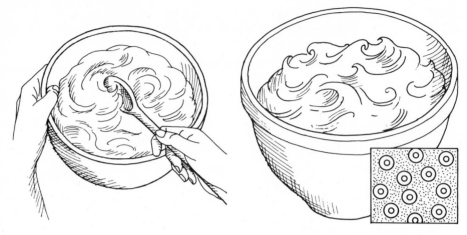

Solid shortening creamed in bowl.   Cake batter.

weaken the structure of a baked product is known as its shortening value. The shortening value of a fat is related to its consistency. Soft fats, such as prime steam lard (the most common type of lard produced in the U.S.) because of their spreadability are superior in this respect to firmer fats such as all-hydrogenated ones. The inadequacy of liquid fats as shortening agents in cakes and flaky pastries (unless special mixing methods are used) is probably related to their lack of plasticity. Creaming quality is important in choosing a fat to use for baked products. In order for fats to cream satisfactorily they usually contain some saturated glycerides. Hydrogenation is effective for the production of good creaming fats. Limited hydrogenation of oil or soft fat will produce a shortening of good creaming quality, as will the addition of a small proportion of highly hydrogenated fat. Lard does not cream well without either hydrogenation or the addition of hydrogenated fat. The creaming quality of butter is variable, depending in part on the temperature when used, and is usually considered inferior to that of hydrogenated fat.

During our discussion of flour mixtures we stated that cake batter is actually an "emulsion" in which the internal phase is the fat and the external phase is composed of the remaining ingredients. However, fat is plastic rather than liquid; thus the fat particles cannot coalesce (combine) as in an ordinary oil-in-water emulsion. They may, however, agglomerate (gather) into large masses. Hence, the problem of producing a good fat dispersion in a batter is analogous to producing an emulsion of oil in an aqueous medium.

Eggs may be added to serve as an emulsifying agent to promote dispersion of the fat. However, the superglycerinated shortenings containing mono- and diglycerides are extremely effective in promoting and stabilizing emulsions. Many vegetable shortenings, and at least one popular animal fat shortening available to the consumer, are superglycerinated to improve their cake-making properties and particularly to permit them to be used in cakes made by the "quick mix" method.

Salad dressings. As you recall, when one liquid is dispersed in a second liquid with which it is immiscible the product is called an emulsion.

Mayonnaise is the semisolid emulsion of an edible vegetable oil, egg yolk or whole egg, an acid (vinegar or lemon juice), and seasonings. Mayonnaise has a pale, creamy yellow color derived from the egg yolks. Physically, mayonnaise consists of an internal or discontinuous phase of oil droplets dispersed in an external or continuous aqueous phase of vinegar and other ingredients. Egg yolk, the emulsifying agent, is concentrated at the surface of the oil droplets. Mayonnaise gradually becomes thinner with age, due to gradual coalescence of oil particles. If kept for a sufficient length of time, it will eventually separate into its two separate phases. Salad dressing, without qualifications, refers to a product which is a modification of mayonnaise with a cooked starch-paste base. The essential ingredients of salad dressing are eggs, vinegar, oil, spices, starch, and water. French dressing is prepared from vegetable oils, vinegar, salt, and spices. The emulsion is developed by beating or shaking to break up the oil into small particles. This kind of emulsion is temporary and the mixture tends to separate immediately upon standing.

Fried foods. Large quantities of oils and fats are used commercially as well as domestically for frying. The food may be sautéed (browned in a small amount of fat) or deep-fat fried. In sautéing, fats prevent the food from sticking to the pan, transfer heat, and produce a characteristic flavor and color. In deep-fat frying, the food is immersed in a large amount of fat. Frying large quantities of food in a frying kettle usually requires a thermostatic control which maintains the fat at a constant temperature. Temperatures of 350° to 385° F are recommended for frying most foods and 385° to 395° F for French fried potatoes. Temperatures above the

VINEGAR

OIL

latter will cause most fats to smoke. However, the tendency of the fat to smoke is in direct proportion to its content of free fatty acids and other factors, as was pointed out earlier.

Fat-flavored foods. Fats are also used extensively in the United States to flavor foods. Often the kind of fat chosen depends on the flavor desired. Some people put butter on vegetables while others prefer bacon fat or olive oil for flavor. The preference for particular fats is largely influenced by cultural backgrounds, established customs, and geographical locations of people.

MAJOR IDEAS

The following statements give the main ideas within the chapter you have just studied. Be sure you know the words underscored in these statements and in the questions to follow.

1. The use of fats in edible products depends upon their physical and chemical properties of oiliness, melting point, smoke point, and solubility.
2. The melting point of a fat or oil is an indication of its degree of saturation. Those fats with a high percentage of unsaturated fatty acids usually have low melting points and are liquid at room temperature; those with a high percentage of saturated fatty acids usually have high melting points.
3. The greater the plasticity of a fat, the greater its spreadability and ability to incorporate air.
4. The shortening power of fat depends on the fat's insolubility in other ingredients, spreading ability, ability to incorporate air, and tendency to soften or melt on heating.
5. The tendency of a fat to smoke during frying is related to its content of free fatty acids.

QUESTIONS TO ANSWER

COMPOSITION AND PROPERTIES

1. In what respects are fats like carbohydrates?
2. Explain the difference between saturated and unsaturated fats.
3. How does the degree of saturation of a fat affect its use in cooking?
4. Why are antioxidants added to some fats?
5. Explain the relationship between the melting point of a fat and its degree of saturation.
6. What characteristics distinguish a solid fat from an oil?

TYPES

1. Explain why cooking oils are usually derived from vegetable sources.
2. Why aren't fish oils considered edible in their natural form?
3. Explain the meaning of the term plastic shortening.
4. Discuss the importance of hydrogenation in the manufacture of fats to be used in cooking and baking.
5. Compare margarine and butter. Consider composition, consistency, food value, melting point, and smoke point.
6. In what way can fats and oils be treated to eliminate unpleasant odors and flavors?

USES IN COOKERY

1. Explain why fat is one of the most important ingredients used in the making of baked products such as pastries and cakes.
2. Explain what is meant by the shortening quality of a fat or an oil.
3. What is the creaming quality of a fat?
4. Give an example of an emulsion in cooking. In what ways can emulsions be stabilized?
5. Compare a salad dressing and a mayonnaise. Consider the methods of preparation, the basic ingredients, and the stability of each.
6. What factors increase the tendency of fats and oils to smoke? What is the advantage of a high smoke point?

BIBLIOGRAPHY

BAILEY, ALTON, *Industrial Oil and Fat Products.* New York, Interscience Publishers, Inc., 1951.

BOEKENOOGEN, H. A., *Oils, Fats and Fat Products.* New York, Interscience Publishers, Inc., 1964.

ECKEY, E. S., *Vegetable Fats and Oils.* New York, Reinhold Publishing Corporation, 1954.

GRISWOLD, RUTH M., *The Experimental Study of Foods.* Boston, Houghton Mifflin Company, 1962.

LOWE, BELLE, *Experimental Cookery*, 4th ed. New York, John Wiley & Sons, Inc., 1955.

MOCK, JOHN P., "Shortenings, Their Processing for Specialized Use." *Baker's Digest*, Vol. 38, 1964, pp. 53–57.

20 PRESERVING FOOD

Man has tried to guard against famine by preserving food during the seasons of abundance. In order to feed himself he has had to use the processes of natural forces to the best advantage. Decomposition is a natural phenomenon in our foods. Plant and animal tissues that are dead are consumed one way or another by biological organisms. There is a contest between man, the lower animals, bacteria, yeasts, and molds as to which one consumes the nutrients first.

In attempting to prevent the deterioration of plant and animal tissue, man has a difficult task in that he must not only preserve the food for his own use but must also exclude the other forces of nature. Although food preservation has been practiced throughout man's history, it was not until the discoveries of Louis Pasteur that man gained insight as to the reasons why foods spoil.

Food Spoilage

The principal causes of food spoilage are the growth of microorganisms—yeasts, molds, and bacteria, the action of naturally-occurring enzymes in food, and physical degradation.

Microorganisms. Putrefaction or decay, fermentation, and molding of food are all caused by the growth of yeasts, bacteria, and molds. These micro-

Yeasts, bacteria, and molds—the principal causes of food spoilage.

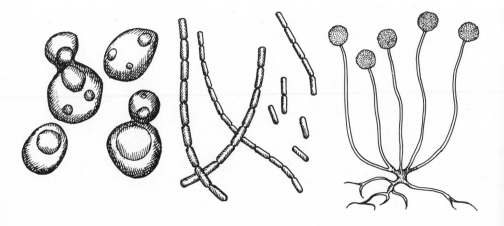

organisms are found on the surfaces of food and in the inner tissues when the outer protective skin, or covering, has been broken.

Enzyme action. Food may spoil through decomposition due to the action of enzymes. Enzymes are found in fresh food, and in plant foods are necessary for the ripening process to take place. However, when enzymatic action continues past the peak of maturity of the food, food decomposition and spoilage result.

Physical degradation. This term simply means damage of food by bruising, cutting, and blighting. The careful handling of plant foods from time of harvest to consumption will do much to prevent physical degradation. Bruises, cuts, insect damage, and disease blight on any food serve to make pathways by which microorganisms can reach the inner tissues and cause further deterioration.

Methods of Preservation

The main objective in the preservation of food is to slow down or prevent the reactions that cause spoilage. The methods that have been found most effective in preserving foods are freezing, drying, canning, fermenting, and pickling. High sugar concentrations, irradiation, and certain chemical additives may be used to insure that the quality of the food is kept at the highest point possible.

Controlled environment. *Most plant foods should be cooled immediately after they are harvested.* Then they should be held under refrigeration until prepared for eating. If the cooked foods are not eaten immediately after cooking, they should be refrigerated as soon as possible. The length of time these foods can be kept edible is increased by storing them at temperatures below 40° F. Some fruits, such as melons, bananas, and pineapples, are usually harvested before they are fully ripened and are allowed to ripen in the home at temperatures above 40° F. If these fruits are stored at temperatures below 40° F after ripening, deterioration is slowed.

Meat must be refrigerated at all stages from butchering to eating. If meat is to be held for a week, it must be rapidly cooled to below 40° F. Otherwise, the meat will begin to spoil. In commercial storage houses, mold and slime formation on chilled animal carcasses is retarded by using ultra-violet light. Fresh fish is extremely perishable. Storage in ice slows the process of spoilage, but with prolonged storage the fish flesh will become soft and flabby.

The *application of wax preparations* to certain foods is also practiced. In addition to preventing or at least reducing moisture losses, products so treated will have a bright appearance. Fruits and vegetables such as citrus fruits, cucumbers, rutabagas, and parsnips have been successfully handled in this way.

Oranges, lemons, limes, cucumbers, and peppers are some fruits and vegetables which are waxed. Such wax preparations reduce or entirely eliminate moisture losses and give the fruit or vegetable a bright appearance.

Prepacking perishable food is another application of controlled environment. The package protects the food and makes it convenient for the consumer to handle. For example, prepackaging fruit cuts down the loss of moisture and damage to fruit from consumer handling and contamination by dirt and insects. Prepackaging of vegetables may prevent excessive trimming waste. Recently a new method has been introduced in connection with the transportation of fresh vegetables. This method is based on the principle that the presence of oxygen causes fruits and vegetables to ripen, rot, and decay. Therefore, refrigerated trailer trucks or railway cars, when loaded with produce, are subjected to the removal of all but 1 percent of the oxygen; this loss is replaced by a carefully controlled atmosphere of inert nitrogen. In nitrogen, produce can endure a five-day cross country trip or even a three-week ocean voyage with virtually no deterioration of quality. This process also does an excellent job in preserving fresh flavor. Tomatoes and melons, for example, previously often picked before they were fully ripened, can be permitted to ripen right on the vine so that peak flavor is developed before and then preserved during shipment.

E. I. duPont de Nemours & Company

Above: Today many fruits and vegetables are prepacked in units by weight. Below: These three heads of lettuce show the effect of a low oxygen atmosphere. Each lettuce was held for 30 days at 2% oxygen, 5% oxygen, or 21% oxygen (normal air). Each was then allowed to stand in normal air for 3 days. The results indicate that low oxygen levels produce less spoilage and longer shelf life.

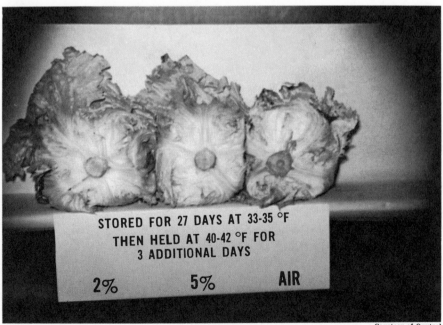

STORED FOR 27 DAYS AT 33-35 °F
THEN HELD AT 40-42 °F FOR
3 ADDITIONAL DAYS

2%   5%   AIR

Courtesy of Oxytrol

Seabrook Farms, one of the largest in the farming-freezing industry, is made up of thousands of acres of fields and plants.

Freezing. This is not a new method of preserving food. Outdoor freezing was formerly used extensively in areas where the temperatures were low enough to slow down the processes that cause food spoilage. Freezing retards bacterial growth and to some extent enzymatic action in foods. This state is maintained as long as the food is stored at a constant low temperature. The growth of microorganisms is usually stopped at 16° F. Freezing kills some yeast cells but bacteria and molds are fairly resistant to freezing. There is general agreement that foods, once frozen, should be stored at 0° F or lower to maintain high quality. The actual length of time a food can be held in frozen storage and still retain its quality depends in part on the prefreezing treatment and packaging.

Prefreezing treatments include blanching vegetables and sugar or sirup packing of many fruits. Blanching of vegetables before freezing is necessary to inactivate enzymes. This means that the vegetables must be plunged into boiling water for a specified time and then cooled rapidly in cold water. The inactivation of the enzymes, you will recall from Chapter 13, prevents discoloration, changes in texture, and the development of off flavors. The time required to inactivate the enzymes varies with each vegetable.

In this pea processing operation, people on assembly lines help rush the peas into freezers to preserve their field-fresh flavor.

Warehouse facilities at this operation in New Jersey can accommodate 40 million pounds of a product at one time.

Tests are made in this quality-control laboratory to check quality from the time the raw produce enters the plant through each processing and freezing step.

Seabrook Farms Company, Inc.

Wrapping meat to be frozen.

Sugar is added to fruits to increase their firmness and to protect them from oxidation which may cause a color change. Dry sugar is used with fruits that readily produce juice, while sugar sirups are used to pack the slow juice-forming fruits. Cyclamates may also be used to sweeten fruits if sugar cannot be used. However, they will not increase firmness or protect the fruit from oxidation. A 40 percent sugar sirup is usually used for most fruits. From Chapter 13 you recall that light-colored fruits such as apples, peaches, apricots, and figs darken when they are exposed to oxygen. Antioxidants such as ascorbic acid are used in pretreating these fruits to prevent the browning action.

It is probable that you have noticed that during freezing, moisture accumulates on the plates or coils of the freezer. This moisture is condensed water vapor lost by food. If food is not carefully wrapped in suitable packaging material, the moisture of the food will vaporize and the food will develop a con-

Proper storage of foods in the refrigerator and freezer is essential to prevent or at least delay food deterioration. In most refrigerators food should always be covered carefully before storage.

dition called "freezerburn." This is characterized by a dry appearance and possible off odor. Furthermore, the food may be subjected to oxidation and contamination. Sturdy, moisture-proof and vapor-proof containers or wrapping materials are recommended to ensure prolonged good quality in frozen foods. Tin, plastic, glass, aluminum foil, or laminated and waxed cardboard cartons may be used successfully in freezer packaging if they are designed to withstand low temperatures. Packaging for meat, poultry, fish, and many cooked foods should not only be moistureproof and vaporproof, but it must also be grease-proof. All packaging materials should be odorless, tasteless, noncorrosive, and flexible enough to avoid cracking. Heavy-duty aluminum foil is one excellent means for packaging irregularly-shaped foods. Glass jars especially designed for freezing may be used to package frozen foods.

There are two general methods for freezing foods: slow-freezing and quick-freezing. Quick-freezing is the preferable method, however, because it promotes the formation of small ice crystals that will not puncture the cell walls of the food and cause the leaking of juices. In slow-freezing, large crystals form which in some foods cause a loss of juices, and this results in a less desirable product.

Freeze-drying and dehydro-freezing are two new methods of food preservation used commercially.

Freeze-drying. Freeze-drying is a two-step process. First, much of the moisture in the fresh food is changed to ice by freezing. The ice is then sublimed (changed from solid directly to gas without liquefaction) under vacuum. Early research in freeze-drying was conducted in Denmark in the 1940's. Basic work was continued in the 1950's in Aberdeen, Scotland. The US Army Quartermaster Food and Container Institute has conducted extensive research in freeze-drying. During World War II freeze-dried foods were used by the Armed Forces. Today, astronauts eat these foods. In tropical regions, where food spoilage is great, and in Arctic regions, where food supplies are limited, servicemen eat freeze-dried foods. Limited amounts of these foods are available on the retail market as well.

Dehydro-freezing. In dehydro-freezing, the food is first partially dehydrated (water is removed) and then frozen. In this process about one-third of the water is removed. Potatoes to be preserved in this manner are first peeled, then cooked and mashed. The moisture in the mash is then reduced from 75–80 percent to 45 percent. This concentrated mash is frozen and kept frozen until it is reconstituted and served. Dehydro-frozen potatoes have excellent quality when reconstituted. They also have good storage quality and offer weight-saving and reduced-shipping costs. At present, there is no indication that there is unusual loss of essential nutrients when either the freeze-drying or the dehydro-freezing technique is used.

Freeze-drying is one of the most accepted methods of preservation for many foods being produced commercially today. Besides being light in weight, freeze-dried products are extremely stable once on the shelf and do not need refrigeration once they have been correctly processed and packaged.

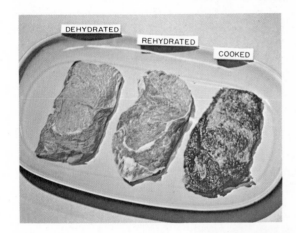

By being freeze-dried, food can be shipped to any place in the world with a minimum of cost and without regard to the growing season. These products can be available at any time and do not require any cold storage. They could be especially useful in underdeveloped countries which do not yet have electrical facilities.

Meats, eggs, and vegetables are only a few of the many foods that can undergo the process of freeze-drying. Strawberries in cereal, fruit bits in desserts, meat cubes in sauce mixes, and sea food dishes are other products which are offered to the consumer as freeze-dried foods.

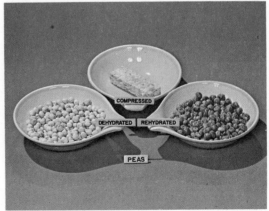

U. S. Army Natick Laboratories

FIGS

DATES

MILK

PEAS

HERBS

Dehydration. The drying of foods to preserve them during seasons when foods are plentiful so that they will be available at times of shortage is an old practice. Production of dehydrated foods in the United States has become a growing part of the food processing industry. In dehydration nearly all the water normally present is evaporated so that the food product is converted to a dry solid. Dehydration offers a method of food preservation which does not require refrigeration for storage. It also reduces the weight of the food by 50 to 80 percent. This makes possible a greater variety of foods in places where refrigeration and transportation facilities are limited. Dried food products available to the consumer are dry fruits, citrus juices, tomato juice, eggs, milk solids, sauces, and soups. Some dried milk powders are now instantized to make them more readily dispersible in cold water.

Food-drying in the home is not done as extensively now as it was a number of years ago. However, in some areas of the United States food is still dried. Fish, for example, is dried by salting it heavily, since the salt draws the moisture from the tissues of the fish. Handling and pretreatment of food for drying should be carefully done to prevent contamination. Sulfuring is used in drying certain fruits, particularly to destroy microorganisms, and to preserve color.

Canning. Canning is the process in which food is heated to inactivate enzymes and destroy microorganisms, and hermetically (made airtight) sealed and stored. This process was invented by a Frenchman, Nicholas Appert, in 1795. Lobsters and salmon were the first foods to be preserved in this manner. In 1819 Ezra Daggett and Thomas Kensett invented the tin can for packing many kinds of food, including meat, poultry, fish, vegetables, and fruits. Acid foods may be successfully canned at boiling temperature (212° F), while nonacid foods require higher temperatures obtained by heating under pressure.

Fermentation. While food preservation systems in general inhibit the growth of microorganisms,

Wes Kemp

Today foods are packaged in multi-shaped glasses, bottles, and cans.

all such organisms are not detrimental. In fact, some are commonly utilized in food preservation. To review terms for a moment, respiration is that process whereby carbohydrates are converted in the presence of oxygen into carbon dioxide and water with the release of large amounts of energy. In fermentation the decomposition of carbohydrates is usually involved. Putrefaction is the degradation of protein material. Each group of microorganisms has an optimum temperature for growth; the temperature of the material upon which they live exerts a positive control on their development. To obtain the maximum performance during fermentation, the optimum temperature for the desired organism must be created. For example, milk held at 32° F is subject to little microbial activity. At 40° F there is a slight growth of organisms and more rapid development of off flavors. At 80° F microbial growth is quite rapid. The temperature at which a food is held will determine, within certain limits, the nature of the organisms capable of growth, either yielding the desired fermentation, or spoilage, whichever the case may be.

Salt is one of the most important substances used in food preservation. In fermentation, salt can exert a role in regulating the growth of organisms. The amount of salt added determines whether or not any organism can grow and what types will develop.

Tarragon, white, garlic, and cider vinegar are some of the vinegars which can be used to season foods, especially salads.

Some fresh fruits and vegetables placed in a dilute salt solution at 86° F or 30° C will soften in 24 hours and begin a slow, mixed fermentation-putrefaction. It is necessary to suppress undesirable microbial activity and create a favorable environment for the desired fermentation. The addition of sufficient salt permits the naturally present lactic acid bacteria to grow, thereby rapidly producing sufficient acid to supplement the action of the salt in suppressing undesirable bacterial growth. For example, in cucumbers the fermentable carbohydrate reserve is changed to acid.

Pickles are sold as sour, sweet, or dill. Sour pickles are prepared by adding vinegar to the salted, fermented cucumber. Sweet pickles are produced by adding a sweet, spiced vinegar solution to freshly salted, fermented cucumbers. Processed dill pickles are prepared much as sour pickles, but dill herbs and spices are added.

Cabbage also may be preserved by subjecting it to bacterial fermentation controlled by salt. During the fermentation, acid is developed and acts as a preservative in addition to producing a desired flavor. Sauerkraut is the German word describing this fermented, salted shredded cabbage.

Another product which is formed by fermentation is vinegar. Vinegar is a condiment (seasoning) prepared from various sugary or starchy materials by means of alcoholic, and subsequent acetic acid, fermentation. Vinegar may be produced from the juices of apples, grapes, cherries, and pears. Cider vinegar has always been popular in American homes.

The use of concentrated sugar solutions as a food preservative has been discussed in Chapter 15.

Irradiation. To understand irradiation, we must know something about radiant energy. Radiant energy may come from the sun, a fluorescent lamp, an X-ray tube, or a radioactive material such as uranium which you may know in

The world's largest cobalt-60 radiation source concentration used in experimental processing of meats, fish, vegetables, fruits, and other foods is located in Natick, Massachusetts. It is resting on the bottom of a 25-foot-deep water-filled storage pool.

U.S. Army Natick Laboratories

Fruit in its raw state is more widely enjoyed than any other food, yet one-fifth of the fruits and vegetables grown in the U.S. are never consumed because of post-harvest deterioration caused by disease organisms, overripeness, chilling injury, sprouting, and dehydration. Radiation pasteurization promises to keep foods edible and acceptable longer. Below are strawberries which were held for eight days. The ones on the right, however, were given a dose of radiation.

U.S. Atomic Energy Commission

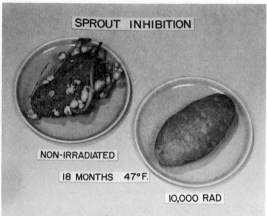

SPROUT INHIBITION

NON-IRRADIATED

18 MONTHS   47°F.

10,000 RAD

U.S. Army Natick Laboratories

Interest in radiation processing of food is worldwide. Potatoes exposed to low-level radiation to inhibit the growth of sprouts were ruled safe for use as food as far back as 1960. Throughout Europe, Russia, and the Far East, radiation research programs are being conducted to lengthen food life, minimize storage requirements, and combat insect pests.

relation to atomic fission. Radioactive materials give off very intense energy which is emitted spontaneously without heat. The energy given off from radioactive material is in three different forms called alpha, beta, and gamma rays. Alpha and beta rays penetrate material to a limited depth with the beta rays penetrating to a considerably greater depth than the alpha rays. Gamma rays, like X-rays and light rays, have a much greater penetrating power. Beta and gamma rays are being used experimentally to kill microorganisms and insects. Limited dosages of radiation (pasteurization) have been used successfully to prevent sprouting of potatoes, destroy insects in flour and spices, and delay the ripening of fruits. Larger dosages of radiation, which are necessary for the sterilization of food, often produce undesirable changes in odor, taste, and texture. These larger dosages cause degradation of carbohydrates, softening of cellulose and pectins, partial denaturation of protein, change in the pigment of meat (myoglobin to metmyoglobin), and the development of off flavors.

Chemical additives. Though chemicals, including salt and sugar, have been used for many years in preservation of foods, it is only in recent years that real progress has been made in this field. Additives can contribute substantially to the preservation of food. They can, therefore, help to prevent the loss of seasonal surpluses. Many are added for purposes other than preservation.

A food additive is usually defined as a substance or mixture of substances—other than the basic foodstuff—which is present in a food as the result of any aspect of production, processing, storage, or packaging. Food additives are usually used in small amounts. Their nature and the extent to which they are likely to be needed vary considerably. Chemical additives in foodstuffs have various functions. They are as follows: (1) preservatives, (2) nutritional supplements, (3) color modifiers, (4) flavoring agents, and (5) chemicals which affect functional properties of food.

Preservatives. The color, texture, and flavor qualities of plant foods are usually at their peak at harvest time. To prevent food from losing its desirable qualities during processing, additives are often used. Among the most undesirable changes in color and flavor are ones caused by the oxygen in the air. To delay or prevent these oxidative changes, antioxidants are added (page 148). Some are used in fats, in the salt used for nuts and potato chips, in dehydrated potato flakes, and in prepared cereals.

Molds, bacteria, and yeasts cause another kind of food spoilage with which most homemakers are familiar. For many years vinegar, salt, and sugar have been used to control the growth of microorganisms in such foods as pickles, sauerkraut, jams, and jellies, as was pointed out earlier in the chapter. Propionates are added to bread to prevent mold growth. Antibiotics are among the newer mold and bacterial inhibitors, but their use in foods is rare. They are especially effective when foods must be held under refrigeration for long periods of time. Some have been approved for use in retarding spoilage in poultry and some fish products.

Nutritive value. At about the beginning of the twentieth century the study of nutrition emerged as an important science. It was learned that certain diseases were caused by a lack of nutrients in one's diet. One of the first studies demonstrated that by adding iodine to the diet, goiter could be prevented. Iodine in salt was the first additive used to improve the nutritive value of a food. Other nutrients added to a limited number of foods are certain B vitamins and iron in the enrichment of white flour and bread to replace nutrients lost in milling, vitamins A and D to margarine, and vitamin D to milk.

Nutritional supplements are often added to foods which have lost vitamins or minerals in processing, such as skim milk, flour, and white bread. Additional nutrients are also added to foods to improve the nutritional value already present, such as vitamin D in milk.

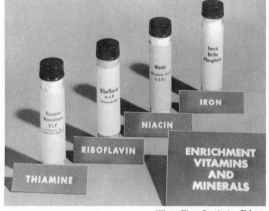

Wheat Flour Institute, Chicago

Skinless

WEINERS

NONFAT DRY MILK ADDED
Ingredients: Beef & Pork, Water, Nonfat Dry Milk, Salt, Corn Syrup, Flavoring, Sugar, Spices, Sodium Erythorbate, Sodium Nitrite, Sodium Nitrate.

NET WT. 8 OZ.

Finest

STEWED TOMATOES

CUT TOMATOES, TOMATO JUICE, SUGAR, DEXTROSE, SALT, DRIED ONIONS, DRIED CELERY, DRIED GREEN PEPPERS, SPICE, TRACE OF CALCIUM, SALT.

PRODUCT OF SCANDINAVIA

Ingredients: Pork, Beef, Veal, Dry Skim Milk, Water, Onions, Salt, Spices, Sugar, Monosodium Glutamate, Sodium Nitrite, Sodium Nitrate.

NET WT. 6 OZ. INCLUDING JUICES

Maraschino Cherries

CONTENTS:
CHERRIES, WATER, SUGAR, CORN SYRUP, CITRIC ACID, ARTIFICIAL COLOR & FLAVOR, SULPHUR DIOXIDE.
1/10 OF 1% BENZOATE OF SODA

NET WT. 12 OZ.

Color additives. As has been said before, we expect foods to have characteristic colors. Effort is made to produce the color that the consumer associates with the particular food. Carotene used in margarine is a good example of a color additive. The food industry uses synthetic colors extensively in maraschino cherries, many frozen desserts, cheeses, jams, and jellies.

Flavoring agents. The consumer and the food industry use flavoring agents to enhance the taste of food. Natural and synthetic (made in the laboratory) flavoring agents, for example, are used in candies, carbonated beverages, and many foods. Synthetic flavorings have some advantages for both the consumer and the food processor. Such flavorings are not seasonal and are easy to standardize, making uniformity possible. Many flavorings are well-known because the group includes naturally-occurring spices and essential oils, such as cloves, ginger, pepper, citrus oils, and vanilla. But equally important are the aromatic chemicals which may induce other flavors. Some additives are flavor enhancers. These agents do not contribute flavor, but instead bring out the natural flavor of a food. Two common examples are hydrolyzed plant protein and monosodium glutamate, known as MSG.

Emulsifiers, stabilizers, and thickeners. Additives which maintain desired textures and thickness in foods include emulsifiers, stabilizers, and thickeners. Emulsifiers permit the dispersion of tiny particles or globules of one liquid within another liquid. For example, they prevent the separation of many commercial French dressings. Added to shortenings, emulsifiers permit even distribution of fat in batters. Cake mixes owe much of their dependability to the presence of emulsifiers (pages 308–309).

Stabilizers thicken chocolate milk and prevent separation of the chocolate. Stabilizers are also used in commercial ice cream to increase the viscosity of the mixture and to prevent the formation of large, coarse ice crystals. Some stabilizers are used to prevent flavor evaporation by surrounding the particles of the flavoring oil. Pectin and gelatin are two thickeners used commercially as well as in the home.

Acids, buffers, alkalies, and neutralizing agents. The control of acidity and alkalinity is very important in determining the flavor, texture, and appearance of many foods. Of this group of additives, acids give the tart taste to soft drinks and compensate for the insufficient acid in certain fruits when making jellies and jams. Buffers stabilize the potassium iodine in iodized salt and permit effective heat processing of certain canned foods without discoloration. Many additives play an important role in leavening agents, many of which contain baking soda, an alkali. Without these agents we would not have such a variety of cakes, biscuits, and many other kinds of baked foods.

Table 14
Food Additives

Additive	Function
Sequestrants (separates or segregates)	Prevent minerals such as copper and iron from acting as catalysts to hasten rancidity in fats and oils.
	Stabilize protein in milk to be evaporated.
Humectants	Prevent drying out of food like coconut, candy, and marshmallows.
Anticaking agents	Keep salt and baking powder free flowing.
Firming agents	Improve texture of processed fruits and vegetables. Aid in the coagulation of milk protein in preparation of cheese.
Clarifying agents	Remove small particles of insoluble substances from liquids.
Curing agents	Produce the pink color associated with cured meat (sodium nitrate and sodium nitrite). Several phosphates are also used to increase the water-holding capacity of cured meat, thereby retaining the meat juice.
Foaming agents	Source of gas in pressurized whipped toppings.
Foam inhibitors	Prevent foaming during processing.
Non-nutritive sweeteners	Sweeten foods without adding any nutritive value. Used in "dietetic foods."

Maturing and bleaching agents. When flour is milled it is yellowish in color but upon aging for several months it becomes whiter and also matures, making it more satisfactory for baking. Because of the amount of time necessary for aging flour and the high cost of storage during this time, certain chemicals have been used to accelerate this process. This treatment neither affects the nutritive value of the flour nor leaves a significant residue. The treatment modifies the gluten characteristics to give improved baking quality and bleaches the yellow pigment. Bleaching agents are also used sometimes to remove the color present in natural fats and oils.

MAJOR IDEAS

The following statements give the main ideas within the chapter you have just studied. Be sure you know the words underscored in these statements and in the questions to follow.

1. Food spoilage is caused by the growth of microorganisms, enzymatic action, and damage due to cuts, bruises, insect infestation, and disease.
2. Food can be preserved by controlling the environment in which the food is stored. This means the elimination of those conditions which would encourage food spoilage.
3. To obtain high quality in preserved foods, care must be taken in selecting the foods to be preserved; food value, color, and flavor of the natural food must be retained.

QUESTIONS TO ANSWER

FOOD SPOILAGE

1. Explain the advantages of preserving foods.
2. Discuss the principal causes of food spoilage.
3. Explain why enzymatic action is an advantage in some instances and a disadvantage in others.
4. Describe the way in which rough handling of fruits and vegetables promotes spoilage.

METHODS OF PRESERVATION

1. What is the relationship of controlled environment to food preservation?
2. Describe the use of nitrogen in the storage of foods.
3. Why are cucumbers waxed?
4. What is the advantage of packaging fresh fruits and vegetables?

5. Explain why foods can be preserved by freezing.
6. What is the purpose of <u>blanching</u> vegetables before freezing them?
7. What causes <u>freezerburn</u>?
8. What qualities must freezer-packaging materials have?
9. Explain why foods must be <u>hermetically sealed</u> in the canning process.
10. Discuss the advantages of foods which are <u>freeze-dried</u> and <u>dehydro-frozen</u>.
11. Explain why fish can be dried by salting them heavily.
12. When freezing fruits what is the purpose of the dry sugar or sugar sirup used with the fruit?
13. Differentiate between <u>fermentation</u> and <u>putrefaction</u>.
14. Describe the process of <u>pickling</u>.
15. Discuss the statement, "Salt is one of the most important ingredients used in preserving foods."
16. What are the most common methods for preserving fruits? Vegetables? Meats?
17. Why is vinegar classified as a fermented product?
18. Discuss the advantages and disadvantages of the use of irradiation as a means of preserving foods.
19. What are <u>food additives</u>? What purposes or functions do they have in food processing and preservation?
20. Why have controls been established in the use of additives?

BIBLIOGRAPHY

LEONARD, SHERMAN, and others, "Aseptic Canning of Food." *Food Technology*, Vol. 18, January 1964, pp. 81–114.

MOTTERN, H. H., and JOHNSON, A. H., "Fifty Years of New Product Development, 1939–1964." *Food Technology*, Vol. 18, September 1964, pp. 87–90.

TRESSLER, DONALD K., and EVERS, CLIFFORD F., *The Freezing Preservation of Foods*, Vols. I and II. Connecticut, The AVI Publishing Company, Inc., 1957.

WELLS, CHRIS, "A New Shipping Process Puts Food to Sleep." *Life*, February 18, 1966, pp. 71–72.

Part III The Management
of Food Resources

21 MEAL PLANNING

The average American homemaker prepares 1,000 meals a year. The total time it takes her to prepare the three daily meals averages $1\frac{1}{2}$ hours; at one time it took $5\frac{1}{2}$ hours. Not only time but also energy and money are important to the person who has the responsibility for planning and preparing food.

Planning Nutritious Meals

In meal planning, first consideration is given to planning meals that are nutritious. One of the most helpful resources for this task is the "Daily Food Guide" (pages 336–337). This Guide recommends that you choose your foods for each day from the four food groups: from the milk group—3 or 4 glasses of milk for children, 4 or more for teen-agers, and 2 or more for adults; from the meat group—2 or more servings; from the vegetables and fruits group—4 or more servings; from the bread and cereals group—4 or more servings. If the homemaker provides at least the minimum number of servings suggested for each member of her family, she can be certain that a large share of the needed nutrients are being met (page 74).

Table 15

Minimum servings according to the Guide from	For an average adult man, the minimum amounts from the four food groups, together provide about.....
MILK GROUP	85% of the protein
	95% of the calcium
MEAT GROUP	90% of the iron
	85% of the thiamine
VEGETABLES & FRUITS	95% of the riboflavin
	100% of the vitamins A, C, and niacin
BREADS & CEREALS	and only around 1200 Calories, or energy value

NUTRITION HANDBOOK, National Dairy Council, 1965, p. 8.

Meal patterns. Meal patterns vary from country to country. For example, in some places the first meal of the day may consist of bread, cheese, jam, and coffee or tea. In other countries the first meal may be a thick soup, eggs (raw or cooked), pickles, rice, and perhaps raw fish. Sometimes the meal may consist of juice, eggs, meat, cereal, bread, and coffee, tea or milk.

In the United States, three meals a day are common. The midday meal is usually a light one because many people are in school or at work and cannot eat this meal with their families. The evening meal is the main one. In other countries, especially in Europe, the main meal may be eaten in the afternoon and is often followed by a nap. The evening meal may be light.

Although in some countries three meals a day are common, in many places only two meals a day are prepared. In Nigeria, for example, these meals may consist of a starch staple, such as yams, and a thick soup or stew. The contents of the latter vary according to the area, season, and income; food likes and dislikes are not often considered. The basic ingredients of water, hot peppers, oil, salt, and perhaps some wood ash are used to make the soup or stew. To this may be added any or all of the following: onions, green leaves, okra, tomatoes, melon seeds, beans, groundnuts, and fresh or dried meat of some sort.

A similar soup called "wat" is eaten in Ethiopia for the evening and noon meals. "Injera," a type of bread or pancake, accompanies the wat. For the first meal of the day Ethiopians may have black coffee, a small amount of injera or some roasted whole grain barley kernels.

Regardless of the number of meals eaten daily, the total food intake for the day should provide the necessary nutrients for the body to function at its best.

On the following two pages is the "Daily Food Guide." This Guide illustrates the four groups of food and suggests the number of servings of each that a person should have every day.

Supplementing the Guide is a series of graphs (pages 338–339) which illustrate (1) the daily nutrient requirements for adults and young children, (2) the additional requirements needed by growing teen-agers, and (3) the percentages of the daily requirements which are supplied by specific amounts of various foods. The colored blocks represent the amounts of calcium, protein, carbohydrates, iron, vitamin A, vitamin B_1, riboflavin, niacin, and vitamin C in relation to the dark line on each graph which represents the minimum daily requirement. Note that while some foods supply low percentages of the daily requirement, others supply more than the recommended amount. It is apparent, therefore, that a knowledge of the basic food groups and the nutritional value of foods can help people plan daily meals that are nutritionally adequate. The "Daily Food Guide" and the daily requirement graphs should be used in conjunction with "Recommended Daily Dietary Allowances" (page 74), "Nutritional Value of Foods" (pages 500–506), and "Food Buying Guides" (pages 508–525). Remember that daily requirements and recommended allowances differ in that the recommended allowances allow for a margin of safety.

Milk Group:
  Children—3 or more glasses
  Teen-agers—4 or more glasses
  Adults—2 or more glasses

Meat Group:
  All ages—2 or more servings

National Dairy Council

Breads and Cereals:
All ages—4 or more servings

Vegetables and Fruits:
All ages—4 or more servings

National Dairy Council

DAILY REQUIREMENTS

Average Adult and Young Children

DAILY REQUIREMENT

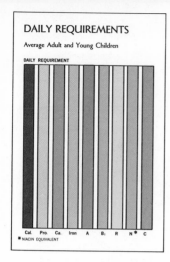

Cal. Pro. Ca. Iron A B₁ R N* C
* NIACIN EQUIVALENT

ADDITIONAL DAILY REQUIREMENTS
FOR BOYS 16-19

DAILY REQUIREMENT

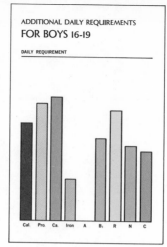

Cal. Pro. Ca. Iron A B₁ R N C

ADDITIONAL DAILY REQUIREMENTS
FOR GIRLS 16-19

DAILY REQUIREMENT

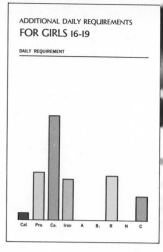

Cal. Pro. Ca. Iron A B₁ R N C

LEAN MEAT-BEEF cooked 3 oz.

DAILY REQUIREMENT

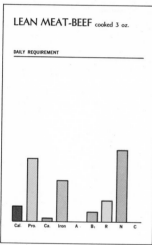

Cal. Pro. Ca. Iron A. B₁ R N C

LIVER-beef - cooked 2 oz.

DAILY REQUIREMENT

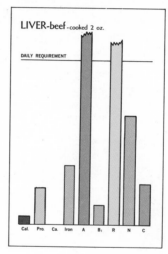

Cal. Pro. Ca. Iron A B₁ R N C

PORK - cooked, 3 oz.

DAILY REQUIREMENT

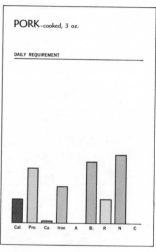

Cal. Pro. Ca. Iron A B₁ R N C

EGG - 1 medium cooked

DAILY REQUIREMENT

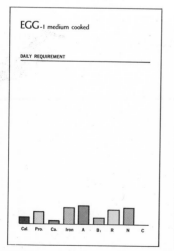

Cal. Pro. Ca. Iron A B₁ R N C

BEANS-dried - ¾ cup cooked

DAILY REQUIREMENT

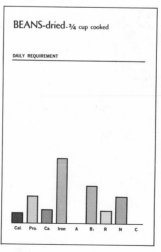

Cal. Pro. Ca. Iron A B₁ R N C

PEANUT BUTTER - 2 tablespoons

DAILY REQUIREMENT

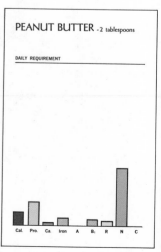

Cal. Pro. Ca. Iron A B₁ R N C

Michigan Department of Health

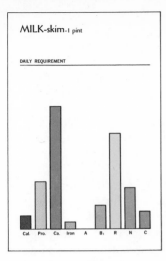

MILK-skim-1 pint

DAILY REQUIREMENT

Cal. Pro. Ca. Iron A B₁ R N C

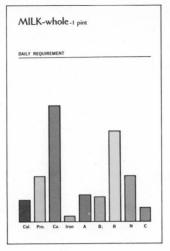

MILK-whole-1 pint

DAILY REQUIREMENT

Cal. Pro. Ca. Iron A B₁ R N C

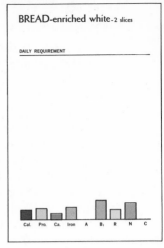

BREAD-enriched white-2 slices

DAILY REQUIREMENT

Cal. Pro. Ca. Iron A B₁ R N C

WHOLE GRAIN CEREAL-
⅔ cup cooked rolled oats

DAILY REQUIREMENT

Cal. Pro. Ca. Iron A B₁ R N C

BREAD-whole wheat-2 slices

DAILY REQUIREMENT

Cal. Pro. Ca. Iron A B₁ R N C

PREPARED CEREAL-
⅔ cup cornflakes

DAILY REQUIREMENT

Cal. Pro. Ca. Iron A B₁ R N C

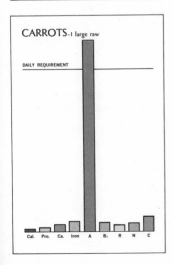

CARROTS-1 large raw

DAILY REQUIREMENT

Cal. Pro. Ca. Iron A B₁ R N C

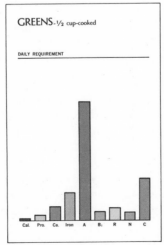

GREENS-½ cup-cooked

DAILY REQUIREMENT

Cal. Pro. Ca. Iron A B₁ R N C

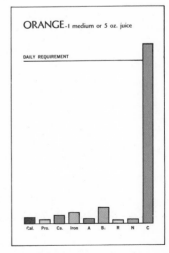

ORANGE-1 medium or 5 oz. juice

DAILY REQUIREMENT

Cal. Pro. Ca. Iron A B₁ R N C

Michigan Department of Health

Food needs of different family members. The whole family, except infants and those on a medically-prescribed diet, can usually eat the same basic meals. Children, teen-agers, adults (including pregnant or lactating mothers), and older adults need the same nutrients. The amount of the various foods which different family members eat should vary according to the size and build of the person, his activity, and his stage of development. The homemaker should take certain factors into account when considering food needs of individual family members.

Preschool children between the ages of one and three are in a period of rapid growth and development. Ample protein to support this rapid growth is important together with sufficient calcium and phosphorus which are necessary for bone tissue. Milk is a major food in the preschooler's daily food intake. As a rule, small children are not able to eat large quantities of food at one time. Their portions are small at regular mealtimes and between-meal snacks may be a part of their eating patterns. Any snack meals should help to complete a well-balanced intake of food for the day. Good eating habits should be encouraged when children are small. Here are some ways in which these habits can be formed more readily:

1. Serve small portions of food.
2. Serve food at medium temperatures.
3. Serve "finger foods" which are easy for a child to handle—wedges of egg, meat and cheese cubes, carrot strips.
4. Serve moderately seasoned food.
5. Do not be unduly concerned if a child eats the same food repeatedly for a period of time—usually he will turn again to a more varied diet if no issue is made.
6. Serve a disliked food in a new way or in a small amount with a favorite food.
7. When introducing a new food, serve a small portion of it together with other familiar foods.
8. Allow the child to eat his food at his own rate of speed. Do not rush him.
9. Establish a regular time for meals.
10. Set a good example.

Teen-agers are in an exciting, active stage of development. Growth is rapid accompanied by many complex physiological and emotional changes. You are probably already aware of these changes. Eating a balanced diet is especially important at this time. Special emphasis should be placed on foods that contain protein and calcium as well as calories. Snack foods add to the overall adequacy of the day's food intake. Healthy physical appearance, healthy hair, and clear skin depend upon having enough of the right things to eat. The teen-age girl needs to know why it is important that she have an adequate diet as preparation for her future role of wife and mother.

In the adult group, men generally tend to have better eating habits than women. Because of her concern for family's food necessities, a mother may neglect her own needs. Older adults' nutritional needs are not fundamentally different from those of younger people. However, lessened physical activity, changes in general health, and changes in the ability to chew, digest, and absorb food do influence the general dietary requirements of the older person. As the aging process advances, there is usually a progressive decrease in physical activity and consequently a decreased need for calories.

Expectant mothers are usually under a physician's care and are given instruction concerning the need for an adequate diet during pregnancy. Having the mother in good physical condition during her pregnancy and delivery is very important both to the mother and to her child. The mother's diet is usually high in protein in order to provide sufficient protein for her body and for the developing baby. Expectant mothers are also instructed to watch their weight because excessive weight places undue strain on the mother and may cause problems at the time of delivery.

Modified diets. Some members of a family may require modified or special kinds of diets for reasons of health. Persons on these diets will be under a doctor's care. His instructions must be followed carefully so that nutritionally adequate diets will be supplied.

Attractive and Varied Meals

Menu planning. Meal plans made with consideration for the season of the year—light, refreshing meals for warm weather inspired by fresh fruits and vegetables in season, cold or quick-cooking meats and main dishes that won't heat up the kitchen, delicate desserts and cold beverages, and for the winter months hearty meals, substantial meats and filling soups, well-seasoned salads and vegetables, hot bread and richer desserts—make meals more interesting and more enjoyable.

Preparing an old favorite in a new way adds variety to a meal. Basic standbys can come to the table in fancy dress by converting a sandwich into a casserole or transforming an ordinary vegetable into a tempting salad. Add some special seasoning and a new taste enhances a familiar favorite. Biscuits become something special with the addition of the right cheese, herb, or sweet filling. Experiment with new flavor combinations. Substitute tomatoes for mushrooms in a favorite meat dish, or mushrooms for tomatoes. Try a sharp cheese sauce instead of a mild white sauce in a creamed dish.

Color, texture, and flavor are important in planning menus that are interesting and appetizing. When you first see food you are usually conscious of its color. For many persons the sight of food stimulates their appetites. Look at the two pictures below. Which one appeals more to you? Why? How might you change any part of the meal?

In planning meals, putting together combinations that are interesting to the taste as well as ones that are colorful to the eye makes people want to eat the food when it is prepared. Some food combinations seem to belong together —like pork and applesauce, lamb and mint jelly, cranberry sauce and turkey, and hot dogs and mustard. The flavors in each of these combinations seem to complement each other. Differences in food textures also encourage hearty eating. Meals should include a variety of textures, since contrasts in crispness,

Green Giant Company

Green Giant Company

chewiness, smoothness, and crunchiness add interest to the food. Variety in food shapes in a meal are also important. Look at the pictures above and try to decide how the various shapes and textures have affected the appearance of each of the meals shown. Which one do you like better?

At the beginning of this chapter it was stated that the management of resources—money, time, and energy—is important in planning and preparing meals. The next four chapters will be concerned with food marketing, marketing decisions, and managing time and energy in selecting food and preparing meals.

MAJOR IDEAS

The following statements give the main ideas within the chapter you have just studied. Be sure you know the words underscored in these statements and in the questions to follow.

1. Having nutritious meals is essential to good health and well-being.
2. The daily total intake of food for a person is more important than whether this food is divided into 2, 3, 4, or 5 meals.
3. All members of a family need the same nutrients, but the amounts needed vary with the sex, age, and activity of each person.
4. Good eating habits should be established early in the lives of children.
5. Special diets require a doctor's guidance.
6. The imaginative use of color, texture, and flavor in meals can stimulate appetite.

QUESTIONS TO STUDY

PLANNING NUTRITIOUS MEALS

1. Explain the advantages of planning meals carefully.
2. What is meant by a nutritious meal?
3. In what ways can between-meal snacks contribute to nutritious food intake for the day?
4. In general, describe ways in which food requirements for the small child, the fifteen-year-old girl, and a grandfather might differ.
5. Why are protective foods considered necessary in the diet of an older person?

ATTRACTIVE AND VARIED MEALS

1. List ways in which meals can be improved through the use of a variety of textures.
2. Describe some ways in which people can be encouraged to eat a greater variety of foods.
3. Plan three menus for summer eating for your family. Check them for variety in color, texture, and flavor. Have you used foods that are quite commonly used in your household?

BIBLIOGRAPHY

DUDGEON, LOLA T., *Meal Planning the Easy Way*. Bulletin 921, New York State College of Home Economics, New York, Cornell University, November 1960 (out of print).

ERICSON, MYRTLE and DUNN, MILDRED, *Family Meal Service*. Cornell Extension Bulletin 774, New York, State College of Home Economics, Cornell University, 1961 (out of print).

Food For You and Your Family. General Foods Kitchens, General Foods Corp., White Plains, New York, 1964.

Majestic Meals with Frozen Prepared Foods. Home Economics Department, Campbell Soup Co., Camden, New Jersey.

Nutrition Handbook. National Dairy Council, 1965, p. 8.

22 THE CHANGING FOOD MARKET

The food industry is certainly big business. It has been estimated by the Agricultural Marketing Service that nearly one-fifth of all the people in the United States are engaged in a facet of the marketing system. Although less than 8 percent of our working population is involved in farming directly, four out of ten jobs in employment are related to agriculture.

Marketing provides many services which are performed by the 6 segments of the industry. These are (1) assembly—gathering raw material and products to one point, (2) processing—making the raw products more marketable by various kinds of treatments or manufacture, (3) wholesaling—transporting products from assembler or processor to the retailer, restaurants, and institutions in large quantities, (4) retailing—selling the product to the consumer, (5) eating places—selling or providing ready-to-eat food to the consumer, and (6) transportation—moving the product from place to place throughout the marketing process.

The six segments of the food industry provide many services to the consumer.

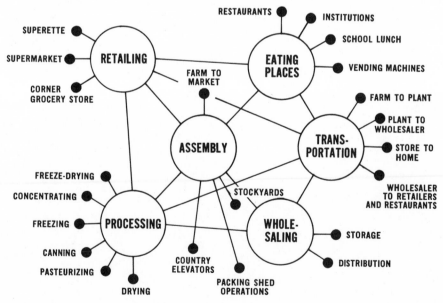

Market Bulletin No. 36, USDA

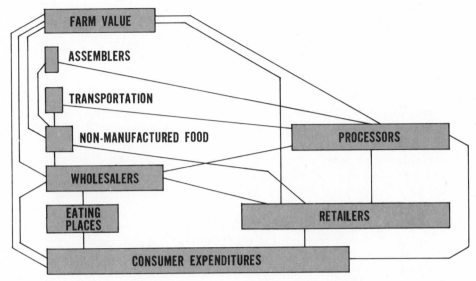

Market Bulletin No. 36, USDA

Farm products usually travel through numerous channels before reaching the consumer.

Most of these marketing services are provided by various private firms, including cooperatives. To improve marketing services, Federal, state, and local governments assist with supplementary services.

The Changing Industry

Agricultural marketing. Agricultural marketing has changed constantly over the years. One significant change is that marketing has increased the value of farm products. In addition, today's market system employs more people, handles a greater variety and volume of products, and serves a larger number of consumers. In general, the areas of processing, food service, retailing, and transportation have become more active, while separate assemblers and wholesalers have lessened in importance. As indicated by the illustration above, nearly one-half of processed foods bypass the wholesaler and go directly to retailers or consumers.

Changes in assembly. Today, assemblers are involved in the handling of only a few products. These agencies include egg-sorting plants, milk and cream receiving stations, fruit and vegetable packing and sorting plants, and livestock terminals. The reduction in assembling practices means that raw products come directly from the farm to the processor.

Other changes in assembly include the increasing number of cooperative grain elevators and the expanding number of country livestock assembly points (separate farms where cattle may be bought) as opposed to the lessening number of terminal stockyards (large areas where great numbers of cattle from many farms are sent to be sold).

Changes in processing. There are many changes which have taken place in this area. The U. S. Bureau of the Census (1958) indicated that the value added by manufacturers to farm products increased from $3\frac{1}{2}$ billion dollars in 1939 to 17 billion dollars in 1958 for food and products associated with food. This increase, translated into consumer terms, means that in 1958 about $100 was spent for the same amount of food a person could buy for about $63.00 in 1939. This accounts for some of the cost of food handling from farm to factory to the home.

Many small processing plants have been incorporated into large processing factories which operate with a lower cost per unit. Another change is the relocation of plants closer to the sources of raw products. Although food processors sell a large part of their products to wholesalers, retailers have been buying an increased proportion of these goods directly.

The primary factor influencing processing changes is the increasing number of innovations. The processor has combined new techniques with efficient older ones and has been able to cut costs and produce goods more attractive to the consumer. Some innovations are machine chicken-pluckers and eviscerators (devices which take out the entrails of animals), and new kinds of packaging.

Rise of the supermarket. In 1938, stores were specialized, and instead of buying food at one establishment, as people tend to do today, people had to go to the meat market, fish market, and bakery to get the necessary items. The self-service idea of the supermarket was unheard of three decades ago. Today, a modern supermarket carries as many as 8,000 articles, whereas the store of the 1920's handled about 1,000 products, and a shop in the 1860's sold only about 100 items. Many of today's goods are the same basic products sold years ago, but they are in new eye-catching packages of different size, shape, and color. Many new brand names competing for the sale of products have increased the amount of merchandise in a supermarket. A tour through today's supermarket will give you some idea of the innovations which processing has introduced in the goods available to the consumer. To quote a recent article:

"In our hypothetical food super-market of today we are faced with a selection of 7,000 to 8,000 items. First, we find that lard, used widely in 1938, is hard to find today. It has been replaced by liquid and solid vegetable shortenings hydrogenated and protected by antioxidants.

"Next, the bread counter has changed. The selection has broadened, unsliced bread is difficult to find, and unpackaged bread is almost impossible to locate.

The bread is packed more and more in plastic instead of paper. Examination of the product shows more homogeneity, and the old "blow holes" are gone.

"Elsewhere in the store we can find frozen and refrigerated baked products (control staling) in abundance. The working woman appears to relish the "brown and serve" concept of baked goods, although with a little more time she can produce cakes and rolls from a ready-to-use dry mix.

"Next, the beverage section. Here the coffee in a bag is almost gone and even the key-opening can is being replaced. Instant coffee in jars, cans, and even carafes is in large supply. The growth of this product since 1945 has been explosive, and, technically, today's product results from volatile entrapment and control in the processing plant. In contrast to five or eight years ago, the 6-oz. unit has grown to 12 and 16 oz.

"Next are dried synthetic drinks, where the addition of water will produce high-vitamin beverages. For those who want to have the water already added, synthetically flavored drinks are available, ready to consume.

"Nearby are soft drinks. Equal in volume to the few classical names and types of 1935 are the synthetically sweetened beverages, for diet or calorie control. Instead of individual 6 oz. units we now find six-packs, of 12 and 16 oz.

"The fresh-meat section is completely new. The separate meat market or store and the fish store of the early '30's are no more. Even the butcher shop has nearly disappeared. Nothing remains but the chilled, cut, packaged meat. A complete section of fabricated "snack" foods and sausages has developed. Further convenience is apparent in the slicing and packaging. Luncheon meat is back from World War II in several forms. Cured meats show more desirable quality, partly because of injection curing, and polyphosphate cures are used for improved texture, and ascorbates for maximum color developments. Underlying all these products is the rapidly increased understanding of meat pigments, lipid chemistry, and use of antioxidants.

"In the refrigerated case, homogenized milk is everywhere. The day of relating quality to visual measurement of the "cream line" is gone. Butter substitutes are in abundance, and some dairy products now contain chives, parsley, onions, and caraway seeds for added taste.

"The fresh-vegetable-and-fruit department, too, has changed in these twenty-five years. Almost every item is prepackaged, from four tomatoes or a bunch of radishes, to five pounds of potatoes. If fresh potatoes are not desired, the store offers dehydrated instant potatoes, canned potatoes, frozen potatoes, potato chips, or flakes, or convenience potato dishes with cheese.

"Almost every shelf and department shows a food product that was not available in 1938 and is there now for convenience. These range from instant dried soups, salad dressings and gravies, to cake mixes, dried milk, freeze-dried meats, dried yeast, and TV dinners."*

*Reprinted from FOOD TECHNOLOGY, Volume 18, No. 7, pp. 43–44. Copyright © 1964 by Institute of Food Technologists. All views stated are solely those of the author.

Courtesy Kitchens of Sara Lee

First in the entire food-processing industry is this Honeywell 610 digital computer control system which embraces plant-wide central processing and quality control at the Kitchens of Sara Lee, in Deerfield, Illinois. The computer simultaneously monitors some 3,000 variables of the production process, scanning two-thirds of these every minute to assure uniform baking. It performs analysis of the entire Holding Freezer complex (page 351) every fifteen seconds. Using formulas stored in its "memory," the computer meters and weighs liquid and dry ingredients for each product batch, eliminating human errors and assisting skilled bakers in maintaining high quality standards. From a desk console an operator can order the computer to report the status of any item of equipment it directs. Although the computer can control every process in the cake-baking operation, certain deft touches are still done manually. For example, after the icing is applied to the cakes automatically through the directions of the computer, women spread the icing evenly. On the panels shown above is the sequence of mixing operations for various products. The computer enables one hundred and twenty batter cakes to be produced each minute.

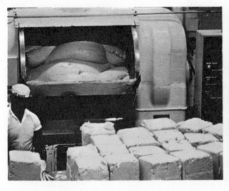

Waiting to go in hopper are 60-pound blocks of 93 score butter.

Cheesecake batter mixer emptying into hopper.

Cakes passing through metering gates on their way to the oven.

Pecan coffee cake passing beneath an icing depositor.

Courtesy Kitchens of Sara Lee

World's largest automated freezer as seen from the top of stacking cranes. Freezer is 180 feet wide, 300 feet long, and 45 feet high. It is maintained at − 10°F.

Other noticeable changes in today's supermarket are the special foods area, shelf space expansion, and introduction of foreign foods.

Special foods. With the large group of people over 65 (18 million) in the United States, the supermarket has developed an area for *geriatric foods*. A *low-calorie food* area can also be found in almost every supermarket. The *baby food* section has been expanded and now has food for children of various ages.

Shelf space. The space for fresh, frozen, and refrigerated foods has greatly expanded. The food refrigerator for dairy products of 1938–1939 has expanded to many refrigerated areas for food today.

Foreign food. Another major change in American foods is the introduction of exotic foods from other countries. Recipes for foods of many lands have been introduced or adapted to our tastes, and this trend will probably be of great impact in the future as Americans do more traveling around the world. Some of the other factors which have affected the availability of foreign food during the 20th century are the advances in agriculture, sanitation standards, packaging, transportation, and new methods of food preservation.

Changes in wholesaling and retailing. The rise of supermarkets is one of the most dramatic changes in food retailing. These stores account for three-fourths of all grocery sales in this country.

Another change in retailing is the growth of affiliated independent stores. The retailers are using more sophisticated and aggressive merchandising and advertising methods than was previously true. They are also spending more money on "promotional give-aways" and trading stamps.

Out of every dollar received from the consumer, the store uses about $.78 to buy the merchandise it sells. The other $.22 goes for the store's operating expenses. After all bills are paid, including income taxes, the store will have a little over $.01 left.

The retailers and wholesalers are using automation in operations in terms of selecting, ordering, billing, and taking inventory. The wholesaler serves the group of affiliated independent grocery stores, and most of his business is in the away-from-home eating or restaurant trade.

Changes in eating places. In 1929 Americans ate about 13 percent of their meals outside private homes; in 1958, 17 percent; and in 1968, this figure will probably be at least 20 percent. These figures are indicative of the fact that people are satisfied with the food they receive outside their own homes, including price and quality, and are willing to spend part of their earnings in order to eat in restaurants. One result of this trend is that many eating places are using precooked and preportioned foods since the transfer of part of the food preparation from the restaurant to the food plant saves money and minimizes problems connected with the serving of the food.

Another major innovation concerning the feeding of people is the growing number of vending machines found in cafeterias, institutions, and along major highways and turnpikes.

Transportation changes. The mechanical refrigerator car which could transport perishable food for long distances was first used in 1949. Today, such cars are able to maintain constant temperatures ranging from 70° to below 0° F. Transportation has also been improved by the addition of "piggyback" handling of loaded truck trailers on railroad flatcars. Motor truck transportation has also expanded. Using these two methods, delivery time can be reduced and larger loads can be carried than was previously possible.

Railroads have improved rail transportation by shifting from the old steam locomotive to the more efficient diesel engine, improving traffic-control systems, and developing special cars to transport meat, vegetables, and other perishables.

The Changing Farmer

Mechanization of farms. Farmers today have a more mechanized operation. They have made better use of fertilizers, pesticides, and other farm chemicals. Additionally, they have adapted better cultural practices in crop growing and have improved the management and breeding of livestock. A larger and better supply of food for the consumer is therefore possible.

As farm mechanization grows, farm operators are able to handle more land. Thus, more farms are being combined to make efficient use of modern power and equipment.

Specialization of farmers. As the farmer has become more specialized, new commercial areas of production have developed. The large specialized growers can produce and sell goods at lowest cost because they can afford expensive, efficient equipment and techniques which are not possible on a small scale.

Concern with market. Many farmers are growing crops for processing. Indeed, many products are grown under a contract signed early in the season, before the crop is planted, in some cases. This method gives the farmer some security if the fresh market is unfavorable one year, but it does limit his profit if returns are particularly good. The farmer is able to plan his time, resources, and labor schedule when he signs his contract before the product is ready for marketing. Farmers have also been selling more of their crops through their own cooperative associations.

A mechanical tomato harvester is used to pick special strains of tomatoes which can withstand the rough handling of the conveyor belts. Each harvester needs a crew of 15 persons.

Ripe tomatoes move from the harvester by a conveyor belt to a large field box. When a box is half full it is taken with 200 others by truck to the packing shed or cannery.

Madison Devlin

Huge semi-trailers haul the tomatoes from the fields near Salinas, California, to the packing sheds in San Jose, a distance of approximately 50 miles.

Green tomatoes (hand-picked) move up a conveyor belt into the packing shed where they will be sorted according to ripeness. These are large salad tomatoes, not for canning or catsup.

The tomatoes are then sorted according to standards of ripeness. All of these workers are members of labor unions and are predominantly Mexican women.

Boxes of choice, ripe tomatoes are on display at a produce market. These have ripened either in transit or at the market. Buyers select the fruit very early in the morning.

Madison Devlin

Green tomatoes are hand-trucked to railroad cars and large trucks. These vehicles are not refrigerated as the fruit cannot stand low temperatures. They are trucked to markets quickly.

A fork-lift at the produce market transfers tomatoes and other vegetables from the loading platform onto a supermarket truck. The vegetables, selected at about 5:00 a.m., will be delivered for sale the same morning.

The Changing Consumer

Today's homemaker-consumer is one of the most sophisticated, value-conscious buyers anywhere in the world. Even so, she may be tempted to make unwise decisions because of advertising appeals, deceptive packaging practices, and incorrect or misleading information regarding food theories or fads. Nevertheless, she knows what she wants and she does not hesitate to make her desires known. Her 5 requests concerning the market are:

1. Less kitchen work. As mentioned previously (page 334), the industry has reacted by saving her almost 1400 hours of meal preparation a year.
2. Less cost for food. The marketplace now allows her to spend seven cents less of her after-tax dollar on food than she spent 15 years ago.
3. Improved quality. Research has discovered new and better ways to raise livestock and plants for better quality foods.
4. More nutritious food. Processors, with the help of nutrition experts, have learned how to retain more essential nutrients in food.
5. More variety in food. The industry has created foods with appealing design, shape, color, texture, and taste combinations.

Trends in consumption. The food patterns of average Americans have changed significantly in the past and are likely to do so again in the future. There has been a decrease in the consumption of cereal foods while the demand for fruits and vegetables has increased. Pork consumption has also declined but the desire for beef and veal has increased and is expected to increase even more in the future. Technological developments may be one cause of an increase in the consumption of a particular food. For example, such developments in the poultry industry have contributed to the sharp decline in the price of chicken, turkey, and eggs. Although the consumer has responded by eating more chicken and turkey, he has resisted the incentive to buy additional eggs, perhaps due to his own food preferences.

Potato consumption (except for potato chips) drastically declined until the early 1950's after which it had a slight recovery. It is generally agreed that the new methods of potato processing at this time led to the increase in consumer consumption. As processing became more important, potato production shifted geographically. Idaho is now the major producer of potatoes for processing; nearly one-half of the crop is sent to this state.

Higher income and improvements in the market system have made a substantial change in consumer buying. Some foods which have been fortified with nutrients have improved the health of many people. The consumer is now able to obtain foods not produced locally; he has a greater choice of all kinds and brands of products and he is assured of clean, well-protected food. In other words, the consumer has benefited substantially from the advances in agricultural marketing.

The Changing Food Costs

Food prices have continued to rise at a rapid rate in the last decade. Prices of other goods and services have also risen, yet so have wages and salaries. It is good to remember that the price of food is relative. Even though food prices are higher now than formerly, we can now buy more food with one hour's work because wages have increased faster than food costs. It should also be noted that today the consumer has the use of many built-in services which were not available a decade or two ago.

It is often easy to confuse added service such as frozen prepared foods or individual serving-size packages with increased food costs. Now, even the basic food items frequently have added service (prepackaging of meat or vegetables is an example).

Convenience costs. Today's homemaker-consumer has become accustomed to buying food often and in small quantities. She wants her food store to have fresh bread and pastries every day and expects a fresh and continuous supply of fruits and vegetables. She also takes for granted prepackaged produce and meat, small packages of flour and beans, frozen foods, and prepared or partially prepared foods in a variety of brands, packages, and sizes. Yet, she might ask herself, How much do conveniences at the grocery actually cost the consumer?

The consumer also should consider the cost of food in terms of time as well as money. In a survey conducted by the U.S. Department of Agriculture in 1953, it was found that it took the homemaker 5.5 hours a day to make home-prepared foods, in which bakery bread was usually the only prepared food. When she used partly prepared foods, including such items as apple pie from canned apples and a bakery mix, approximately 3.1 hours were required in preparation. When the homemaker used ready-to-serve foods, with frozen apple and beef pies but not completely frozen dinners, she worked only 1.6 hours per day. The

Wes Kemp

Wes Kemp

Convenience foods are available in many different forms. They include canned goods (such as soups, vegetables, fruits, meats, and desserts), frozen products (such as appetizers, soups, fruits and fruit juices, complete dinners, and baked goods), dehydrated foods (such as beef and chicken bouillon cubes, milk, and yeast), packaged mixes (such as baked goods, casserole dishes, soups, and puddings), instant foods (such as cooked cereals, beverages, cheesecakes, and

Wes Kemp

mashed potatoes), and ready-to-eat foods (such as baked goods, processed meat, barbecued chicken, and canned puddings). The use of convenience foods saves time and energy for the person cooking a meal because these products cut down or eliminate assembling ingredients and equipment, measuring and mixing food, and washing the equipment which has been used. With a little bit of imagination, convenience foods can be combined together with other convenience foods or basic ingredients to produce original gourmet dishes.

dollar cost was the reverse of the time cost—$4.50 per day for home-prepared foods, $5.80 for the partially prepared, and $6.70 for the ready-to-serve.

This study points up the fact that it usually takes longer but costs less to start with raw food; it saves time but costs more to buy prepared or partially

Table 16
Food Cost for Some Home-prepared and Convenience Foods

| | Food Cost at One Portion | |
Food Item	Convenience	Home-prepared
Chicken Vegetable Soup	6.2¢	5.1¢
Cream of Tomato Soup	6.6	6.5
Vegetable Soup	4.8	6.2
Beef Dinner	59.0	61.4
Beef Patties	24.3	18.9
Mushroom Gravy	4.6	4.5
Beef Stew	16.3	15.8
Chicken Pie	24.8	21.8
Mushroom Soup (as sauce)	4.6	4.9
Flounder	14.4	17.1
Pork and Beans	4.9	5.7
Green Beans	4.9	6.5
Mixed Salad Greens	6.3	3.0
French Dressing	3.1	2.2
Russian Dressing	4.7	4.2
Boston Brown Bread	4.5	4.5
Muffins	2.0	2.1
Rolls	5.5	1.2
Cheese Cake	19.8	12.1
Cookies	5.5	4.0
Cream Puff Shells	2.8	2.3
Vanilla Pudding	3.8	3.8
Fruit Segments	14.9	13.3
Fruit Cocktail	5.2	8.8

FOOD TECHNOLOGY, Vol. 19, No. 7, July 1965, p. 80. Reprinted by permission. Copyright © Institute of Food Technologists.

prepared food. However, "Drexel Institute of Technology recently completed a comprehensive study of the cost and preparation time for convenience foods and their homemade counterparts. Thirty-one different food items were arranged into a number of typical meals prepared for a family of four people. The results showed that, out of 31 convenience foods, 25 could be prepared in less than 5 minutes. Of 31 home-prepared counterparts, only 2 could be

Table 17 Preparation Time and Cost for Seven Meals

		Convenience	*Home-prepared*
MEAL 1	Chicken Vegetable Soup Roast Beef Dinner (with Gravy, Potatoes, Peas, Corn) Club Rolls Cream Puff Vanilla Filling Coffee	34 min. $3.12	143 min. $3.03
MEAL 2	Beef Stew Lettuce Wedge Salad Russian Dressing Lemon Turnover Tea	16 min. $1.52	130 min. $1.17
MEAL 3	Beef Patties Mushroom Gravy Stuffed Baked Potato Green Beans Grapefruit Segments French Dressing Cheese Cake Coffee	35 min. $3.11	124 min. $2.32
MEAL 4	Vegetable Soup Cheese Sandwich Radishes Sponge Cake Shells Strawberries Milk	22 min. $1.52	80 min. $1.54
MEAL 5	Cream of Tomato Soup Chicken Pie Tossed Salad French Dressing Fruit Bowl Tea	13 min. $2.28	127 min. $1.89
MEAL 6	Baked Fillet of Flounder Mushroom Sauce Broccoli Spears Stewed Tomatoes Banana-Nut Salad Plain Muffin Ice Cream Coffee	36 min. $2.08	61 min. $2.14
MEAL 7	Grilled Frankfurters Baked Beans Cabbage Slaw with Pepper Rings Boston Brown Bread Fruit Cocktail Cookies Tea	68 min. $1.98	168 min. $1.93

FOOD TECHNOLOGY, Vol. 19, No. 7, July 1965, p. 81. Reprinted by permission. Copyright © Institute of Food Technologists.

prepared in less than 5 minutes. Drexel's food and nutrition department found that direct food costs for 10 of the 31 convenience products are actually less than the cost of the ingredients for home-prepared products.

"The Drexel study also discovered that the average 'convenience food' meal for four people has an average direct cost of only 23¢ more than the cost of the ingredients of the home-prepared meal. In fact, this cost came to $2.23 for the average of seven different convenience food meals, compared to an average of $2.00 for the same ingredients of seven comparable home-prepared meals. These figures include only direct costs, and do not take into account the housewife's time in preparation. Preparation time for the average of the seven convenience meals was about one-fourth as long—32 minutes, versus 119 minutes for the home-prepared meal. This amounts to the housewife's trading 23¢ for about $1\frac{1}{2}$ hours of kitchen work, not to mention the extra shopping time involved."*

As a consumer it will be necessary for you to decide what choices you will make in regard to convenience foods. If you enjoy food preparation and have enough time, you will probably prepare your meals from the beginning. If you are a working homemaker, or a full-time homemaker with small children, or if you enjoy spending your time outside the home in other activities, you may choose to spend the money and save time and energy. Probably most women fall between the two extremes, taking advantage of some prepared foods but doing some of their own preparation.

In the following chapter we shall see the influence of the consumer as a decision-maker in the market.

MAJOR IDEAS

The following statements give the main ideas within the chapter you have just studied. Be sure you know the words underscored in these statements and in the questions to follow.

1. The food industry is a constantly changing business. These changes affect the farmer, assembler, processor, wholesaler, retailer, and eventually the consumer.
2. Consumers' choices are a major determinant of marketing practices, prices, and the quality of food in the market.
3. The changes in the number of foods available in the market have contributed to the variety of goods for the consumer.
4. Improved transportation increases the food supply and contributes to the availability of many foods which otherwise would be seasonal to many consumers.

*W. B. Murphy, "Convenience Foods: A Young Giant," FOOD TECHNOLOGY, Vol. 19, No. 7, July 1965, p. 80. Reprinted by permission, © The Institute of Food Technologists.

5. Mechanization and specialization of the farmer has increased the quality and quantity of food available to the consumer.

QUESTIONS TO STUDY

THE CHANGING INDUSTRY

1. What changes have occurred in agricultural marketing? Why are these changes important to the consumer?
2. Explain the statement "Most of the food we eat today has been processed."
3. What changes have occurred in the supermarket in the last few decades?
4. What changes have occurred in retailing and wholesaling in the past few years?
5. How does the fact that more people are eating out affect the food industry?
6. How has transportation affected the food available to the consumer?

THE CHANGING FARMER

1. How have farmers changed the market?
2. How does specialization of the farmer contribute to the food supply?

THE CHANGING CONSUMER

1. What role has the consumer played in changing the market?
2. How have food habits changed the food available to the consumer?

THE CHANGING FOOD COSTS

1. What affects the price of food?
2. What determines the cost of convenience foods?

BIBLIOGRAPHY

Agricultural Marketing—Vital Link Between Farmer and Consumer. Marketing Bulletin No. 36, Marketing Economics Division Economic Research Service, U. S. Department of Agriculture, Washington, D. C., October 1965.

Agricultural Statistics 1957. U. S. Department of Agriculture, Washington, D. C., p. 597.

Agricultural Statistics 1959. U. S. Department of Agriculture, Washington, D. C., p. 500.

American Trucking Trends. American Trucking Association, Inc., Washington, D. C., 1960, p. 5.

"Consumer's View of Food Controls." *Consumer Bulletin,* Vol. 49, July 1966, pp. 19–24.

COOK, C. W., "Consumer Confidence—Major Food Industry Asset." *Food Technology,* October 1964, pp. 66–68.

"Crops Fail, Food Crisis Mounts." *Science News,* Vol. 90, October 1966, p. 327.

DALY, R. F., and EGBERT, A. C., "A Look Ahead for Food and Agriculture." *Agricultural Economics Research,* Vol. 18, No. 1, January 1966, p. 3.

DOWLING, E., "To Market We Go, with Editorial Comment." *New Republic,* Vol. 156, January 1967, pp. 9, 19–24.

"Fat Cats in the Food Market: Study by National Commission on Food Marketing." *Consumer Reports,* Vol. 31, June 1966, pp. 306–309.

"Food: The Changes Ahead." *Changing Times,* Vol. 20, June 1966, p. 6.

"Great Food Markets of the World." *Life Magazine,* Vol. 62, May 1967, pp. 64–81.

"Harvester Crops." *New Republic,* Vol. 152, April 3, 1965, pp. 6–7.

HILLERY, R., "Inside Tips on the Supermarket; Questions and Answers." *Changing Times,* Vol. 19, February 1965, pp. 7–11.

HOOVER, D., and STOTZ, M. S., "Food Distribution Changes and the CPI." *Monthly Labor Review,* Vol. 87, January 1964, pp. 58–64.

LODGE, G. C., "Food Processing, Key to Economic Development." *Harvard Business Review,* Vol. 44, September 1966, pp. 6–8.

MORGAN, W. B., "Today: A Quarter Past One." *Food Technology,* July 1964, pp. 43–44.

"MRCA Gets Rich Supermarket Data." *Business Week,* April 1966, p. 134.

MURPHY, W. B., "Convenience Foods: A Young Giant." *Food Technology,* July 1965, pp. 80–82.

"New Foods for Fighting Famine." *Newsweek,* Vol. 69, February 1967, pp. 87–88.

"New Ways to Preserve Food." *Good Housekeeping,* Vol. 157, August 1963, p. 147.

RASMUSSEN, CLYDE, "The Dynamic Food Industry and Our Eating Concepts." *Food Technology,* December 1965, pp. 36–42.

"Shopping for Food: How It's Changing." *U. S. News and World Report*, Vol. 60, May 1966, p. 12.

"Stretch Your Food Dollar." *Changing Times*, Vol. 21, January 1967, p. 18.

"Swinging a Scythe on Farm Surplus; Omnibus Bill Launches a New Subsidy Program." *Business Week*, October 23, 1965, pp. 29–30.

WEISS, GERTRUDE, "Time and Money Cost of Meals Using Home and Prekitchen-Prepared Food." *Journal of Home Economics*, Vol. 46, No. 2, February 1954, pp. 98–100.

"What's in Food Standards for You?" *Consumer Bulletin*, Vol. 48, March 1965, pp. 31–33.

"Why Farmer's Share Is Shrinking; Study by National Commission on Food Marketing." *Business Week*, May 15, 1965, pp. 174–176.

"Why You Spend So Much On Groceries." *Changing Times*, September 1965, pp. 25–28.

WIECK, P. R., "Ups and Downs of Food Prices." *New Republic*, Vol. 154, June 1966, pp. 9–10.

WRIGHT, CARLTON, *Food Buying*. New York, The Macmillan Company, 1962.

"Yankee Marketeers; Italy's Largest Supermarket." *Time*, Vol. 85, April 23, 1965, p. 97.

23 MAKING DECISIONS IN THE MARKET

Every homemaker is faced with the problem of spending her food money as wisely as possible. It is important for her to buy a variety of nutritious foods for her family, yet it is also necessary for her to stay within the bounds of her food budget. The homemaker's decisions in the market are made more complex by the diversity of foods, as well as the disparate qualities, sizes, and prices of similar kinds of food.

How Much to Spend

With so many items to choose from—8,000 or more—in the supermarket, how can a homemaker do a better job of making decisions about family food needs? Probably the first thing she should do is establish with her husband a set of values on which they can base their choices of goods and services as well as the use of their time. Those values to which they give preference should include both short-term and long-term goals. No family can reasonably think of its food budget as an isolated factor since the amount to be spent for food must be seen in relation to all expenses which have to be met.

Spending patterns. This brings us then to how much of the family's income will be spent for food. Just as families have different living habits, they have different spending habits. The way they spend their money varies with their incomes and with their interests. Those with more money to spend may spend more. Those with limited funds must learn to curtail their expenses and plan with greater care the use of the money they have. Family spending patterns for food vary as do those for the other things people buy. However, most often food is the largest single item for which money is spent. In the last few years Americans, on the average, have spent almost 22 percent of their disposable income (after taxes) for food. With larger incomes people tend to spend more money for food per person, as well as per family, yet the percentage of income they spend is lower. Why? Study the table on the next page.

If a family's income is $30 a day, how much might be spent for food? First let's consider how this income is broken down. According to national figures, 12 percent of our income goes for taxes and non-tax payments (social security) leaving 88 percent of our total income at our disposal. From surveys done by the U.S. Department of Commerce in 1959 it was seen that we spent 5 percent on savings, 12 percent on taxes and non-tax payments, 33.6 percent on services, and 49.4 percent on goods.

366

Table 18

INCOME AFTER TAXES	$3,100–5,500	$5,600–9,500	$9,600–14,000
		Percent of Income	
Food	30–40	18–30	15–20
Housing	15–25	15–25	15–20
Household Operation	5–10	5–10	5–10
Furnishings	3–4	3–4	4–5
Clothing	10–15	10–12	5–10
Transportation	6–8	4–7	3–5
Medical Care	5–10	5–10	3–6
Personal Expenses	3–10	3–7	3–7
Recreation & Education	5–10	5–10	5–10
Gifts & Contributions	2–5	2–5	4–10
Life Insurance	2–5	4–5	5–8
Operating Margin	1–15	1–20	1–25

USDA figures from Cook County (Illinois) Extension Service, University of Illinois, and United States Department of Agriculture, 1966.

Applying this information. With an income of $30 a day, during a 5-day week the income would be $7800 a year and the disposable income would be $6864. If the family members spend their money as the average family does, they would spend about $28.87 for food per week. This figure, of course, is just an estimate because many factors such as family size, ages, and occupations have to be considered. The homemaker's role in securing and preparing the food must also be considered in planning the food expenditure. Consideration has to be given as to whether the expenditure represents the "food bill" or the "shopping bill." The supermarket these days has changed our shopping habits. We buy not only food in the market but also soap, detergents, tissues, toothpaste, pet food, light bulbs, glassware, kitchen equipment, sponges, silver polish —things we once bought at the drug store, hardware store, variety store, or pet store. Thus, many of these items are not food and should not be included as part of the food expenditure.

Before considering how the family's expenditures might be reduced, it is important to note where the food dollar goes. According to a study done in 1955 on how we spend our food dollar, it was noted that consumers spent 32¢ for meat, poultry, and fish and 19¢ for fruits and vegetables. Dairy products represented 17¢, including butter, fresh milk, and cream which cost over 10¢, ice cream 2¢, and butter 1½¢. Flour, cereals, and bakery products accounted for 12¢, with baked goods costing nearly 10¢ and white bread accounting for 3½¢ of the 10¢. Beverages, other than milk, cost 6¢, eggs 4¢, and sugar and sweets 3¢, as did fats and oils. Miscellaneous foods (condiments, canned soup, jams and jellies, frozen prepared foods, and others) accounted for 4¢.

FOOD DOLLAR GRAPH

.32	MEAT, POULTRY, FISH
.19	FRUIT & VEG.
.17	DAIRY
.12	FLOUR, BAKED GOODS, ETC.
.06	BEVERAGES
.04	EGGS
.03	SUGAR & SWEETS
.03	FATS & OILS
.04	MISCELLANEOUS

$1.00

On the average, each person in an American household eats 10 pounds of fruits and vegetables, 4.5 quarts of milk or a corresponding amount of cheese and ice cream, 4 pounds of meat, 7 eggs, 1 pound of fat, 1.5 pounds of sugar, and 3 pounds of cereal products in a week.

Although these figures may vary from year to year, they still point out the fact that meat, fish, and poultry take the largest share of the food dollar followed by fruits and vegetables, dairy products, the bread group, and beverages.

The spending of the food dollar involves many choices which the homemaker must make if she is to get full value for the money spent for food. Some of these choices are: Where are the "best" shops? What food is to be bought? What constitutes a "good choice"? Will a freezer save money? Who will protect the homemaker and you, as consumers?

Where to Shop

Types of stores. Choosing the "best" stores depends on you and your needs. In most communities there are several types of stores. It is wise to study the possibilities and decide which store (or stores) best fits your needs. There are many kinds of stores available in most communities.

The *chain store* is one of several under common ownership and management and is usually a cash-and-carry store. It bases its stock on large quantities so it may provide real savings to the customer. There are usually no charge accounts or delivery services.

The *independent store* is usually independently owned and operated. This kind of store usually buys in relatively small quantities, so large volume purchasing gains are limited. However, independent store owners make an effort to stock hard-to-get food items that cannot be purchased at other stores. Sometimes this type of store offers credit and delivery service to its customers.

The consumer may also shop in stores which specialize in certain products such as meat, fish, baked goods, candy, and fruits and vegetables. These *specialty shops* may be independently owned or part of a chain operation.

The *supermarket* has become an important part of the shopping center of today. Most supermarkets follow the cash-and-carry policy on merchandising. These stores buy and operate in large volume with a minimum of operating expense (self-service).

The *farmer's market* is one which sells food directly from the farmer. This is one means for the city dweller to obtain fresh produce direct from the producer. Shopping at a farmer's market has advantages if you can identify quality and know the current retail prices of the food to be purchased.

The *discount supermarket* is a store which sells food at reduced prices. The products may be the same as those purchased elsewhere, or they may be damaged (cans dented, packages slightly open, etc.). The discount supermarket may also receive goods which have been harmed during transit (for instance, in a train wreck). This type of store is growing rapidly. For example, there were six discount stores in Detroit in 1961 and seventy-nine only two years later. Prices at these supermarkets should be watched carefully, since they tend to rise after initial opening and customer inspection.

It is unlikely that any one store will meet the needs of a family. It may be that in shopping for food, use will be made of several types of stores. Trading stamps are another factor to consider. There is still debate over whether receiving trading stamps is beneficial to the consumer. The grocer knows stamps cost him $2\cent$ to $2\frac{1}{2}\cent$ out of every dollar, but who actually absorbs this cost is still in question. Trading stamps may be advantageous to the consumer if the store offering them attracts more customers and can therefore buy goods in larger quantities at lower cost. Once a majority of stores in an area adopt trading stamps as a promotional technique, however, prices in the different stores tend to become similar. Many shoppers prefer lower prices to receiving stamps.

Comparison shopping is important so that you know if the prices are really lower. How would you go about determining which stores are best for your particular needs?

Norman Matheny, *The Christian Science Monitor*

What to Buy

Planning. Before you go to a store to buy food you must know what you need. Careful pre-shopping planning is a necessity in order to do the most efficient shopping. Once the menus are planned, a *shopping list* should be prepared. The shopping list made according to the menu plan will help you buy the right food at the right price. The list should be carefully planned so that it provides for possible substitutions.

Food advertisements give tips on season's supply, prices, grades, and brands. This information can be used to good advantage in making a shopping list. The shopper should be alert to particular items in the store which may be purchased at a savings. A shopping list which classifies food into departments such as meats, dairy products, produce, and so on makes shopping easier. Checking menus and recipes with the list will help you be sure that you haven't overlooked any necessary ingredient or food.

Knowing what you need, getting it, and resisting the impulse to pick up food you neither really want nor need are ways to control food expenditures.

Specials. Stores feature special sales for many reasons: to bring traffic into the store, to adjust overstocking of various items by the store, to anticipate storage loss among perishables. Whether or not the homemaker buys these specials depends on the amount of money she has to spend for food, the need for these items, and the available storage space if the items are not to be used immediately. The purchase of perishables at special sales requires careful judgment. A special food may be overripe. This involves the possibility of waste or loss in nutritive value. Capitalizing on special food sales when possible can cut food expenditures.

Comparing costs. Price comparison is another way of controlling the cost of food. When items are sold in multiples, figure out first what you pay for one; then decide if you have a need for the product and if there is a price advantage in buying the several offered on sale. Observing the same practice when buying food sold by weight will give you a solid basis for comparing prices. The consumer should also be alert to the methods a store uses to sell merchandise. For example, consider this story which appeared in *Changing Times*. "One Saturday recently a mountain of canned fruit punch stood at the end of an aisle. A modest blue-lettered sign announced it was a 'spotlight-of-the-week' item. But the price was the same as usually charged.

"Meanwhile, further back and harder to reach was another stack of a similar fruit punch. Over this hung a very large red sign marking these as specials, which indeed they were. Yet the 'special' lay almost untouched while the 'spotlighted' item—offering no bargain at all—was moving briskly."*

In another instance, cans of food were marked on sale for 4 for $1 and others, 3 for 99¢. Single cans were marked respectively 25¢ and 33¢. There is no difference in price per item or "sale" price. Yet it has been shown that by marking items as sales, purchases of those goods may zoom as much as 70 percent. The next time you visit your grocery, see if you can spot items which are being merchandised in this way.

Cost per serving is one way of determining how much the food will cost for the family meal. The two factors which affect the cost per serving are (1) the price of the unit and (2) the number of servings the unit yields. The cost per serving can easily be determined for fruits and vegetables, meats, eggs, fish, poultry, and dairy products. To be able to compare the cost per serving of various fruits and vegetables requires a knowledge of how much edible food is provided in each retail unit—a pound, head, package, or can. Once you know how many servings can be expected from a specific unit it is easy to determine the cost per serving by dividing the retail cost per unit by the number of serv-

*"Why You Spend So Much on Groceries," CHANGING TIMES, September 1965, p. 26. Excerpted by permission from CHANGING TIMES, Copyright 1965 by The Kiplinger Washington Editors, Inc.

THE MANAGEMENT OF FOOD RESOURCES

ings. Although the number of servings obtained from a given unit will vary from family to family, a standard serving for fruits and vegetables is considered to be one-half cup of the product including its juice. A smaller allowance is used for foods such as celery, cranberries, and mushrooms since one-half cup would be a larger portion than is generally served. For example, let's compare the cost per serving of peaches.

	Weight	Retail Price (cents)	Serving per Unit	Cost per Serving (cents)
Fresh peaches	1 lb.	19	4	5
Canned peaches	1 lb. 4 oz.	29	7	4
Frozen peaches	12 oz.	39	3	13

One can readily see that the canned peaches are the least expensive while the frozen peaches are the most expensive per serving. The figure being used in this illustration was at a time when peaches were in season. The price for seasonal perishables varies from season to season.

In choosing which item to buy, one has to consider (1) the quality of the food, (2) how it is to be used, (3) time and labor necessary for its preparation, and (4) the family's preferences and dislikes. The table on the next page gives

The amount of bone and fat on meat is important in cost per serving (chicken, lamb).

American Lamb Council

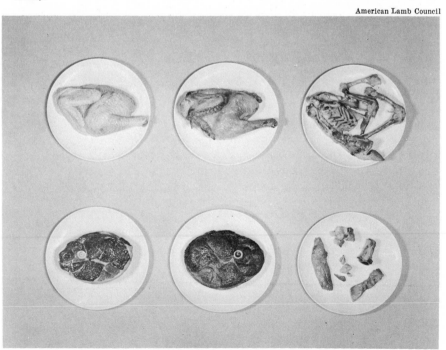

Table 19

Retail Cut	Servings Per Pound	29	39	49	59	69	79	89	99	109	119	129	139
						Cost Per Serving							
Beef													
Sirloin Steak	2½	12	16	20	24	28	32	36	40	44	48	52	56
Porterhouse, T-bone													
Rib Steak	2	15	20	25	30	35	40	45	50	55	60	65	70
Round Steak	3½	8	11	14	17	20	23	25	28	31	34	37	40
Chuck Roast—bone-in	2	15	20	35	30	35	40	45	50	55	60	65	70
Rib Roast—boneless	2½	12	16	20	24	28	32	36	40	44	48	52	56
Rib Roast—bone-in	2	15	20	25	30	35	40	45	50	55	60	65	70
Rump, Sirloin Roast	3	10	13	16	20	23	26	30	33	36	40	43	46
Ground Beef	4	7	10	12	15	17	20	22	25	27	30	32	35
Short Ribs	2	15	20	25	30	35	40	45	50	55	60	65	70
Heart, Liver, Kidney	5	6	8	10	12	14	16	18	20	22	24	26	28
Frankfurters	4	7	10	12	15	17	20	22	25	27	30	32	35
Stew Meat—boneless	5	6	8	10	12	14	16	18	20	22	24	26	28
Lamb													
Loin, Rib Shoulder													
Chops	3	10	13	16	20	23	26	30	33	36	40	43	46
Breast, Shank	2	15	20	25	30	35	40	45	50	55	60	65	70
Shoulder Roast	2½	12	16	20	24	28	32	36	40	44	48	52	56
Leg of Lamb	3	10	13	16	20	23	26	30	33	36	40	43	46
Pork—Fresh													
Center Cut or Rib Chops	4	7	10	12	15	17	20	22	25	27	30	32	35
Loin or Rib Roast	2½	12	16	20	24	28	32	36	40	44	48	52	56
Boston Butt—bone-in	3	10	13	16	20	23	26	30	33	36	40	43	46
Blade Steak	3	10	13	16	20	23	26	30	33	36	40	43	46
Spare Ribs	1⅓	22	29	37	44	52	59	67	74	82	89	97	104
Pork—Cured													
Picnic—bone-in	2	15	20	25	30	35	40	45	50	55	60	65	70
Ham—fully cooked													
bone-in	3½	8	11	14	17	20	23	25	28	31	34	37	40
boneless and canned	5	6	8	10	12	14	16	18	20	22	24	26	28
shankless	4¼	7	9	12	14	16	19	21	23	26	28	30	33
center slice	5	6	8	10	12	14	16	18	20	22	24	26	28
Poultry													
Broiler, ready-to-cook	1⅓	22	29	37	44	52	59	67	74	82	89	97	104
Legs, Thighs	3	10	13	16	20	23	26	30	33	36	40	43	46
Breasts	4	7	10	12	15	17	20	22	25	27	30	32	35
Turkey, ready-to-cook													
under 12 lbs.	1	29	39	49	59	69	79	89	99	109	119	129	139
12 lbs. and over	1⅓	22	29	37	44	52	59	67	74	82	89	97	104

Price Per Pound (column headers 29–139)

How to Use

Let us assume chuck roast (bone-in), lamb shoulder roast, and Boston butt (bone-in) are all 59 cents per pound. Which is the more economical choice? Just match the price per pound with the meat cut you are comparing. Reading the table under the 59 cents per pound column shows chuck roast at 30 cents per serving, lamb shoulder roast at 24 cents per serving, and bone-in Boston butt at 20 cents per serving. Servings are from 2½ to 3½ ounces of cooked lean meat.

Marketing Information for Consumers · Cooperative Extension Service
The Ohio State University, Columbus, Ohio

the cost per serving of different cuts of meat. Table 32 in the Appendix gives the number of servings in common retail units of food. For example, if beef chuck steak costs $0.59 per pound, the cost per serving would be $0.59 (cost per pound) ÷ 3 (number of servings per pound) = $0.19 per serving.

If porterhouse steak is $1.18 per pound, the cost per serving is as follows: $1.18 (cost per pound) ÷ 2 (number of servings per pound) = $0.59. If you want to know the cost of porterhouse steak for your entire family, multiply the cost per serving by the number of people in your family; for example, $0.59 × 4 = $2.36 for a family of 4. If, however, certain members of the family require more than one serving, the price increases accordingly. You will also notice that some meats—flank steak, for instance—give you 4 servings per pound while a rib steak gives only 2 servings per pound. You will find in some cases that boned cuts at higher prices may be less expensive to serve because they yield more servings than cuts containing bone.

The unit in which you purchase an item may also affect its price. As a rule, larger boxes or cans of an item will cost less per ounce. However, the consumer should be aware of ways in which the packaged material may create the illusion that it is larger than it really is. For this reason, note the weight of the contents before deciding whether the item is a good buy.

The cost of food varies according to brand, grade, and style. Because of extensive advertising, many products are bought because of their brand names. In fact, some consumers may make all of their buying decisions on brand names. Brand names are used to identify a food product of a manufacturer and usually refer to a consistent quality. Determining the brand best for your needs requires reading the labels or trying many brands to discover which are satisfactory. In other words, it takes experience to determine the right brand for your use. In many cases, however, it will be easier to familiarize yourself with quality associated with a brand or trademark carried by the store than to purchase foods according to grade. Many foods are only graded at the wholesale level and some foods do not have established grades. A brand name often indicates the grade. For this reason, in many cases you will find that foods which normally are graded are sold by brand and do not carry a grade label. Some foods, however, are sold by grade, and there are Federal and state laws that prescribe the quality of these products.

The style in which a product is sold is another consideration which relates to cost. For example, sliced cheese usually costs more than bulk cheese. Nuts in the shell may be less costly than shelled ones. These facts can help to decide your final choice.

Whether to buy a ready-prepared product or to prepare the same item from scratch is a common question. This is especially true regarding cakes. If an angel food cake mix costing 59¢ contains the equivalent of the whites of 1 dozen fresh eggs (which cost 59¢) plus the other ingredients, it may be more desirable to use the mix. However, if a cake mix requires additional eggs, the cost increases, and a cake from scratch may be cheaper. Whether the home-maker buys a mix depends on several other factors such as her skill in making a quality cake and the time available to her.

Good buys. The good buy always calls for decisions on the part of the consumer. Good buys for one family may not be good buys for another family. To determine if a certain food is a good buy for you, consider the following questions: Is it a food that is nutritious and one your family enjoys? Is its cost within the amount available for food? Is the size of the container appro-priate for your family? How much preparation is necessary? Is storage space available?

Buying food which your family will not eat is a poor buy. A homemaker is usually familiar with her family's preferences and dislikes, however, and plans her purchases accordingly. The cost of food is always a consideration in making a good buy since the homemaker has only a certain amount of money to spend. To purchase the "good buy" may mean that she will have to sacrifice another item on her list for the item she considers superior.

For some families with only two members, items packaged in large con-tainers may cost less but may be poor buys because of the possible waste in-volved. For the two-person family the smaller container costing more may be a better buy in the long run Unless you plan to use the food immediately, nothing is a good buy unless there is adequate storage for your purchase. For example, buying large quantities of frozen foods at one time may be a poor decision if you do not have a freezer. The homemaker who buys a bushel of fresh peaches for her family of two may be making a mistake if she has neither the time nor the equipment for preservation of the peaches. These peaches would then not be a "good buy."

Preserving food. Whether or not to preserve foods depends on several factors: the quality and cost of the raw food, the need for added ingredients, the necessary equipment, the fuel needed, and the time necessary for preparing and processing. There is a cost involved in processing food. This is true whether you grow your own food or whether it is given to you by a neighbor. Growing your own food requires purchasing seeds or plants and time and money for cultivation.

Consumer Information and Protection

Label information. Any descriptive label on foods you buy, especially when choosing a product you haven't used previously, will give you informatian about the product. The label probably will tell you the brand name, name and address of the manufacturer, packer or distributor, and the weight or liquid measure. You may also be given explicit directions for the product's use and some suggested recipes.

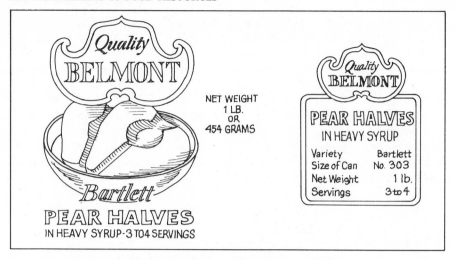

The consumer can put food to best use if the label clearly indicates the form or style of the food in the can or package.

While the ingredients in canned goods are usually given, with the ingredients in larger quantity listed first, there are certain products which have so-called "standards of identity" according to government regulations. In general, manufacturers are not required to state the ingredients on the labels for standardized foods, except that the presence of any artificial flavorings, artificial colorings, or chemical preservatives must be declared. A descriptive label states the style or form of the canned product. You are told, for instance, whether tomatoes are whole or in pieces, and if pineapples are sliced, crushed, cubed, or diced, in spears or tidbits. In addition, the number of cups and approximate servings may be stated on the label. Dietetic foods are clearly labeled as such and their contents are listed. Such a label also shows the amount of seasoning, if any, that has been added.

The Food, Drug and Cosmetic Act (1938) requires all labels on foods which are sent out of their home state (interstate commerce) to list the following information:

1. The name of the product and the variety, type, or style, when this is applicable.
2. The complete name and address of the manufacturer, packer, or shipper of the product.
3. An accurate statement of quality.
4. A list of the ingredients when two or more foods go into an unstandardized product.
5. Enough facts to inform the purchaser if it is a food for special dietary purposes.

6. A statement regarding the presence of artificial colorings, flavorings, imitations or chemical preservatives.

7. An indication and explanation of substandard quality or substandard fill of containers.

The placement of this required information must be easy to find and easy to understand.

Consumers were helped in their marketing decisions when the "Fair Packaging and Labeling Act" went into effect on July 1, 1967. This law provided that (1) descriptions such as "giant" quart could no longer be used, (2) servings, if stated, had to be in terms of weight ("two 4-ounce servings"), (3) amounts had to be expressed in two ways ("1 pint or 28 ounces"), and (4) "cents off" labeling could only be used if the item was offered at a price lower than the regular retail price.

Sources of information. Among these sources is the U.S. Department of Agriculture which conducts studies and prepares reports for consumers. The Food and Drug Administration of the U.S. Department of Health, Education, and Welfare is continuously protecting people against misrepresented products

besides providing miscellaneous information for the consumer. State government agencies also distribute excellent information for the public. Furthermore, university and extension specialists are constantly conducting research and publishing materials to aid the consumer.

Many trade associations such as the Poultry and Egg National Board, The American Meat Institute, The National Livestock and Meat Board, The American Dairy Association, and the United Fresh Fruits and Vegetables Council also provide information which helps the consumer.

Consumer responsibility. It is the responsibility of the family shopper to be informed, and there are many other places where this person can get accurate, helpful information. Intelligent consumers who make rational and discriminating choices can influence our market for the benefit of everyone.

U. S. Public Health Service. This service is concerned with helping state and local agencies which are directly involved in safeguarding the public's health and safety. For example, all states now have milk and food sanitation programs that are based on recommendations by the U. S. Public Health Service. This agency also cooperates with local authorities to pinpoint the causes of any diseases which may be traced to food. The agency's communicable disease center is available to investigate outbreaks of food poisonings.

The U. S. Public Health Service also conducts experiments on toxic agents and on chemical and radiological contaminants in foods. Extensive programs in nutrition research are also supported.

The Meat Inspection Act. This act is enforced by a branch of the Bureau of Animal Industry within the U. S. Department of Agriculture. It requires all meat and meat products in interstate commerce or imported from abroad to be packed under government license and inspected as specified in the regulations.

The Poultry-Products Inspection Act. This act provides for the inspection of processed poultry which will enter interstate commerce. It is governed by the Agricultural Marketing Service of the U. S. Department of Agriculture.

The Agricultural Marketing Service. This agency develops quality standards on which grades for various foods are based.

The Federal Trade Commission. This agency is responsible for preventing the use of unfair methods of competition in commerce. Its work includes the prevention of misleading advertising, misbranding, and the misrepresenting of secondhand or made-over products as new. The Commission's jurisdiction is generally limited to companies which deal in interstate commerce.

State and municipal food laws. All states and cities have certain food laws which are often modeled after Federal laws and recommendations. These laws usually make provisions for inspection of food-handling operations and examinations of the food handlers.

The Consumer Advisory Council. This organization was established by President Kennedy and is one of the most recent organizations formed to help the consumer. It works directly with the Council of Economic Advisers. The function of this organization is to examine and provide advice to the Government on issues of broad economic policy, governmental programs protecting consumers' needs, and needed improvements in the flow of consumer information to the public.

MAJOR IDEAS

The following statements give the main ideas within the chapter you have just studied. Be sure you know the words underscored in these statements and in the questions to follow.

1. A decision-maker's choices are affected by his motives, needs, and goals; by his abilities, habits, and attitudes; by the situation; and by the expected outcome of each alternative.
2. Satisfaction from a decision is influenced by the relative importance of short-term and long-term goals, the amount of risk and uncertainty inherent in the situation, and the cost of the results.
3. Rational choice becomes more complex when there are many food products available and many ways of merchandising them.
4. Informed consumers who make rational and discriminating choices in the purchase of food can improve the functioning of our market economy.
5. Changing prices of consumer goods affect the purchasing power of family income.
6. The safety of food is controlled through the procedures used in its production and processing and by the sanitary measures employed in the handling and storing of food in the market and at home.
7. Federal, state, and local agencies give protection and guidance to consumers in their purchases of food by certifying its wholesomeness and freedom from adulteration, establishing standards of identity, requiring truthful labeling, and by prohibiting false statements in advertising.

QUESTIONS TO STUDY

HOW MUCH TO SPEND

1. What determines how much a family spends for food?
2. What is the difference between the shopping bill and food bill?

WHERE TO SHOP

1. What is the difference between an independent store and a supermarket?
2. What knowledge is important when buying from a producer?
3. What is the difference between the chain store and the independent store?
4. What factors determine where you shop?

WHAT TO BUY

1. What are the advantages of the shopping list?
2. What is a "good buy"?
3. When is a special a good buy?
4. What factors determine cost per serving?
5. What is the advantage of determining the cost per serving?
6. Why may it be advisable to buy food by brand name?
7. How does a knowledge of grade help the consumer?
8. When is the preservation of food at home desirable?

CONSUMER INFORMATION AND PROTECTION

1. Why should the consumer read the label before making a purchase?
2. What information is required by law to be on the label?
3. What is the role of the Pure Food and Drug Administration?
4. How does the U. S. Public Health Service protect the consumer?
5. What is the role of the Federal Trade Commission with regard to food?

BIBLIOGRAPHY

The Food Dollar: Food Purchases by Household of Two or More Persons (One Week Spring 1955)." *Household Food Consumption Survey*, 1955, Report No. 1, U. S. Department of Agriculture, Washington, D. C., December 1956.

General Regulations for the Enforcement of the Federal Food, Drug, and Cosmetic Act, Title 21, Part 1, June 1958 Revision, Sections 1.2–1.14.

"How We Use Our Total Personal Income—United States 1959." *Survey of Current Business*, Vol. 40, No. 7, July 1960, pp. 10, 16.

MARGOLUIS, SIDNEY, "*Buyer, Be Wary.*" Public Affairs Pamphlet, December 1965.

Read the Label on Foods, Drugs, Devices, Cosmetics. Miscellaneous Publication No. 3, Revision No. 2, Department of Health, Education and Welfare, Food and Drug Administration, Washington, D. C., 1957.

"Why You Spend So Much on Groceries." *Changing Times,* September 1965, pp. 25–28.

SELECTION AND STORAGE OF
FRUITS AND VEGETABLES
EGGS AND DAIRY PRODUCTS
MEAT, POULTRY, AND FISH
CEREALS AND CEREAL PRODUCTS
CANNED GOODS

24 FOOD SELECTION AND STORAGE

Selection and Storage of Fruits and Vegetables

The informed consumer knows what to look for in choosing top quality fruits and vegetables. These foods should have uniform size, color, and the desired degree of ripeness. They must also be free from defects and blemishes. In the selection of all fruits it is most economical to buy fruit best suited for the purpose intended.

Citrus fruits. Oranges, grapefruits, lemons, citrons, kumquats, and limes are citrus fruits. In general, when selecting citrus fruits, one checks to see that the fruit is heavy for its size, moderately firm, and fine-textured. These qualities usually indicate juiciness and ripeness. When these fruits are light-weight, very hard or soft, with thick coarse-textured skin, they are usually lacking in juice. The good taste of citrus fruits is dependent upon a good juice content in the fruit.

Tangerines, satsuma oranges, and temple oranges cannot be judged in quite the same way as other citrus fruits because they have a loose skin which can be easily peeled off. Color cannot always be used as a guide. For example, valencia oranges reach the market with their greenish color. At times these oranges are treated to change their color to orange before they are sold since many consumers are unaware of the fact that this particular orange may be fully ripe although its color is still green. Lemons have a characteristic yellow shade. The skin of the grapefruit may vary from pale yellow to russet. Even though the yellow-skinned grapefruit is preferred for appearance, many russet-colored grapefruit are juicier and have a better flavor. The pink meat grapefruit has become popular because of its sweet flavor. Limes should be green in color when bought.

The final selection of citrus fruits depends on their intended use. If oranges are to be used for a salad or dessert where separate orange segments are wanted, seedless navel oranges—sometimes called California oranges—may be the best choice. This variety is easily segmented. If oranges are needed for juice, the valencia will perhaps be the best choice because it contains a substantial amount of juice. The fact that it does not readily separate into segments is not important in this case.

1

2

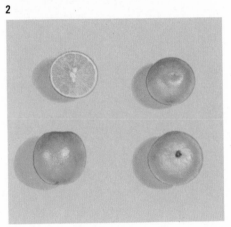

3

Varieties of oranges:
(1) Valencia
(2) Hamlin
(3) Jaffa
(4) Seedling
(5) Parson Brown

4

5

Florida Citrus Commission

1

2

Other citrus fruits:
(1) Ruby Red Grapefruit
(2) Seedless Grapefruit
(3) Tangerines
(4) Lemons
(5) Limes

3

4

5

Florida Citrus Commission

Melons also belong to the citrus group. They are divided into two classes: the muskmelons (honeydew, cantaloupe, and casaba) and the watermelon.

The flesh of the muskmelon and cantaloupe is dark yellow or orange; that of the honeydew, greenish-white; that of the casaba, yellowish-white. The watermelon is usually elliptical, green or green striped on the exterior and smooth finished. Lycopene and carotene are the color pigments found in watermelon. All of these melons must be picked ripe to be sweet.

Honeydew, cranshaw, cantaloupe, netted gem cantaloupe, Fordhook Hybrid Watermelon, and Charleston Gray Watermelon are some varieties of melons.

Burpee Seed Company

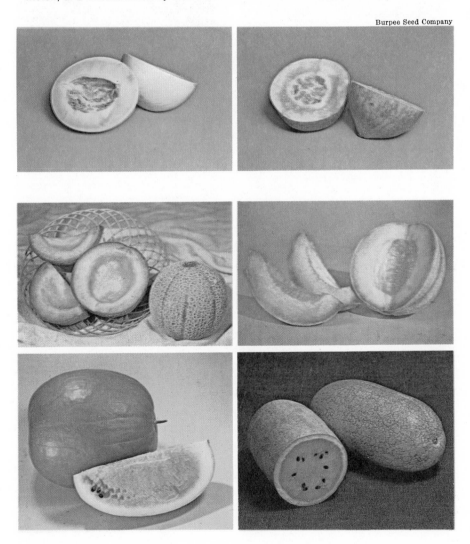

Washington State Apple Commission

Summer varieties of apples include (1) Lodi, (2) Yellow Transparent, (3) Tydeman Red, (4) Beacon.

Fall varieties of apples include (1) Golden Delicious, (2) Winesap, (3) Rome Beauty, (4) Red Delicious.

Selection of other fruits. Pomes are a group of fruits characterized by an enlarged fleshy body. Apples are pomes. There are many varieties of apples which vary in size and range in color from green to yellow to red. Certain apples have better cooking quality than others.

Table 20

Some Varieties of Apples and Their Use

Variety	Season	Use
Rome Beauty	Nov.–May	Baking—cooking
Winesap	Jan.–May	Excellent for all purposes
Delicious	Oct.–March	Raw
Northern Spy	Oct.–March	Raw—cooking
Rhode Island Greening	Oct.–March	Cooking—pies
McIntosh	Oct.–March	Raw—cooking
Jonathan	Oct.–Jan.	Raw—cooking
Baldwin	Nov.–April	Raw—cooking

"Fruits and Vegetables," QMFCIAF, Vol. 1, May 1946.

Like the apple, the pear is also a pome. Pears are harvested when mature, but not completely ripe. As they ripen, their color changes to yellow with a red or brown flush. Generally pears are eaten raw, but they may also be canned, dried, or pickled.

Table 21

Some Varieties of Pears and Their Use

Variety	Season	Use
Kieffer	Oct.–Dec.	Cooking—canning
Winter Nelis	Oct.–April	Raw
Seckel	Oct.–April	Raw—canning—pickling
Comice	Oct.–March	Raw
Bosc	Oct.–April	Raw
Bartlett	July–Oct.	Raw—canning
Anjou	Late fall & winter	Raw—canning

"Fruits and Vegetables." QMFCIAF, Vol. 1, May 1946.

An apricot resembles a small peach. Its skin is smooth and turns orange-yellow when ripe; the flesh is sweet and juicy. Apricots should be an orange color with a "blush" tone, firm and plump.

Peaches are similar to apricots but larger, sweeter, and less pungent to taste. Peaches are selected on the basis of flesh color which is white or yellow with a red blush. The fruit should be firm but not hard. Nectarines are a variety of peach having a smooth skin. Nectarines should be closely examined for cracking since their smooth skin makes them vulnerable to cracking and disease.

Cherries are available in several varieties—Bing, Black Tartauan, Royal Ann, Montmorency, and others. Cherries, like other fruits, should be selected with regard to the purpose for which they are to be used. Red sour cherries should be chosen for canning and pies; the dark sweet cherries for desserts.

Table 22

Characteristics of Some Varieties of Cherries

Variety	Size-Appearance	Season	Use
Black Tartauan	Medium, purplish-black, sweet	Early June	Dessert
Royal Ann	Large, yellow with red blush		Canning
Bing	Large, dark red to purplish-black, sweet	June	Dessert
Montmorency	Medium, light red, sour		Pies and Canning

"Fruits and Vegetables." QMFCIAF, Vol. 1, May 1946.

Plums are also available in several varieties. The Japanese plum is yellow and red, while the European varieties are green and blue. Fully ripe plums are dark in color, whether red or yellow, and are usually eaten raw, although large quantities are also preserved, dried, or canned.

Berries are fruits in which the layers of the pericarp are pulpy and succulent, and seeds are contained in the mass. Among the different kinds of berries are blackberries, blueberries, strawberries, raspberries, gooseberries, grapes, and cranberries.

Berries should be the representative color of their kind; for example, strawberries, red; blueberries, blue. This fruit bruises easily if not very carefully handled, and this is a factor which should be considered before selecting high quality berries.

Avocados are pear-shaped fruits with a green or purplish skin. They are high in fat content and have a pleasant smooth texture. Avocados should be firm and not shriveled.

Bananas are tropical fruits which are imported to the United States. Bananas of good quality are plump or full, and yellow in color flecked with brown. Green fruit may be a good buy if not to be used immediately. Brown skinned, soft bananas may be a good buy if they are to be used in making banana bread or in some other cooked or baked product.

Pineapples are also tropical fruits. When fully ripened, the pineapple flesh is orange-yellow in color and has a fragrant odor.

Remember to ask yourself these questions when selecting fruits: How is the fruit to be used? Is it in season? Must it be used immediately? What is the best variety for the intended purpose?

Storage of fruits. Fruits are perishable foods and will deteriorate rapidly. Apples and ripe pears may be stored in a cool place such as in the cellar or in the refrigerator. In storing these fruits a circulation of air around the fruit must be present. Wrapping individual apples in newspaper for longer storage is helpful in preventing the fruit from spoiling. If you plan to use the fruit fairly soon, put it in your refrigerator, but remember that some kind of ventilated container is necessary to prevent the fruit from losing moisture during storage. Fresh fruits also absorb and emit odors so they should be separated from other foods when stored.

Bananas are not kept in the refrigerator because when kept too cold they do not ripen properly and have a poor flavor. Their skin color also changes when they are later moved to room temperature. Berries also are not adapted to long periods of storage either at home or at the store.

As mentioned previously, fruits such as eggplant, squash, melons, tomatoes, and avocados can remain at room temperature if more ripening is desired. Otherwise, these fruits should be refrigerated promptly after they are purchased.

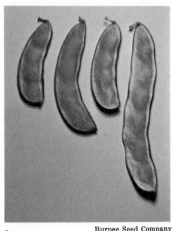

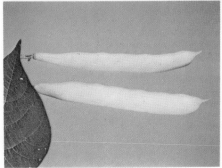

Burpee Seed Company

Beans should be crisp with shiny green or yellow pods.
(1) Richgreen Bush Snap Beans
(2) Pole Lima, Best Pole Lima, Improved Bush Lima, Fordhook Bush Lima
(3) Golden Pole Beans

Dried fruits, such as raisins, prunes, and figs, are usually stored at room temperature in a cupboard. In humid weather, however, they should be placed in the refrigerator to prevent the absorption of moisture from the damp room air.

Selection of vegetables. Although the standards for the selection of vegetables will vary with individual vegetables, factors such as degree of ripeness, freedom from defects and bruises, color, and uniformity of size are always important.

When selecting vegetables, nutritional value should also be considered. Vegetables of a deeper yellow or green color will be higher in vitamin A content than those which are pale in appearance. For example, deep green leaves contain more provitamin A than do leaves which are a lighter green, yellow, or white color.

Regional differences are another factor which should be kept in mind. Geographical location may determine what vegetables are available, their price, and whether they have been imported from another area or are native. Vegetables which have been transported from one region to another may be higher in price and if they are out of season, they may be difficult to obtain. In addition, out of season vegetables may be markedly inferior in quality. Sometimes this inferior quality results from storage of the vegetables before they reach the market.

Table 23

Selection of Vegetables

Vegetable	Qualities
Asparagus	Firm, fresh compact tips
Beans, snap	Tender, firm, clean, shiny, dark green or yellow pod, free from mold
Beets	Smooth surface, relatively free from dirt and uniform in size
Broccoli	Stalk and branches are tender but firm, fresh, clean and compact bud clusters (wilted, flabby stalks and a bloom of bright yellow or purple color indicates overmaturity)
Brussels sprouts	Bright green in color, firm, compact heads
Cabbage, Danish	Firm heads, fairly heavy for size, green in color
Cabbage, red	Resembles Danish cabbage in shape, dark red or purple in color, compact head
Carrots	Spindle-shape, clear orange color (wilted, soft, flabby roots indicate poor quality)
Cauliflower	Heavy head, white or cream colored with fresh and green outer leaves (yellow flowers and leaves indicate poor quality)
Celery	Stalks that are brittle enough to snap easily (yellow or dry leaves indicate aging)
Corn	Yellow or white kernels, plump with little resistance to pressure
Cucumbers	Bright fresh green color, firm, crisp, tender flesh
Eggplant	Firm, heavy, uniform dark, rich purple color, free from scars and decay
Greens: chard, collards, kale, spinach	Young tender leaves free from wilted yellow leaves
Lettuce: Boston, butter head	Fresh, easily separated leaves—not as compact as Iceberg lettuce

Vegetable	Qualities
Lettuce, iceberg	Compact, relatively large head with medium green, crisp outer leaves
Lettuce, leaf	Tender, green, curled loose leaves
Lettuce, romaine	Elongated, crisp, tender, dark green leaves
Mushrooms	Creamy white color (discolored caps indicate poor quality)
Okra	Small to medium size pods, young and tender
Onions, dry	Bright, clear, hard and well-shaped with dry skins
Onions: green, leeks, shallots	Crisp, tender green tops, young tender bulbs
Parsley	Green tops, free from dirt (yellow color indicates overmaturity)
Parsnips	Smooth, firm, clean, well-shaped roots of uniform medium size
Peas	Bright green pods, somewhat velvety to touch and fresh in appearance; pod fairly well filled
Peppers	Fresh, firm, bright appearance
Potatoes, sweet	Well-shaped, smooth, firm, creamy white to deep orange in color, free from scars and decay spots
Potatoes, white	Smooth, shallow eyed, clean
Radishes	Mild flavored, firm, crisp, tender
Rhubarb	Tender, bright colored stalks, crisp
Squash, summer	Fresh, fairly heavy for size, free from blemishes, skin can be easily punctured
Squash, winter	Cream to light green in color, hard rind, firm body
Tomatoes	Firm, but not overripe, uniform red color and plump bodies
Turnips, rutabaga	Thick yellow or buff skin; very firm, crisp, fresh
Turnips, white	Smooth, firm with few leaf scars around the crown, tender white skin with a purple tinge
Watercress	Fresh, young, crisp, tender leaves, medium green in color

Tampala (Red)

Tampala (Green)

Kale

Salad Bowl Lettuce

Iceberg Lettuce

Burpee Seed Company

Burpeeana Lettuce

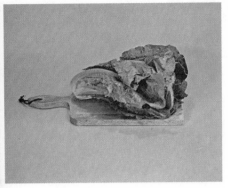

2

(1) Swiss Chard Rhubarb
(2) Romaine Lettuce
(3) Loose-Leaved Chinese Cabbage
(4) Allhead Early Cabbage

1

3

4

The term "greens" applies to any wild or cultivated green vegetable which is eaten raw or cooked. Greens that are commonly used in salads are lettuce (all varieties), escarole, chicory, endive, and watercress. Beet tops, dandelion, spinach, collards, mustard, kale, Swiss chard, and turnip tops are greens most usually cooked. Green leafy vegetables contain many minerals and vitamins, especially iron, calcium, and riboflavin, and are the best sources of vitamin A. They are very low in caloric value.

Cherokee

Irish Cobbler

Katahdin

Pontiac

Green Mountain

Norgold Russet

Chippewa

Kennebec

Netted Gem

Idaho

Sebago

White Rose

Rohm and Haas Company

Keswick   Hunter

Vegetable storage. Most vegetables, like fruits, are perishable foods and should be stored in a cool place promptly after purchasing. Vegetables will lose moisture and shrink in weight and size unless stored in a container which retains this moisture.

Fresh vegetables such as asparagus, snap beans, broccoli, cauliflower, Brussels sprouts, and all leafy vegetables should be loosely wrapped, kept refrigerated, and used as soon as possible.

When fresh vegetables are stored in a place with insufficient moisture, they will become limp and rubbery. The term "flaccid" is used to describe this condition. Placing flaccid vegetables in water helps them revive. For example, when wilted celery is immersed in water, it becomes firm again. The principle behind this process is the loss and gain of water in the cells by osmosis since the water will travel from an area of higher concentration to one of lower concentration.

Since fruits and vegetables bruise easily, they should be handled carefully both at the store and at home. Dropping them on the floor, squeezing them, or crowding them among heavier objects may result in the almost immediate appearance of brownish areas on otherwise quality fruits and vegetables.

Leftover cooked fresh fruits and vegetables can be covered and stored in the refrigerator for several days. They can then be reheated or used in salads or casseroles.

Frozen vegetables should be kept in the freezer section of the refrigerator at 0° F or lower until they are ready to be used. If they are taken out and thawed (or partially thawed), they should be cooked immediately; do not refreeze them.

Guides to produce buying. In summary, these are some guides for wise produce shopping: (1) select your fruit and vegetable market wisely so that you get the freshest possible merchandise, (2) shop before the best fruit and vegetable produce has been already chosen, (3) buy fruits and vegetables when their flavor, color, and texture are at

peak quality and their cost at a minimum, and
(4) buy only quantities that you can use while
the produce is still fresh.

For example, if green peppers are six for 25¢ and
you use them frequently, buy them six at a time.
If, on the other hand, you use only a couple a week,
you'll do better to buy just one or two. Today fresh
produce is frequently packaged in transparent plastic sacks, paper and cellophane bags, and baskets
covered with clear wrap. Make sure that you can
see what you're getting, and be certain that the
quantity is right for your needs.

Select sizes according to use: large tomatoes to
stuff, smaller ones to slice for salad; tiny beets to
cook whole, larger ones to dice; small, heavy
oranges for squeezing, plump, navel oranges for
eating. Remember that the largest is not always
the best. Learning to recognize the many types of
fruits and vegetables available will help you add
variety to your menus and enable you to take advantage of good buys. For example, there are many
varieties of potatoes from which to choose but
Idaho potatoes are especially suited for baking, norgold russets are best boiled or used as French fries,
and cherokees are good for both baking and boiling.
Onions, too, should be selected according to the
purpose for which they will be used. Scallions and
Bermuda onions are at their best in salads, leeks
are more suitable for soups, and the small white
onions are particularly good in stews. In selecting
fruits and vegetables know and check characteristic
color, shape, and odor. Green vegetables should be
crisp and bright. Potatoes should be firm, smooth,
and shallow-eyed. Pick fresh, plump, and non-leaky
berries. Citrus fruits are best when firm and heavy
for their size. At home, handle fruits and vegetables
properly. Store perishable produce in the refrigerator in bins, bags, or vegetable crispers that permit
circulation of air. Potatoes, rutabagas, and onions
can be stored for fairly long periods in a dry, dark,
cool spot—bananas should be kept cool, but not
refrigerated.

THE MANAGEMENT OF FOOD RESOURCES

Selection and Storage of Eggs and Dairy Products

Selection of eggs and dairy products. In Chapters 16 and 17, we discussed the grades of eggs and the kinds of milk. Here our concern will be with some aspects of selection and storage.

The wise food shopper is aware of the ups and downs of food prices and frequently can save money by shifting from one food to another. Eggs are an example. You recall that eggs are sold according to grade and size. In certain areas of the United States homemakers can save money on eggs by buying medium and small eggs. August through November are the months when pullet and other small eggs are abundant. When purchasing eggs, the consumer must decide how he plans to use them. If they are to be poached or fried, a higher grade may be desired because of appearance. If the eggs, however, are to be used in a product such as a pudding or shortened cake, a lower grade egg may be acceptable.

Storage of eggs. Eggs are perishable and must be stored in the refrigerator in a covered container since they tend to lose moisture and absorb odors readily.

Selection of milk. In Chapter 17 you studied about the different kinds of milk available from which the consumer can make a choice. The amount of money spent for milk can be reduced by using evaporated milk or dried milk solids for cooking. Buying milk in larger containers also reduces the cost. Having milk delivered to your door may be more expensive but may be a convenience for which you are willing to pay.

Storage of milk. Milk is stored in the refrigerator in a covered container to retard the growth of bacteria and protect it from odors and undesirable flavors. Dried milk may be stored at ordinary room temperature. Higher temperatures will cause deterioration of the product. To prevent deterioration of the milk, dried milk should be stored in a container with a tight-fitting cover to keep out air and moisture. Evaporated milk may be stored at room temperature on the shelf until it is opened. Once the can is opened, however, the milk should be refrigerated. Sweetened condensed milk must also be stored in the refrigerator once the can has been opened.

Cheese. The most expensive variety of cheese is not necessarily the one with the highest food value. Most expensive cheeses are valued because of their flavor and texture. Cheese, like other products, should be selected according to use. Cheese for cooking should have excellent blending and melting qualities as well as good flavor. Soft cheese spoils quickly and must be placed in a covered container and refrigerated until consumed. Hard and semi-hard cheese should also be stored at low temperatures to avoid deterioration.

Selection and Storage of Meat, Poultry, and Fish

Selection of meat. Meat is probably the most expensive item in your food budget and accounts for roughly 32¢ of your shopping dollar. If meat is packaged in film, the label appearing on the package may help you in making your selection. Usually this information consists of name of cut, packer, retailer or government grade, weight, price per pound, and total price.

Buying meat from a dealer who handles high-quality meat is important. Take advantage of lower prices which result from heavy seasonal supplies of particular meats. Watch for merchants' "specials" on various cuts. Use less tender cuts and cook them by methods recommended for tenderizing. For instance, flank steak is one of the cheaper cuts in the hind quarter of beef. It is nutritious and can be prepared most appetizingly. Figure the cost per serving of meat. The amount of bone and fat not eaten varies with different cuts. In some cuts there is little or no waste.

Meat storage. Fresh meat such as chops, steaks, roasts, and stew pieces should be unwrapped and then rewrapped loosely in wax paper to allow some air to enter. All fresh meat should be stored in the coldest part of the refrigerator and cooked within a few days. Ground meat is especially perishable. Left-over cooked meat should be stored in the refrigerator in a covered container to retain the moisture.

Selecting ready-to-eat meats. Prepared meats have increased in kind and variety and have been improved in quality to meet consumer demands. Ready-to-eat meats which are sliced and wrapped in cellophane, waxed paper, or foil will keep about three or four days in the refrigerator. Unsliced, semi-dry sausage will keep about two weeks when refrigerated.

Selecting smoked and cured meats. Meat packers have their own recipes for curing and smoking each product. Learn the brands you like. Price alone should not influence your purchase. Cured hams should be golden brown on the outside, firm, uniformly pink on the inside, and finely streaked with fat. Bacon of best quality should be well streaked with lean. It will be more expensive than bacon with little lean but it will hold its size when cooked.

Storage. All cured meat should be sealed from air. It keeps longer than fresh meat but may change flavor during storage. If it is to be stored for a long period of time, wrap for freezing and place in the freezing compartment of a refrigerator or in a freezer.

THE MANAGEMENT OF FOOD RESOURCES

Selection of poultry. Poultry labels should be read and grade markings and official inspection marks checked. Your selection of poultry, especially chickens, will depend largely on how you plan to cook the bird and how many servings you need. Younger chickens are used for frying, broiling, and roasting, while older chickens are used for stewing. For a roasting turkey, about one-half pound ready-to-cook weight per serving is adequate. For a broiled, fried, or fricasseed bird, allow one-half to three-fourths pound ready-to-cook weight per serving.

Another consideration you will want to make in selecting poultry is the style of processing—ready-to-cook or dressed. Dressed poultry includes the head, feet, and viscera. You pay for this waste. A ready-to-cook bird will cost a few cents more per pound than a dressed bird. Some turkeys and chickens complete with stuffing are sold ready for the oven and you will have to decide whether to buy a bird stuffed or unstuffed. The stuffed product may cost more.

Storage of poultry. The wrapping of chilled, tightly packaged poultry should be loosened and the poultry should be refrigerated immediately. Poultry should be used as soon as possible because it is highly perishable and will show signs of deterioration very rapidly.

Selection of fish. Fresh fish is easily identified: the eyes are bright, clear and bulging; the gills are reddish-pink; the surface is free from dirt or slime; the flesh is firm to the touch. A fish just taken from the water has practically no "fishy" odor. The odor of the fish becomes more pronounced with the passage of time, but it should not be disagreeably strong when the fish is bought. Fish is marketed in several forms. Among these are the following:

Table 24	
Market Forms of Fish	
Whole or round	Fish as they come from the water. They must be scaled or skinned, and eviscerated before cooking. Head, tail, and fins may be removed.
Drawn	Fish is marketed with only entrails removed.
Dressed	Fish is scaled and drawn. Steaks are cross sections of larger sizes of dressed fish.
Fillet	Sides of fish cut lengthwise away from the backbone.
Butterfly fillet	Two sides of the fish are cut away from the backbone, but are held together by the uncut under-part of the fish.
Sticks	Sections may be cut crosswise or lengthwise from fillets into portions of uniform length and thickness.

Market forms of fish.

The market forms of shellfish vary with the type: alive, in the shell, shucked, headless, and cooked.

Table 25

Market Forms of Shellfish

Kind	Market Form
Oysters	Alive in shell, or shucked
Clams	Alive in shell, or shucked
Scallops	Shucked, fresh
Mussels	Alive in shell
Crabs	Cooked, picked crabmeat
Lobster	Alive, cooked, frozen, or canned
Shrimp	Frozen in shell, canned, raw, headless, and cooked in the shell

Fish and shellfish spoil very rapidly; thus, they are usually packed and stored in ice until bought. Fish and shellfish should be refrigerated until used and used promptly.

Today, almost any variety of fish can be bought already cleaned and dressed, in fillets or steaks. Knowing how to clean and prepare fish for cooking is important, however, especially if you live in an area where you can catch your own fish, if you wish fillets or steaks of a certain size and thickness, or if you wish to economize by buying whole fish and cleaning it yourself. The preparation of shellfish is another valuable technique to know since many shellfish are alive and in the shell when purchased. On the following eight pages are photographs which illustrate how to clean fish, cut a fillet or steak, open clams and oysters, shell and devein shrimp, and boil and cut lobsters.

Since scales are more easily removed from a wet fish, soak the fish in cold water for a few minutes before scaling. Lay the fish on the table and with one hand hold the fish firmly by the head. Holding a knife almost vertical, scrape off the scales, working from tail toward head. Take care to remove all scales near the base of the fins and head.

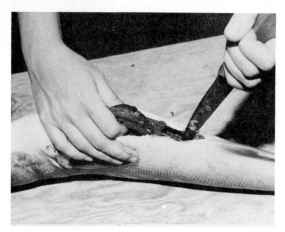

Cut the entire length of the belly from the vent (anal opening) to the head and remove the entrails.

Remove the head, including the pectoral fins, by cutting above the collarbone.

U.S. Bureau of Commercial Fisheries

If the backbone is large, cut down to it on each side of the fish, and then snap the backbone by bending it over the edge of the cutting board or table. Cut any remaining flesh which holds the head to the body. Cut off the tail.

Remove the dorsal or large back fin by cutting the flesh along both sides of the fin.

Give the fin a quick pull forward toward the head of the fish and remove the fin with the root bones attached. Remove the other fins in the same manner. Never trim the fins off with shears or a knife since the bones at the base will be left in the fish. Wash the fish in cold running water, removing the blood, any remaining viscera, and membranes. The fish is now dressed or pan dressed, depending on its size, and is ready for cooking.

U.S. Bureau of Commercial Fisheries

THE MANAGEMENT OF FOOD RESOURCES

With a sharp knife, cut through the flesh along the back from the tail to just behind the head.

Then cut down to the backbone just above the collarbone. Turn the knife flat and cut the flesh along the backbone to the tail, allowing the knife to run over the rib bones.

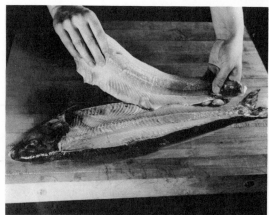

Lift off the entire side of the fish in one piece. Turn the fish over and repeat the steps on the other side.

U.S. Bureau of Commercial Fisheries

U.S. Bureau of Commercial Fisheries

If you wish, you may skin the fillets. Lay the fillets flat on the cutting board or table, skin side down. Hold the tail end with your fingers, and with a knife cut through the flesh to the skin about one-half inch from the end of the fillet. Flatten the knife on the skin and cut the flesh away from the skin by pushing the knife forward while holding the free end of the skin firmly between your fingers.

Large fish may be cut crosswise into steaks. Steaks are usually cut three-quarters to one inch thick but this thickness can be varied according to individual taste.

U.S. Bureau of Commercial Fisheries

Wash the clams thoroughly, discarding any broken-shell or dead clams. Hold the clam in the palm of one hand with the shell's hinge against the palm. Insert a slender, strong, sharp knife between the halves of the shell and cut around the clam.

Twist the knife slightly to pry open the shell.

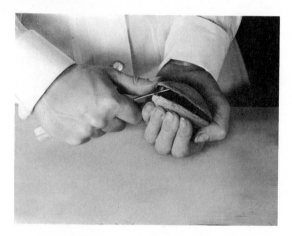

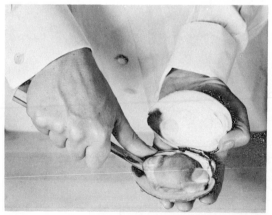

Cut both muscles free from the two halves of the shell. If the clam is to be served on the half shell, remove only one-half of the shell. If the clam is to be used in a recipe, remove and rinse the meat.

U.S. Bureau of Commercial Fisheries

Wash and rinse the oyster thoroughly in cold water. Place it on a table, flat shell up, and hold it with the left hand. Break off the thin end or "bill" with a hammer.

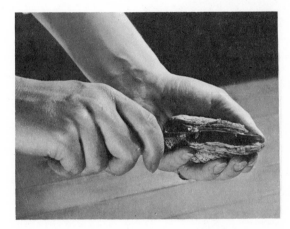

Next, force an oyster knife between the shells at or near the thin end. Cut the large adductor muscle close to the flat upper shell to which it is attached and remove the shell.

Cut the lower end of the same muscle, which is attached to the deep half of the shell. Leave the oyster loose in the shell if it is to be served on the half shell. After shucking, examine the oysters for bits of shell, paying particular attention to the muscle, to which pieces of shell sometimes adhere.

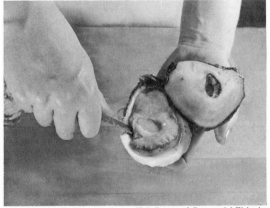

U.S. Bureau of Commercial Fisheries

THE MANAGEMENT OF FOOD RESOURCES

Hold the shrimp in your left hand and carefully peel the shell off with your right hand. The shell should peel off easily in segments.

Make a shallow cut down the middle of the back of the shrimp with a slender, sharp knife. Carefully pull the vein out. If the vein breaks, insert the knife again and repeat the process in as many places as necessary.

Boiling is the basic method of cooking raw shrimp. The shrimp may be boiled and then peeled, or they may be peeled and then boiled. The order is largely a matter of personal preference. Either way, 1½ pounds of raw shrimp will yield about ¾ pound of peeled, cleaned, and cooked shrimp.

U.S. Bureau of Commercial Fisheries

Plunge live lobster headfirst into boiling salted water. Cover and return to boiling point. Simmer for 20 minutes. Drain.

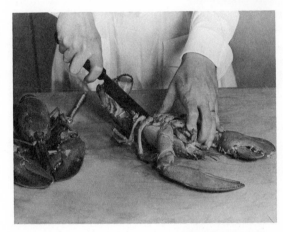

Place lobster on its back. With a sharp knife cut in half lengthwise. Remove the stomach, which is just in back of the head, and the intestinal vein, which runs from the stomach to the tip of the tail. Do not discard the green liver and coral roe; they are delicious.

Use a lobster-cracker or nutcracker to break the shell of the big claws. Small cocktail forks can be used to remove the meat from the tail. Otherwise a regular knife and fork can be used to cut the rest of the lobster meat.

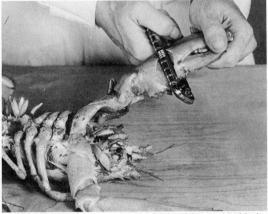

U.S. Bureau of Commercial Fisheries

Selection of frozen meat, poultry, and fish. Many frozen meats are available and may be good buys if the consumer has adequate storage space for items not to be used immediately. The United States government has defined standards for frozen poultry pies, the labels of which must also list the ingredients. Grades A, B, and Substandard have been defined for fish sticks.

Storage of frozen foods. All frozen products should be stored at 0° F and kept frozen until used. All products should be thawed according to the manufacturer's directions. If products thaw before the desired time for use, *they should not be refrozen* but cooked immediately.

Selection and Storage of Cereals and Cereal Products

Selection of cereals. Grains are processed into many kinds of flour and meals, breakfast cereals, spaghetti, macaroni, and noodles. When selecting flour you should consider how you intend to use it. All-purpose flour will take care of many needs, but cake flour or some other flour may be needed for special purposes. The amount of flour you purchase will depend upon how much you need, how long it may be on hand, and facilities for storage. Flour is marketed in 25, 10, 5, and 2 pound bags. Cornmeal is used more in some parts of the United States than others. Both white and yellow cornmeal are available.

Either dry breakfast cereals or ones which are to be cooked are on the market. Family preference is always a guide to selection. Ready-to-serve cereals may be more expensive than those to be cooked. However, saving time may be your objective, and therefore the first kind may be your choice. Read the labels to be sure of the best value in terms of weight and nutrients.

Pastas such as macaroni, spaghetti, and noodles are offered to the consumer in many sizes and shapes. Again, the one you select should be determined by your needs. The price of breads and rolls of various kinds may also vary widely. Bread prices may range from 19¢ to 44¢ for a one-pound loaf. You as the consumer need to be aware of how much bread you are getting for your money.

Storage of cereals and cereal products. Cereals should be sealed in airtight containers and stored in a dry place at a temperature of about 70° F. Otherwise, exposure to moisture will cause ready-to-eat cereals to become less crisp and change in flavor. Bread may be frozen for future use.

Selection and Storage of Canned Goods

Selecting canned food. How many cans and jars of food would you say the average family uses annually? It is estimated to be 680. That is approximately 600 pounds of food per household and 137.5 pounds per person. From

Table 26

Size and Content of Cans and Common Use

Industry Term	Approx. Net Wt. or Fluid Meas. (Check Label)	Approx. Cups	Principal Products
8 oz.	8 oz.	1	Fruits, vegetables, specialties* for small families. 2 servings.
Picnic	10½ to 12 oz.	1¼	Mainly condensed soups. Some fruits, vegetables, meat, fish, specialties.* 3 servings.
12 oz. (vacuum)	12 oz.	1½	Principally for vacuum-packed corn. 3 to 4 servings.
No. 300	14 to 16 oz.	1¾	Pork and beans, baked beans, meat products, cranberry sauce, blueberries, specialties.* 3 to 4 servings.
No. 303	16 to 17 oz.	2	Principal size for fruits and vegetables. Some meat products, ready-to-serve soups, specialties.* 4 servings.
No. 2	1 lb. 4 oz. or 1 pt. 2 fl. oz.	2½	Juices,† ready-to-serve soups, some specialties,* pineapple, apple slices. No longer in popular use for most fruits and vegetables. 5 servings.
No. 2½	1 lb. 13 oz.	3½	Fruits, some vegetables (pumpkin, sauerkraut, spinach and other greens, tomatoes). 7 servings.
No. 3 cyl. or 46 fl. oz.	3 lb. 3 oz. or 1 qt. 14 fl. oz.	5¾	Fruit and vegetable juices,† pork and beans. Institutional size for condensed soups, some vegetables. 10 to 12 servings.

Note: Meats, fish, and seafood are almost entirely advertised and sold under weight terminology.

*Specialties—Food combinations prepared by special manufacturer's recipe. For instance, spaghetti and meat sauce, Spanish-style rice, etc.

†Juices are now being packed in a number of other can sizes, including the one-quart size.

National Canners Association

these figures you can see that it is important to know how to shop for canned foods in order to get the desired flavor, texture, and quality at the most economical prices. Your best guide to buying canned foods is the label on the can. By experience in shopping you will learn what size can to buy based on the number of servings you want. Remember that the large, economy size of a product is only economical when you are able to use the entire amount at one time or have room to store the unused portion for use in the near future.

Storage of canned goods. If you see a bulging or leaking can of food on a shelf in the market or at home, don't buy or use it. This is an indication the food is spoiling. However, slight dents in cans, light rust, or stains on the label should not affect the contents. Without tasting, discard the contents of any can of food about which you have any doubts.

Store canned foods in a dry, moderately cool area, away from heat. To save yourself time, arrange canned foods in categories on the shelf—vegetables in one place, soups in another, and fruits in still another. This arrangement will make it easier for you to keep your food stocks in good supply. As soon as you use an item, mark it down on your list for replacement. An emergency shelf of easy-to-prepare canned foods is an invaluable aid when someone is ill or housebound or when unexpected guests visit.

Once food has been carefully selected and cared for, the next important step is the cooking of it. Whether a family will actually benefit to the fullest degree from the chosen food depends a great deal on its careful preparation.

MAJOR IDEAS

The following statements give the main ideas within the chapter you have just studied. Be sure you know the words underscored in these statements and in the questions to follow.

1. The quality of fresh fruits and vegetables is determined by their variety, size, color, degree of ripeness, and number of defects or blemishes.
2. Because of their high degree of perishability, fresh fruits and vegetables must be handled, selected, stored, and prepared with care if their appearance and nutritive value are to be retained.
3. Eggs are marketed according to grades which indicate size and general quality. Maintenance of quality is controlled by proper handling and storage.
4. Milk can be purchased in several different forms. The forms differ in the ways in which they can be used; how they can be stored successfully; how they can influence total food expenses.

5. The grade, the proportion of bone to muscle tissue, the cost per serving, and the length of time required for preparation are all factors to consider when selecting meats and poultry. Once meat and poultry are purchased, proper wrapping and storage are required if quality is to be retained.

6. Fresh fish and seafood spoil quickly, so care must be taken in making selections of these foods in the market.

7. Cereal foods, available in many forms, must be stored in dry airtight containers or packages if they are to keep their best quality.

8. Labels which give full information as to contents, measure, quality, number of servings, weight, and additives are most helpful to the consumer.

9. Choosing cheaper items, although they may not be as well suited for a particular use as more expensive products, is one way of curbing costs.

QUESTIONS TO STUDY

SELECTION AND STORAGE OF FRUITS AND VEGETABLES

1. What are some of the factors that you would consider in buying oranges?

2. Describe the way in which you would decide the variety of apples to buy for making an apple pie.

3. In what ways are avocados different from other fruits?

4. What precautions must be taken in storing citrus fruits?

5. Describe the standards used in the selection of fresh vegetables.

6. In general, what guides do you follow in selecting produce such as lettuce, carrots, potatoes, and green beans?

7. Why are cans of food which have bulging tops and bottoms considered unsafe for use?

8. Why is it important that canned goods be stored away from heat?

9. When shopping for fresh produce in the market, why is it best not to pinch and handle each item?

SELECTION AND STORAGE OF EGGS AND DAIRY PRODUCTS

1. List the factors which should be considered when buying fresh eggs.

2. Describe the recommended method for storing fresh eggs. Why is this a good method?

3. Milk is sold in various forms. Describe the way in which each type is best stored.

4. What factors most greatly influence the cost of cheese? How should cheese be stored?

SELECTION AND STORAGE OF MEAT, POULTRY, AND FISH

1. Today many meats are marketed in packages with labels which give some information to the consumer. In what respects is this prepackaging an advantage? A disadvantage?

2. Describe the way in which fresh meat should be stored at home.

3. Explain the differences between ready-to-cook and dressed poultry.

4. List the means of identifying fresh fish.

5. In what forms is fish marketed?

6. Describe the best methods for keeping fish and shellfish at home.

SELECTION AND STORAGE OF CEREALS AND CEREAL PRODUCTS

1. List some cereal products that are available on the market.

2. What are the general steps to remember in storing cereals and cereal products?

3. Name as many different kinds of pasta as you can. Describe them.

4. What factors do you consider in deciding what cereals to buy?

SELECTION AND STORAGE OF CANNED GOODS

1. What information should appear on the labels of canned foods?

2. Why is it important to store cans of food properly?

BIBLIOGRAPHY

CARSON, RACHEL, *Food from the Sea.* Bulletin 33, Fish and Wildlife Service, U. S. Department of the Interior, Washington, D. C., 1941.

DEAN, G. C., "Keeping Food Safely at Home: Role of Bacteria in Food Poisoning, With Questions and Answers on Food Safety." *PTA Magazine*, Vol. 60, June 1966, pp. 14–16.

Fish and Shellfish of the Middle Atlantic Coast. Bulletin 38, Fish and Wildlife Service, U. S. Department of the Interior, Washington, D. C., 1941.

Fruit and Vegetables, Vol. I. Chicago Quartermaster Food and Container Institute for the Armed Forces, 1946, pp. 4, 9, 17, 20, 27, 31, 36.

Green Vegetables for Good Eating. Home and Garden Bulletin 41, U. S. Department of Agriculture, Washington, D. C., 1954.

How to Buy Eggs. Home and Garden Bulletin 26, U. S. Department of Agriculture, Washington, D. C. (undated).

"How Long Foods Keep in Your Refrigerator, in Your Freezer." *Changing Times*, Vol. 20, November 1966, pp. 13–14.

"How to Store Foods." *American Home*, Vol. 70, March 1967, p. 119.

The Inspection Stamp as Guide to Wholesome Meat. Agricultural Information Bulletin 92, U. S. Department of Agriculture, Washington, D. C., 1952.

McColloch, L. P., *Home Storage of Vegetables and Fruits.* Farmers Bulletin 1939, U. S. Department of Agriculture, Washington, D. C., 1960.

Poultry Inspection: A Consumers' Safeguard. Agricultural Marketing Service Bulletin PA–299, U. S. Department of Agriculture, Washington, D. C., 1959.

Shell Eggs: U. S. Standards for Quality of Individual. U. S. Department of Agriculture, Washington, D. C., 1955.

Shopper's Guide to U. S. Grades for Food. Home and Garden Bulletin 58, U. S. Department of Agriculture, Washington, D. C., 1958.

"Shopping for Food; How It's Changing." *U. S. News and World Report*, Vol. 60, May 1966, p. 12.

"Summer Vegetables." *Better Homes and Gardens*, Vol. 44, August 1966, pp. 85–86.

Tips on Selection of Fruits and Vegetables. Marketing Bulletin No. 13, U. S. Department of Agriculture, Washington, D. C., 1961.

U. S. Grades for Beef. Marketing Bulletin No. 15. U. S. Department of Agriculture, Washington, D. C., 1960.

"What's in a Brand of Frozen Food?" *Consumer Reports*, Vol. 31, May 1966, p. 218.

25 MEAL MANAGEMENT AND SERVICE

In the first chapter of Part III it was stated that when the homemaker plans meals she must be concerned with the amount of time and energy it will take to prepare each meal. This chapter will present some of the ways the homemaker can save time and energy in the management of family meals.

Management of time is a way of life in the United States. If you think about it, you will probably realize that most of your life is controlled by time—time to go to bed, time to go to school, time to do your homework, time to get married, etc. The person who can manage time probably attains his goals much more easily than the person who is unable to manage his time effectively. Preparing a meal also requires efficient management of time.

Saving Time, Steps, and Motions

To know how you're going to manage your time in relation to a meal, you will need to know how long it takes to prepare the food planned for in the menu. Naturally some menus take much longer than others. For example, a menu calling for canned soup, sandwich, and relish dish will take a great deal less time to prepare than one calling for roast stuffed turkey with all the trimmings.

A *written time schedule* is one way to organize a meal more effectively. Your plan should be flexible and practical.

Your schedule should include the jobs to be done, the steps to be followed, and a rough allotment of the time you believe it will take you to carry out each job. Some of the advantages of having a schedule, especially when you are first learning to prepare meals, are these: (1) it prevents you from forgetting some part of the job, (2) it enables you to have everything ready at the same time, (3) it helps you know what jobs need to be done and how to dovetail jobs when possible, (4) it helps you to decide what jobs to do and when, and (5) it gives you an idea of the total amount of time which the menu requires.

If you are the kind of person who does not think a written schedule is necessary, you may want to try a little experiment to see how long it takes to prepare and serve a meal with a schedule and how long it takes for the same meal without a schedule. Of course, if you have prepared the same menu many times, you are probably so familiar with the preparation that a written schedule would not be necessary. Here is how we might develop a work plan for the following menu.

414

The American Home

MENU

Chicken Oriental
Romaine and Cucumber Salad
Hot Buttered Rolls
Lemonade Souffle
Fortune Cookies
Tea   Milk

Job to Be Done	Time to Begin	Time to Finish
Prepare lemonade souffle 3 to 4 hours ahead or night before	8:00 A.M.	8:30–chill 3 to 4 hours
Prepare salad, put in refrigerator	10:00 A.M.	10:35 A.M.
Set table	10:35 A.M.	10:45 A.M.
Prepare chicken oriental	10:45 A.M.	11:55 A.M.
Turn on oven	11:15 A.M.	
Heat rolls	11:40 A.M.	11:55 A.M.
Heat water and make tea	11:40 A.M.	11:55 A.M.
Place dishes on tray for dessert, include fortune cookies	11:43 A.M.	11:48 A.M.
Pour tea or milk	11:55 A.M.	
Place salad on table		
Put heated rolls in basket		
Serve chicken oriental	11:58 A.M.	
Meal is served	12:00	

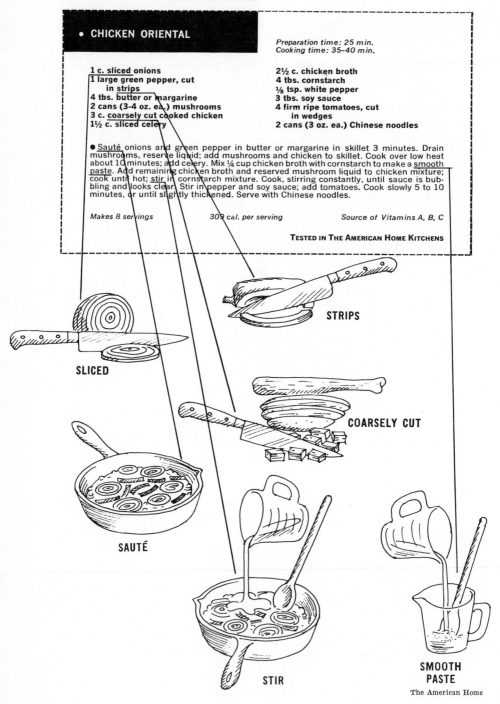

● CHICKEN ORIENTAL

Preparation time: 25 min.
Cooking time: 35–40 min.

1 c. sliced onions
1 large green pepper, cut
   in strips
4 tbs. butter or margarine
2 cans (3-4 oz. ea.) mushrooms
3 c. coarsely cut cooked chicken
1½ c. sliced celery

2½ c. chicken broth
4 tbs. cornstarch
⅛ tsp. white pepper
3 tbs. soy sauce
4 firm ripe tomatoes, cut
   in wedges
2 cans (3 oz. ea.) Chinese noodles

● Sauté onions and green pepper in butter or margarine in skillet 3 minutes. Drain mushrooms, reserve liquid; add mushrooms and chicken to skillet. Cook over low heat about 10 minutes; add celery. Mix ¼ cup chicken broth with cornstarch to make a smooth paste. Add remaining chicken broth and reserved mushroom liquid to chicken mixture; cook until hot; stir in cornstarch mixture. Cook, stirring constantly, until sauce is bubbling and looks clear. Stir in pepper and soy sauce; add tomatoes. Cook slowly 5 to 10 minutes, or until slightly thickened. Serve with Chinese noodles.

Makes 8 servings   *309 cal. per serving*   *Source of Vitamins A, B, C*

TESTED IN THE AMERICAN HOME KITCHENS

STRIPS

SLICED

COARSELY CUT

SAUTÉ

STIR

SMOOTH PASTE

The American Home

● LEMONADE SOUFFLÉ

Preparation time: 30 min.
Chilling time: 3 to 4 hours

⅔ c. sugar
3 envelopes unflavored gelatin
6 egg yolks, slightly beaten
1½ c. water
2 tsp. grated lemon rind

½ c. lemon juice
6 egg whites
⅓ c. sugar
2 c. heavy cream, whipped

● Fold long strip of wax paper in half lengthwise. Tie securely around 1-quart soufflé dish, so collar will hold soufflé mixture above dish until it sets. Combine sugar and gelatin in saucepan. Blend egg yolks and water; stir into sugar mixture. Cook over medium heat, stirring constantly, until mixture just comes to boiling; do not boil. Cool; add lemon rind and juice; chill until mixture mounds slightly when spooned. Beat egg whites until frothy; add sugar slowly; continue to beat until stiff and glossy. Fold meringue into chilled mixture; fold in whipped cream. Pour into prepared dish; chill 3 to 4 hours, or until set. Carefully peel off wax paper. Garnish with orange slices, lime wedges, and additional whipped cream, if desired.

Makes 8 servings   *323 cal per serving*   *Source of Vitamins A, B, C*

TESTED IN THE AMERICAN HOME KITCHENS

BLEND

STIFF

WEDGES

FROTHY

FOLD

Saving time by changing the menu. How could this menu be changed to use less time? One time-saving idea would be to change the dessert to canned mandarin oranges which would carry out the theme but eliminate the preparation of the souffle. An oriental casserole which could be prepared hours ahead and then reheated would also save time.

Reading directions. Once you have a schedule developed, you will need to proceed logically from step to step. Read through special directions. Think through each process. Consider in advance the utensils you will need and the steps you will follow. Try to avoid unnecessary interruption and backtracking.

Understanding the recipe. Understanding the recipes used is another necessity in meal management. As a beginning, consider the recipes used in the menu on page 415.

A few terms which may help you prepare recipes more successfully are listed below:

Bake—to cook by dry heat

Beat—to make a mixture smooth or to introduce air by using a brisk, regular motion that lifts the mixture over and over

Blanch—to pour on boiling water, drain, and rinse in cold water

Cream—to work one or more foods until soft and creamy

Cut and fold—to combine by using two motions, cutting vertically through the mixture and turning it over and over

Dice—to cut into cubes

Dredge—to sprinkle or coat with flour or another fine substance

Knead—to manipulate with a pressing motion accompanied by folding and stretching the product

Marinate—to treat with a marinade or oil-acid mixture

Scallop—to bake food, usually cut in pieces, with a sauce or other liquid

Simmer—to cook in a liquid at a temperature of about 185° F.

Stir-fry—to toss food lightly in a skillet either by using a fork or shaking the pan

Whip—to beat rapidly to produce expansion due to incorporation of air

Experimenting with seasonings. There are many types of seasonings which give additional flavor to foods. Spices, such as cinnamon, mustard, cloves, anise, caraway, nutmeg, and curry, are made from various parts of tropical plants, shrubs, and trees. Flavoring extracts, such as vanilla, are solutions of aromatic oils in alcohol. Ginger and horseradish (roots) and mushrooms and truffles (fungus plants) are also used to season foods.

Grown especially for condimental purposes, herbs are used in small amounts, green or dried. Since herb flavors are volatile, they should be added at the last of the cooking process. The following chart suggests how herbs can be used to flavor different foods.

HERB BUTTER: BLEND 1 TBSP. FRESH OR ⅓ TSP. DRIED HERBS WITH 4 TBSP. (2 oz) FRESH BUTTER. ADD DASH OF LEMON JUICE. USE WITH COOKED VEGETABLES... SPREAD ON BROILED MEATS — HAMBURGERS

SAVORY

BASIL
IN ITALY—LOVE
IN GREECE—HATE

SAGE
IMMORTALITY

- **WINTER SAVORY**—GIVES IMPORTANT ACCENT TO CHICKEN—TURKEY STUFFING. ADD TO SAUSAGE MEAT, COMBINE WITH PARSLEY AND ONION JUICE TO GIVE ZEST TO FRENCH OMELETTES. (PERENNIAL—MINT FAMILY)
- **SUMMER SAVORY**—IMPROVES FLAVOR OF ANY MEAT, POULTRY OR EGG DISH. USE IN SOUPS, MUSHROOM SAUCE. (ANNUAL)

BASIL — SPRINKLE LIGHTLY ON LAMB CHOPS—BROIL. ADD TO TOMATO, EGG, SHRIMP DISHES. GARNISH CUCUMBERS. TOSS IN GREEN SALADS. SPICY ODOR AND TASTE (ANNUAL)

SAGE — USE SPARINGLY WITH ONION FOR STUFFING PORK, DUCKS AND GEESE. RUB ON OUTSIDE OF FRESH PORK. BLEND SOUPÇON WITH COTTAGE OR CREAM CHEESE. STEEP DRIED LEAVES FOR TEA. (PERENNIAL—MINT FAMILY)

DILL
TO LULL

CHERVIL

CHIVES
AN ALLIUM —THE UNIVERSE

DILL — USE FRESHLY CHOPPED LEAVES ALONE IN BUTTER FOR BROILED OR FRIED MEATS, FISH. ADD TO FISH SAUCES, — CREAMED OR FRICASSEED CHICKEN. FRUITING UMBELS USED FOR FLAVORING PICKLES. (ANNUAL)

CHERVIL — ADDS DELIGHTFUL FLAVOR TO SALADS, SALAD DRESSINGS. USE IN OMELETTES, SOUPS, STEWS. IMPORTANT INGREDIENT IN "LES FINES HERBES." MILDLY ANISE IN FLAVOR. (ANNUAL)

CHIVES — GARNISH CREAM SOUPS, BOILED, BAKED, WHIPPED POTATOES. USE IN CREAM CHEESE, BUTTER SPREADS, SALADS, OMELETTES. (PERENNIAL)

MARJORAM
JOY

THYME
BRAVERY

ROSEMARY
REMEMBRANCE

MARJORAM — GOOD WITH VEAL—LIVER. NICE IN HERB BUTTER SPREAD ON COLD ROAST—BEEF SANDWICHES. ADDS NEW FLAVOR TO STRING BEANS—SPINACH. USE IN EGG DISHES, POULTRY STUFFING, STEWS, POT ROASTS. WARM AROMATIC FLAVOR. AIDS DIGESTION. (PERENNIAL)

THYME — BLEND WITH OTHER HERBS. USE IN SOUPS, CLAM CHOWDER, IN GRAVIES, POULTRY STUFFING, IN MEAT, EGG, CHEESE DISHES. (PERENNIAL)

ROSEMARY — ANOTHER MEMBER OF MINT FAMILY, VERY SPICY ODOR. USE SPARINGLY FOR NEW ACCENT IN CREAM SOUPS, SAUCES, POULTRY, STEWS. BLEND PARSLEY, BIT OF ROSEMARY WITH SWEET BUTTER—SPREAD UNDER SKIN OF CHICKEN BREASTS—ROAST. (PERENNIAL)

OREGANO
JOY-OF-THE-MOUNTAIN

TARRAGON
TO SHARE

MINT
WISDOM

OREGANO — PUNGENT COUSIN OF MARJORAM. SPRINKLE ON LEG OF LAMB—ROAST. SHAKE ON PIZZA, ADD TO ITALIAN SAUCES. FINE IN OMELETTES, PORK, CHICKEN. (PERENNIAL)

TARRAGON — ADDS TOUCH TO TARTER SAUCE. USE IN FISH SAUCES, CHICKEN DISHES, GREEN SALADS, SALAD DRESSINGS, VINEGAR. A SWEET, ANISE-SCENTED HERB OF THE ASTER FAMILY. (PERENNIAL)

MINT — FOR SAUCES TO ADORN LAMB—ICE CREAM. FOR MINTED CARROTS—PEAS—CREAM OF PEA SOUP—TEA—FRUIT DRINKS. (PERENNIAL)

PUNGENT HERBS	HERBS FOR ACCENT	HERBS FOR BLENDING
ROSEMARY	MARJORAM	SUMMER SAVORY
SAGE	BASIL	CHERVIL
WINTER SAVORY	DILL	CHIVES
	MINT	PARSLEY
	TARRAGON	
	THYME	

1. USE HERBS WITH A LIGHT HAND.
2. SELECT A LEADING FLAVOR AND COMBINE TWO TO FOUR LESS PRONOUNCED FLAVORS WITH IT.
3. NEVER EMPHASIZE MORE THAN ONE OF THE PUNGENT HERBS IN A BLEND.

PASTRIES, CANDIES, AND DRINKS.

Learning Measurements. Learning equivalent measures and approximate substitutions for ingredients is also an important time-saver.

Table 27

Unit	Equivalent Unit
1 tablespoon	3 teaspoons
16 tablespoons	1 cup
$\frac{1}{4}$ cup	4 tablespoons
$\frac{1}{3}$ cup	$5\frac{1}{3}$ tablespoons
1 pint	2 cups
2 pints	1 quart
1 gallon	4 quarts
1 pound	16 ounces
1 pound sugar	2 cups
1 pound rice	2 cups
1 pound of potatoes	2 cups diced
$\frac{1}{4}$ pound marshmallows	15–16
juice of 1 lemon	about 3 tablespoons
juice of 1 orange	about $\frac{1}{2}$ cup
1 ounce of chocolate	1 square

Table 28

1 tablespoon flour	$\frac{1}{2}$ tablespoon cornstarch, or 2 teaspoons quick-cooking tapioca
1 cup cake flour	$\frac{7}{8}$ cup all-purpose flour
1 cup honey	$1\frac{1}{4}$ cups sugar plus $\frac{1}{4}$ cup liquid
1 cup butter	1 cup margarine
	$\frac{7}{8}$ to 1 cup hydrogenated fat plus $\frac{1}{2}$ teaspoon salt
1 ounce chocolate	3 tablespoons cocoa plus 1 tablespoon fat
1 cup coffee cream (20 percent)	3 tablespoons butter plus about $\frac{7}{8}$ cup milk
1 cup heavy cream (40 percent)	$\frac{1}{3}$ cup butter plus about $\frac{3}{4}$ cup milk
1 cup whole milk	1 cup reconstituted nonfat dry milk plus 2 teaspoons table fat
1 cup buttermilk or sour milk	1 tablespoon vinegar or lemon juice plus sweet milk to make 1 cup (let stand 5 minutes)
1 teaspoon tartrate baking powder	$\frac{1}{4}$ teaspoon baking soda plus $\frac{1}{2}$ teaspoon cream of tartar

Collecting the tools. Assemble all the utensils at one time and then all the supplies. Grease baking pans before you begin to mix together the ingredients. The oven should be preheated well in advance of the time it will be needed for a baked product. If a rubber scraper is available, use it for cleaning out mixing bowls as well as scraping dishes before washing either by hand or machine.

Saving use of cooking utensils. A big item in saving time, steps, and motions is using as few cooking utensils as you can. Using equipment to measure dry ingredients and then wet ingredients can cut down on the pieces of equipment to wash.

Some other helpful ideas to consider are to measure or sift dry ingredients onto wax paper or a paper towel; rinse out all equipment as used to cut down on scouring and soaking of dishes; cook and serve in the same utensil whenever possible.

Selecting right tool for the job. In selecting the tools for your work choose efficient tools and, of course, select the best tool for each particular job. Gadgets are sometimes more convenient but does their use justify space in the kitchen drawer or cupboard?

Combining related jobs. Combining related jobs can also save time and energy. For example, if you need to be in the kitchen to keep an eye on the food, do some necessary job such as washing, drying, and putting away dishes which have been used for preparation, setting the table for the meal, organizing your recipes, preparing a shopping list, relining shelves, mopping the floor, cleaning the refrigerator or maybe even straightening the kitchen drawers. This use of time will prevent extensive cleaning to be done all at one time. In the menu illustrated on page 415 both the dessert and the main dish could be served in the utensil in which they were prepared.

Preparing one-dish meals. One-dish meals, those prepared on top of the stove, in a pressure saucepan, or in the oven, are an advantage when it comes to saving time and effort and avoiding dishwashing.

Preparing food in quantity. Preparing food in quantity may also save time and energy and sometimes money. You can prepare a whole ham for dinner and use the remainder later in sandwiches, sliced, or in various prepared dishes at several other meals. Leftover chicken can be sliced or made into chicken salad. Baking extra cookies will provide a supply later when you do not have time to bake.

Short cuts. There are many short cuts which can be followed in preparing a meal. Some of these are listed in Table 29.

Table 29

Short Cuts in Meal Preparation

1. When setting the table, use a tray to carry most of the materials to the table at one time.
2. Wipe greasy fry pans etc. with paper towels before washing.
3. Scrape, rinse, and stack all the dishes before beginning dishwashing.
4. For easier dishwashing, soak all sirupy and greasy dishes in hot water, and dishes spotted with egg, milk, or starch in cold water. (Why?)
5. Line the broiler with disposable foil to make the cleanup job after broiling easier.
6. Use kitchen shears to cut pieces of bacon, parsley, scallions, figs, chives, dates, or pimentos.
7. Cut foods such as vegetables, bread, and cheese on a cutting board to make the job easier and safer.
8. Remove food spilled on the range immediately to prevent a more difficult job of cleaning at a later time.
9. Wipe up immediately any water or food spilled on the floor to prevent falls.
10. Use a small amount of bleach plus water in a glass container used for ice tea to quickly remove stains.
11. Use casserole or earthenware dishes in which food can be both cooked and served at the table.
12. For easy disposal of waste and to make the cleaning of work surface quicker and easier, pare and peel fruits and vegetables over paper.
13. Dovetail tasks.

Table Service

Simplicity in table setting. Attractive, delicious food is important, but the smoothness with which it is served and the atmosphere you create combine to make your family and guests look forward to each meal. Feel free to express your individuality when planning your table service. In homemaking today, an informal, simplified style of living has become the rule. Servants are few even among the wealthy. In food service, most homemakers have adopted fewer courses and fewer foods in each course than was once the custom. Our trend toward casual living has made mealtime a time of relaxation and companionship.

Moving the eating center. The family today has also moved the eating center all about the home, both indoors and out, depending on where food can be enjoyed the most. The patio, the TV room, a casual bar, the kitchen, and the dining room are all areas used for eating.

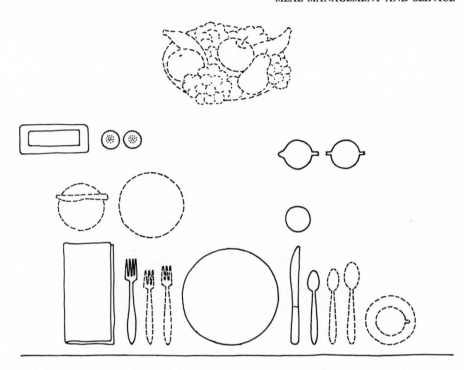

Wherever you have the location, it should be cheerful and inviting, and the appointments should harmonize with the environment and express your personality. *Be creative.*

Setting the table. The way you set the table is probably based on family tradition and the equipment which is available. In fact there have been many rules set down concerning table setting. Today with the informality present in American society many of these rules are no longer applied. The very elaborate settings of the past are probably only found in fine restaurants where waiters and waitresses are available to help with the service. Some rules, however, are good to follow in table setting because they are helpful in making mealtime more pleasant. A simple table setting is illustrated above.

You will notice that the knife and spoon are placed to the right of the plate and the fork and the napkin are put on the left of the plate. The glass is placed at the tip of the knife. Cup and saucer are placed to the right near the spoon. The salad plate, if used, is put above and to the left of the fork. Bread and butter plates if used are placed to the left and above the fork.

Service. The type of service you choose for your meals will again depend on family traditions and customs. However there are some common types of service used in the United States. In *informal service* (American style) if a first course is served, it is on the table when the meal begins. The first course is then removed, the main course is placed on the table in serving dishes, and the host (father) or hostess (mother) serves the food. The host serves the meat, potatoes, and vegetable, and the hostess distributes the salad, and later the dessert and beverage. Also in this type of service, part of the food may be served by host and hostess and part from the kitchen. For example, soup as a first course and the dessert may be served from the kitchen, and salad may be on the table at the beginning of the meal.

Country or *ranch style* is another type of service used in the United States. Food in serving dishes and platters is placed on the table. Whoever is sitting nearest a dish is asked to help himself and pass it. This type of service has also been referred to as *family service*.

Buffet service has become very popular in the United States because with this type of service you can handle a large group even though your dining area may be small. In this service the flatware, napkins, dishes, and food are arranged on the table or buffet. Guests may then help themselves. They can be seated at small tables, or trays can be provided. If trays are used, the menu should be planned to require only a fork, since trying to cut food with a knife can be difficult on a tray.

Appointments. The menu should be carefully planned to consider what is available in table appointments. Serving a formal meal without enough table equipment will be difficult to manage. Choosing table appointments will depend on the personal taste of the homemaker. Experimenting with a few creative ideas will also increase table setting possibilities.

The next chapters will include suggestions for various types of meals based on cookery which comes from many countries. These meals will help you apply the scientific principles you have learned. The chapters will provide a creative approach to meal planning and a chance to become familiar with the foods which are a part of America's heritage.

MAJOR IDEAS

The following statements give the main ideas within the chapter you have just studied. Be sure you know the words underscored in these statements and in the questions to follow.

1. Management is the act of planning, controlling, and guiding the use of resources to get something one wants or what one thinks is worthwhile.
2. Time schedules, meal short cuts and understanding the recipes

all contribute to efficient management of a meal.

3. The kind of tablesetting and the type of service used in today's homes are based on family traditions and time and equipment available.

QUESTIONS TO STUDY

SAVING TIME, STEPS, AND MOTIONS

1. Why is a written time schedule desirable?
2. Describe some of the ways in which the use of time in meal preparation can be reduced.
3. Explain how careful reading of directions may save time and energy.
4. Explain the statement, "Successful use of a recipe depends a great deal on one's understanding all the special terms used."
5. Give some examples of ways in which making use of substitutions of ingredients can be advantageous to you.
6. Describe some short cuts in meal preparation. Give some examples where these short cuts would be most helpful to you.

TABLE SERVICE

1. In what ways is the success of a meal influenced by the way in which the meal is served?
2. Describe some of the ways in which meals are served. Think of situations in which one way of serving might be preferable to another.
3. Plan a luncheon for a group of your friends. Decide ways in which you might serve the food.

BIBLIOGRAPHY

CARSON, BYRTA, and RAMEE, MARUE CARSON, *How You Plan and Prepare Meals*. New York, McGraw-Hill, Inc., 1962.

FITZSIMMONS, CLEO, *Management for You*. Philadelphia, J. B. Lippincott Company, 1958.

STARR, MARY CATHARINE, *Management for Better Living*. Boston, D. C. Heath and Co., 1956.

26 ENGLISH AND IRISH COOKERY

Introduction

You will remember that in Chapter 2 we said that the United States was settled by people from all over the world who brought their favorite foods, recipes, and ways of cooking to America. The next eight chapters will be concerned with the preparation and serving of some of these foods which have become a part of American cookery.

Each of the following chapters is divided into five major ideas: (1) suggested menus, (2) recipes, (3) review of cookery principles, (4) table settings, and (5) other suggested foods. All of the suggested menus are representative of the food which the various groups of people brought to America. Since these menus are only suggestions, you may choose to use all or part of them for your study. The other suggested foods will also give you an opportunity to plan any number of meals representative of each of the countries included in these chapters.

The recipes for each suggested menu are given following the menu. The recipes for the other suggested foods can be found in most cookbooks or in your manual, *Students' Activities and Experiments*. Also included are table settings which will help you develop a creative approach to the serving of food.

Your table setting should be simple, developed from materials which are available and representative of the people being studied. Remember that in all of these experiences you are trying to create an impression, or mood, representative of the culture of each of the groups. The meals in these chapters which you prepare and serve should be a review of the principles which you have learned in nutrition, food, science, and management of human resources. In many cases you may want to refer back to this material before proceeding with your preparation.

English Cookery

The English were one of the first groups of people to bring their food habits and recipes to the United States. Most of the new "American" dishes prepared by the English settlers in this country included such foods as beans, corn, and fish, since these were the foods available to the early colonizers.

426

Courtesy of the New York Historical Society, New York City

"Ye Boston Baked Beans" by H. E. Covill, 1886

MENU

New England Boiled Dinner
Crisp Coleslaw
Old-Fashioned Indian Pudding

New England Boiled Dinner was always served once a week from early fall until late spring. Cabbage often went into a netted cotton bag and was taken from the kettle with the quarters whole. A boiled dinner is a very old version of a perfect one-plate meal.

RECIPES

New England Boiled Dinner

4 pounds corned beef	8 parsnips, peeled
1 pound salt pork, unsliced	8 large potatoes, peeled
1 large turnip, peeled and cut large	1 large cabbage, quartered
10 large whole carrots, peeled	12 small beets, unpeeled

Simmer corned beef and salt pork in unsalted water to cover, in a large covered saucepan, about 1 hour. Add turnips, carrots, and parsnips. Cook 1 more

THE MANAGEMENT OF FOOD RESOURCES

Courtesy Woman's Day Encyclopedia of Cookery. Copyright 1965, Fawcett Publications, Inc.

hour, then add potatoes and cabbage. Meanwhile, cook beets in a large covered saucepan in salted water to cover, until tender. When corned beef is very tender, remove to platter with salt pork. Drain vegetables and place around meat on platter. Drain beets, immerse in cold water, slip off skins, and place on platter. Serve at once. *Serves 6 to 8.*

Equipment: 2 large saucepans with covers
Preparation Time: 20 minutes
Cooking Time: 2 hours
To shorten the cooking time, a pressure saucepan may be used for this dish.

Coleslaw

3 cups shredded cabbage
1 cup hot slaw dressing
salt and pepper to taste

Crisp the cabbage by covering it with cracked ice, or refrigerate. Mix with Hot Slaw Dressing or old-fashioned sour cream dressing and season to taste. *Serves 6.*

Equipment: vegetable grater, 2 bowls
Preparation Time: 10 minutes

Hot Slaw Dressing

1 tablespoon butter	$\frac{1}{4}$ teaspoon dry mustard
1 teaspoon flour	$\frac{1}{2}$ teaspoon salt
$\frac{1}{2}$ cup vinegar	$\frac{1}{8}$ teaspoon pepper
2 teaspoons sugar	1 egg yolk, well beaten

Melt fat and blend in flour. Add vinegar and stir until mixture thickens. Mix together sugar, mustard, salt, and pepper, and add to liquid. Cook for 4 minutes. Pour over beaten egg yolk and mix well. Return to heat and cook 1 minute longer. *Makes about 1½ cups dressing.*
Equipment: saucepan
Preparation Time: 5 minutes
Cooking Time: 10 minutes

Old Fashioned Indian Pudding

"At first the pioneer women put a mixture of cornmeal, water, and salt in a bag, suspended it in boiling water and cooked it—this was hasty pudding. The story goes that a Pilgrim mother was making her pudding one day when the alarm sounded to go to the stockade at once, since unfriendly Indians were approaching. Trying to hide her precious food supply, she put the pudding, bag and all, into the smouldering embers of her hearth fire. Six hours later after the "all clear," she returned home and found a delicious dessert with a thin brown crust. From then on Indian pudding was baked and not boiled. Molasses was served over hasty pudding but was added to the baked pudding."*

5 tablespoons yellow cornmeal	1 teaspoon cinnamon
4 cups milk, scalded	$\frac{3}{4}$ teaspoon ginger
2 tablespoons butter	1 teaspoon salt
1 cup dark molasses	1 cup cold milk
2 eggs, beaten	

Add cornmeal to hot milk, stirring constantly. Cook over low heat until thickened, again stirring constantly. Remove from heat, add butter, molasses, beaten eggs, spices, and salt. Mix well and pour into buttered baking dish. Bake in 300° F. oven† for about 1 hour. Remove from oven. Stir and add the 1 cup cold milk. Then continue baking for 1 more hour. Serve warm with plain or whipped cream. *Serves 8 to 10.*
Equipment: baking dish
Preparation Time: 1 hour
Cooking Time: 2 hours

---

*Easton, Alice ,"Old Massachusetts Recipes in the New Boston," The Massachusetts Restaurant Service, 1966.

†Whenever the oven is to be used, be sure to turn it to the specified temperature before proceeding with the rest of the directions.

Irish Cookery

In Ireland the basic food is the potato, or pratie, as the Irish call it. Soda bread, of course, is a tradition in Ireland. Other breads which are popular are the treacle (molasses), oaten (oatmeal), and baxty (combination of potatoes, flour, butter, and salt). Perhaps the best known of all Irish foods are stew and stirabout. The original Irish stew was made with spare ribs, not lamb as we

Courtesy Gourmet Magazine

know it today. Stirabout, a staple of ancient Ireland, is a cereal made with oatmeal. Ireland is surrounded by waters rich with fish of every description, yet fish is the least popular of Irish foods.

MENU

Irish Stew
Green Salad
Irish Soda Bread

RECIPES

Irish Stew

6 large potatoes, peeled and
sliced thick
4 large carrots, scraped and
sliced
4 large onions, peeled and
sliced

4 shoulder lamb or mutton
chops
salt and pepper
2 cups beef bouillon or
2 cubes dissolved in
2 cups of water

In a deep casserole or bean pot put a layer of the sliced potatoes, a layer of carrots, and one of onions. Then put in the chops, season with salt and pepper lightly, and then repeat layers of vegetables, being careful to end up with the potatoes on the top. Pour bouillon over mixture. Cook at 350° F. for 1½ hours, removing the cover the last hour to brown the potatoes. *Serves 4.*

Equipment: casserole dish
Preparation Time: 30 minutes
Cooking Time: 1½ hours

Green Salad

Any one of the green salads suggested in the following chapters.

Irish Soda Bread

4 cups sifted all-purpose flour
¼ teaspoon sugar
1 teaspoon salt
1 teaspoon baking powder
¼ cup butter or margarine

2 cups seedless raisins
1⅓ cups buttermilk
1 egg
1 teaspoon baking soda

Mix and sift the flour, sugar, salt, and baking powder. Cut in butter or margarine with pastry blender or two knives until mixture resembles coarse cornmeal. Stir in raisins. Combine buttermilk, egg, and baking soda, and stir into flour mixture until just moistened. Bake in greased 1-quart pudding pan or casserole in moderate oven (375° F.) 45 to 50 minutes, until golden brown.

Equipment: casserole dish
Preparation Time: 20 minutes
Cooking Time: 45 to 50 minutes

Review the cookery principles found on the following pages:		
pp. 278–288	Meat Cookery	New England Boiled Dinner
pp. 160–167	Vegetable Cookery	
pp. 158–160, 382–395	Vegetable Selection	Coleslaw
pp. 247–248	Milk Cookery	Old-Fashioned Indian Pudding
pp. 177–192	Flour Mixtures	
pp. 160–167	Vegetable Cookery	Irish Stew
pp. 278–288	Meat Cookery	
pp. 158–160, 382–395	Vegetable Selection	Green Salad
pp. 177–192	Flour Mixtures	Irish Soda Bread

Table Settings

As a whole, the English people have a history of appreciating the sea, tradition, and freedom. Creating a setting based on a nautical or freedom theme would be appropriate for this meal. A nautical setting could include a fish net, seashells, rocks, and perhaps an old lantern or navigator's map.

Since green is Ireland's traditional color, this color should be prominent in the setting. A few Irish potatoes placed in a soup tureen with shamrocks cut from green construction paper could form part of the decoration. A small number of corncob pipes tied with green ribbons and put among the potatoes will give added effect.

Other Suggested Foods					
Food	Part of Meal	Preparation Time	Cooking Time	Special Equipment	Review
Boston Brown Bread	bread	20 min.	3 hr.	deep kettle steaming rack	Flour Mixtures, pp. 177–192
Yorkshire Pudding	bread	10 min.	25 min.	mixing bowl muffin tin	Egg Cookery, pp. 231–237 Flour Mixtures, pp. 177–192
Scones	bread	20 min.	12–15 min.	baking sheet	Flour Mixtures, pp. 177–192
Berry Grunt	dessert	20 min.	1 hr.	kettle rack	Flour Mixtures, pp. 177–192 Fruit Cookery, pp. 160–167

The recipes for these foods may be found in your manual or cookbooks. The times suggested in this table are the times found in the recipes checked. Some recipes may require longer times.

MAJOR IDEAS

The following statements give the main ideas within the chapter you have ust studied.

1. The food of New England is basically English and Indian in its origin.
2. Typical foods of New England are New England Boiled Dinner and Old-Fashioned Indian Pudding, a cornmeal and molasses dessert.

QUESTIONS TO STUDY

1. Suggest ways by which the New England Boiled Dinner can be prepared more quickly.
2. How should the cabbage in the Boiled Dinner be prepared to preserve the nutritive value in it?
3. What is the purpose of the cornmeal in the Indian Pudding?
4. What were some of the historical factors which affected the development of New England cookery?

BIBLIOGRAPHY

MOSSER, MARJORIE, *Foods of Old New England.* New York, Doubleday and Company, 1957.

VAUGHAN, BEATRICE, *Yankee Hill Country Cookery*. Brattleboro, Vt., Stephen Green Press, 1963.

27 CREOLE COOKERY

Creole cookery represents some of the finest cooking in the world. This cookery combines the Spanish enthusiasm for highly seasoned dishes, the peasant cookery of early French immigrants, the more delicate cookery of newly arrived noblemen from the French Revolution and their trained chefs, the natural skill of the Negro cooks they taught, and the native Indian knowledge of wild herbs and vegetables. Two menus are included, thereby suggesting unusual food for the cook who wants to be creative, and less expensive food for the budget-conscious cook.

"Charleston Square" by C. J. Hamilton, 1872

Abby Aldrich Rockefeller Folk Art Collection

434

The main dish of the first menu features Bouillabaisse which has been described in this fashion:

The Ballad of Bouillabaisse

This Bouillabaisse a noble dish is—
    A sort of soup, or broth, or stew,
Or hotchpotch of all sort of fishes,
    That Greenwich never could outdo;
Green herbs, red peppers, mussels, saffron,
    Soles, onions, garlic, roach, and dace:
All these you eat at Terre's Tavern
    In that one of Bouillabaisse.
            WILLIAM THACKERAY

The American Home

MENU I

Bouillabaisse
Green Salad
Lime Mallow
French Bread

RECIPES

Bouillabaisse

4 pounds firm-fleshed fish (equal parts of any: snapper, bass, cod, haddock, perch)
$\frac{1}{3}$ cup olive or pure vegetable oil
2 cups sliced onion
3 cloves of garlic, minced
4 carrots, pared and chopped
1 pound fresh tomatoes, peeled and chopped (or a 1-pound can of tomatoes)
2 bottles (8 ounces each) clam juice
1 can (1 pint 2 ounces) tomato juice
1 teaspoon thyme, crumbled

$\frac{1}{2}$ teaspoon saffron, crumbled
$\frac{1}{2}$ teaspoon dried orange peel
$1\frac{1}{2}$ teaspoons salt
$\frac{1}{4}$ teaspoon pepper
$\frac{1}{2}$ teaspoon fennel seed, crushed
1 bay leaf, crumbled
2 tablespoons minced parsley
2 pounds live lobster
1 pound raw shrimp, shelled and deveined
2 dozen clams, scrubbed (optional)
1 dozen mussels, scrubbed (optional)

Cut fish into $1\frac{1}{2}$ inch serving size pieces, bone and all. Heat oil in large kettle; add onion, garlic and carrots; sauté 5 minutes. Add tomatoes, clam juice, tomato juice, thyme, saffron, orange peel, salt, pepper, fennel, bay leaf, and parsley; boil 10 minutes. Plunge lobster into boiling water until it turns red. Take it out of the water and cut it into serving-size pieces, shell and all (page 407); layer onto mixture in kettle; layer cut fish over lobster. Boil actively for 10 minutes. Add shrimp (page 406); boil 5 minutes. Add clams and mussels; cover; cook 5 minutes or just until shells open. Remove from heat; serve at once with French bread. Soup may be sprinkled with additional parsley, if desired. (If using frozen fish, select a variety in the same total quantity (4 pounds); proceed according to recipe but boil actively for only 5 minutes after adding it to the kettle. Precooked frozen or canned shellfish should be added last and cooked only 5 minutes.) *Serves 6.*

Equipment: large kettle
Preparation Time: 30 minutes
Cooking Time: 30 minutes

Lime Mallow

2½ cups miniature marshmallows or 24 marshmallows cut in quarters
1 cup orange juice
grated rind of 1 lime

juice of 1 lime
few drops of green food coloring
1 cup heavy cream, whipped
fresh mint and lime slices

Combine marshmallows and orange juice in top of double boiler; cook over boiling water until marshmallows melt. Cool and then chill until almost thickened. Add lime rind and juice and a few drops of green food coloring. Fold whipped cream into lime mixture; turn into a 1-quart mold or refrigerator tray; freeze for several hours. Unmold or spoon into serving dishes; garnish with fresh mint sprigs and lime slices, if desired. *Serves 6.*

Green Salad

4 cups assorted salad greens (leaf, Boston or iceberg lettuce, romaine and curly endive)
8 artichoke hearts
3 medium tomatoes, sliced
1 medium cucumber, sliced

½ cup crumbled Roquefort or blue cheese
½ teaspoon salt
dash of pepper
½ cup French dressing

Bernard L. Lewis, Inc.

Lettuce of various kinds, watercress, endive, celery, cabbage, and escarole are commonly called salad greens. A tossed salad consists of several different greens which are torn apart, mixed in a bowl, and tossed gently with a salad dressing until the vegetables are coated. This particular salad is a basic one and is an attractive and nutritious accompaniment to many different main dishes.

Wash, drain, and chill salad greens; tear into bite-size pieces. Arrange with remaining ingredients in salad bowl. Toss lightly. Serve immediately. *Serves 6.*

Equipment: salad bowl
Preparation Time: 20 minutes

French Bread (quick method)

2 cans refrigerated biscuits
1 egg white, beaten
sesame seed
garlic spread

Stand biscuits on edge on an ungreased baking sheet; lightly press together and shape ends to form a long loaf. Brush with egg white. Sprinkle with sesame seed. Bake at 350° F. for 30 to 40 minutes, until golden brown. Slice and spread with garlic butter or another spread. Return to oven for 3–5 minutes. *Makes 1 loaf.*

Equipment: baking sheet
Preparation Time: 5 minutes
Cooking Time: 30–40 minutes

MENU II

Fresh Fruit Cup
Shrimp Jambalaya À La Louisiana
Baked Onions Au Gratin
Southern Ambrosia
Glacé Nuts

RECIPES

Fruit Cup

$1\frac{1}{4}$ cups pineapple chunks
1 cup orange sections, cut in half
$\frac{3}{4}$ cup fresh or frozen melon balls
$\frac{2}{3}$ cup banana slices

$\frac{1}{2}$ cup fresh strawberries
$\frac{1}{4}$ cup lemon juice
4 drops peppermint extract
2 to 4 tablespoons sugar

Combine fruit. Blend lemon juice with peppermint extract and sugar. Sprinkle over fruit and chill. (After dinner mints may be placed on each serving in place of peppermint extract and sugar.) *Serves 4 to 6.*

Equipment: large bowl
Preparation Time: 30 minutes

Shrimp Jambalaya

1 tablespoon fat
1 tablespoon flour
½ cup chopped onion
1 garlic clove, minced
2 tablespoons parsley
½ cup grated medium sharp Cheddar
   cheese
1 cup tomatoes
½ cup ripe olives, pitted
½ cup water

1 green pepper, finely chopped
½ teaspoon salt
¼ teaspoon red pepper
thyme
1 tablespoon Worcestershire
   sauce
3 cups cooked rice
2 cups shrimp, cooked, peeled,
   and deveined

Make a roux with fat and flour. Add onions to the roux and let cook until they are transparent. Add garlic, parsley, cheese, tomatoes, olives, water, green pepper, salt, red pepper, thyme, and Worcestershire sauce. Boil these ingredients for 5 minutes. Add cooked rice and shrimp. Cook, stirring slowly, 10 minutes on a low heat. Pour mixture into buttered casserole dish. Sprinkle top of casserole with extra cheese and parsley. Bake in 350° F. oven for 15 minutes. Serve hot. *Serves 8 to 10.*

Equipment: large heavy pan, casserole
Preparation Time: 20 minutes
Cooking Time: 40 minutes

Baked Onions Au Gratin

12 medium onions
   boiling salted water
1 cup grated Cheddar cheese
½ teaspoon salt

¼ teaspoon pepper
⅛ teaspoon nutmeg
2 tablespoons heavy cream

Peel onions. Cook in enough boiling water to cover, about 8 minutes or until slightly tender. Drain. Carefully remove centers and chop; mix with remaining ingredients. Fill cavities with mixture. Place in shallow baking pan with ½ inch water. Cover and bake in oven at 375° F. for 30 to 35 minutes. Remove cover 5 minutes before onions are done. *Serves 6.*

Equipment: kettle, baking dish with cover
Preparation Time: 10 minutes
Cooking Time: 40 minutes

Southern Ambrosia

1 cup milk
1 cup heavy cream
4 egg yolks, slightly beaten
¼ cup sugar

1 tablespoon flour
¼ teaspoon salt
4 to 6 oranges, sectioned
1½ cups grated fresh coconut

Scald milk and cream. Into egg yolks, stir sugar, flour, and salt. Slowly add hot liquid to egg mixture, stirring constantly. Cook mixture on low heat until mixture coats spoon; stir constantly. Chill well. In individual dishes, put a layer of custard in bottom, then a layer of orange sections, then a layer of coconut. Repeat. Serve well chilled. *Serves 6 to 8.*

Equipment: pan, bowl
Preparation Time: 10 minutes
Cooking Time: 30 minutes

Glacé Nuts

1 cup sugar
pinch cream of tartar
$\frac{1}{2}$ cup boiling water
$\frac{1}{2}$ pound shelled pecans

Add sugar and cream of tartar to the boiling water and cook sirup to hard crack stage (295° F.). Remove from heat. Drop the nut meats into the sirup one at a time or several together for a cluster. Remove immediately with fork, and drain off excess sirup. Place on wax paper to cool.

Preparation Time: 10 minutes
Cooking Time: 40 minutes

Review the cookery principles found on the following pages:		
pp. 295, 400–407	Seafood and Fish Cookery	Bouillabaisse
pp. 158–160	Vegetable Selection	Green Salad
pp. 414–415, 422	Management of Time	French Bread
pp. 247–248	Milk Cookery	Lime Mallow
pp. 158–160, 382–395	Fruit Selection	
pp. 158–160, 382–395	Fruit Selection	Fresh Fruit Cup
pp. 295, 406	Seafood Cookery	Shrimp Jambalaya
pp. 160–167	Vegetable Cookery	Baked Onions
pp. 253–257	Cheese Cookery	
pp. 231–237	Egg Cookery	Ambrosia
pp. 247–248	Milk Cookery	
pp. 203–205	Sugar Cookery	Glacé Nuts

Table Setting

Many flowers and brightly colored tablecloths and napkins may be used to capture the gaiety and charm of New Orleans. Decorating the table and room to capture the atmosphere of a sidewalk café would be effective.

Other Suggested Foods

Food	Part of Meal	Preparation Time	Cooking Time	Special Equipment	Review
Chicken Gumbo	main dish	20 min.	50 min.	Dutch oven	Starch Cookery, pp. 172–174 Vegetable Cookery, pp. 160–167 Meat Cookery, p. 291
Eggs Benedict	main dish	10 min.	10 min.	heavy pan	Egg Cookery, pp. 231–237
Shrimp Newburg	main dish	15 min.	6 min.	heavy pan	Milk Cookery, pp. 247–248 Egg Cookery, pp. 231–237 Seafood Cookery, p. 295, 406
Green Beans À La Creole	vegetable	10 min.	1 hr.	saucepan	Vegetable Cookery, pp. 160–167
Praline Parfait	sauce for dessert	10 min.	30 min.	heavy pan	Sugar Cookery, pp. 203–205

MAJOR IDEAS

The following statements give the main ideas within the chapter you have just studied.

1. Creole cookery represents some of the finest American cookery.
2. Its distinct blend of spices and herbs with meat, fish, and poultry has made Creole cooking known all over the world.

QUESTIONS TO STUDY

1. What historical factors affected Creole cookery?
2. What is Bouillabaisse? How is it prepared?
3. Why do you think Shrimp Jambalaya is a popular Creole dish?
4. What is Ambrosia?
5. What substitute could be made for the heavy cream in the Ambrosia?
6. How do the principles of sugar cookery apply to the Glacé Nuts?

BIBLIOGRAPHY

KAUFMAN, WILLIAM I., and SISTER MARY URSULA COOPER, O. P., *The Art of Creole Cookery*. New York, Doubleday & Co., Inc., 1962.

28 GERMAN COOKERY

German cookery is not as sophisticated as French cooking nor as plain as English cooking. It is essentially food for families. One of the most striking features in German cookery is the fondness for sour-sweet flavoring, found here in our German derived Pennsylvania Dutch cooking.

German cookery excels in imaginative treatment of vegetables, especially cabbage in the making of sauerkraut and others in the staggering variety of sausages for which the country is famous. Veal and pork seem to be favorite meats of the Germans.

The Germans use a great deal of fruit in their cooking and baking. *Kuchen*, or cakes, with their fruit fillings and Apples in Nightgowns are two examples. Germany has many beautiful orchards (as does the Pennsylvania Dutch area in this country) and in many places fruit trees line the sides of the country roads.

"Outdoor Scene with Feasting and Dancing"

Wadsworth Atheneum, Hartford, Conn.

Menus

Two menus are suggested for the German cooking study. One features the famous sauerkraut and the other includes a veal dish.

MENU I

Spareribs With Sauerkraut
Boiled Potatoes
Green Salad
Pumpernickel Bread
Apples In Nightgowns

Spareribs With Sauerkraut

3 to 4 pounds meaty spareribs
1 tablespoon butter
1 quart (about 1 pound)
  sauerkraut
1 medium carrot, grated

2 teaspoons caraway seeds
salt and freshly ground pepper to taste
2 medium onions, thinly sliced
3 large tart apples, cored, cut in circles
1½ cups water

Cut the spareribs into serving portions. Melt the butter in a skillet and quickly brown the spareribs in it. Wash the sauerkraut under cold running water; squeeze dry with hands. Combine the sauerkraut with the carrots, caraway seeds, salt, and pepper. Place half of the mixture in a buttered baking dish. Cover with half the onions and apples. Top with browned spareribs. Then add the other half of mixture of sauerkraut, and top with the remainder of onions and apples. Add the water. Cover tightly. Bake in a preheated 350° F. oven for 1½ hours. *Serves 4–6.* (Variation: Substitute browned smoked pork chops for spareribs.)

Equipment: skillet, baking dish with tight cover
Preparation Time: 15 minutes
Cooking Time: 1½ hours

Boiled Potatoes

This is the most common German way of cooking potatoes. Peel potatoes and cut them into quarters, or if very large cut into eighths. Cook in rapidly boiling, very heavily salted water until done. Drain. Lower heat and shake— do not stir—potatoes in saucepan over heat until very dry. The potatoes must be extremely dry and mealy.

Equipment: saucepan
Preparation Time: 10 minutes
Cooking Time: 20 minutes

National Canners' Association

Early German immigrants prepared the first sauerkraut in America. After the autumn harvest, housewives chopped many heads of cabbage, which were well sprinkled with salt and placed in earthenware crocks. As the salt drew out the sugary juice which was then fermented by bacteria, a tangy flavor was produced. This "cooking" process took from twelve to fourteen days. Although sauerkraut is available today in cans, packages, and jars, there are still some housewives who prefer to make their own. Sauerkraut is excellent with sausages, spareribs, ham or pork, corned beef, and roast turkey.

Green Salad

Any mixture of greens combined to make a salad is satisfactory.

Pumpernickel Bread

This bread can be purchased at your local food market.

Apples In Nightgowns

4 large apples	2 tablespoons dry bread crumbs
1 recipe pastry dough	pinch of cinnamon
$\frac{1}{4}$ cup almonds, grated	2 tablespoons butter
2 tablespoons raisins	1 egg yolk, beaten
2 tablespoons sugar	extra sugar

Pare and core apples. Prepare pastry dough. Mix together almonds, raisins, sugar, bread crumbs, and cinnamon. Put butter, the size of a hazelnut, in the center of each apple and fill with stuffing. Roll dough out thin and cut in squares large enough to enfold apples. Place apples in center of dough squares, lift up corners, and press tightly together. Set apples on baking sheet, brush with egg yolk, and bake in a moderate (350° F.) oven for approximately 30 minutes or until apples are tender. Sprinkle with sugar to serve. *Serves 4.*

Equipment: peeler, mixing bowl, baking sheet
Preparation Time: 20 minutes
Cooking Time: 30 minutes

MENU II

Veal Cutlet Garni
Dutch Beans
Tomato Salad
Shoo-Fly Pie

RECIPES

Veal Cutlet Garni

4 veal cutlets ($1\frac{1}{4}$–$1\frac{1}{2}$ pounds)	$\frac{1}{2}$ cup salad oil
6 eggs	8 anchovy fillets
flour, seasoned with salt and pepper	2 tablespoons chopped parsley
fine dry bread crumbs	capers, lemon wedges, pickles
$\frac{1}{2}$ cup butter	

Beat the veal cutlets to slightly flatten them, or ask your butcher to do so. Slightly beat 2 of the eggs. Dip the cutlets into the seasoned flour, then into the beaten eggs, then into bread crumbs, coating evenly. Shake off excess crumbs. If possible, refrigerate for 30 minutes. Melt butter and add with salad oil to a depth of ½ inch in a large skillet. When just below the smoking point, add the cutlets. Sauté on both sides until brown and tender—about 10 to 15 minutes in all. Drain the cutlets on absorbent paper, arrange on a hot platter and keep warm. Fry the remaining 4 eggs in the fat remaining in the skillet. Top each cutlet with a fried egg. Crisscross each egg with 2 anchovy fillets. Sprinkle gently with chopped parsley and a few capers. Garnish with lemon wedges and some pickles. *Serves 4.*

Equipment: large skillet
Preparation Time: 15 minutes
Cooking Time: 15 minutes

Dutch Beans

1 quart quartered green beans	½ teaspoon dried mustard
3 slices bacon	½ teaspoon salt
4 small onions	¼ teaspoon paprika
2 tablespoons flour	½ cup vinegar
1 tablespoon sugar	½ cup water

Cook beans in boiling salted water for about 35 minutes. Drain. Cut bacon into small pieces and fry until crisp. Reserve 2 tablespoons of the bacon fat. Add the whole onions to bacon and cook until golden brown. Add to beans. Combine flour, sugar, mustard, salt, and paprika, and blend with 2 tablespoons of the bacon fat. Brown well. Add vinegar and water and cook until thickened. Pour over beans and let stand in a warm place for ½ hour before serving. *Serves 4–6.*

Equipment: saucepan, skillet
Preparation Time: 10 minutes
Cooking Time: 50 minutes

Tomato Salad

4 large tomatoes
2 onions
lettuce
salt and pepper

Slice tomatoes into thick pieces and garnish with thickly sliced onions. Serve on chilled lettuce, using salt, lots of freshly ground pepper, and no dressing. *Serves 4.*

Equipment: bowl
Preparation Time: 5 minutes

Shoo-Fly Pie

1 recipe of plain pastry	$\frac{1}{4}$ cup shortening
$\frac{1}{2}$ cup sifted flour	$\frac{1}{2}$ teaspoon baking soda
1 cup brown sugar	$\frac{1}{2}$ cup hot water
$\frac{1}{8}$ teaspoon salt	$\frac{1}{2}$ cup molasses

Line 2 pie pans with pastry dough. Make crumbs by combining flour, sugar, salt, and shortening. Dissolve soda in hot water. Combine with molasses and pour into pastry-lined pan. Top with crumbs and bake in a very hot oven (450° F.) for 10 minutes. Reduce to moderate oven (350° F.) and bake 20–30 minutes longer or until firm. Makes two 9-inch pies.

Equipment: pie pans, mixing bowl
Preparation Time: 25 minutes
Cooking Time: 40 minutes

Review the cookery principles found on the following pages:

pp. 278–288	Meat Cookery	Spareribs With Sauerkraut
pp. 160–167	Vegetable Cookery	Boiled Potatoes
pp. 158–160	Vegetable Selection	Green Salad
pp. 177–192	Flour Mixtures	Apples In Nightgowns
pp. 160–167	Fruit Cookery	
pp. 278–288	Meat Cookery	Veal Cutlet Garni
pp. 160–167	Vegetable Cookery	Dutch Beans
pp. 158–160, 382–395	Vegetable Selection	Tomato Salad
pp. 177–192	Flour Mixtures	Shoo-Fly Pie

Table Setting

The Germans who settled in the United States were plain people who enjoyed peasant designs in their homes. A table setting might be based on the use of such designs. These can be found in a German or Pennsylvania Dutch cookbook. A cutting board or iron trivet which has the peasant design might also be a part of the table setting.

Since the people who settled in the Pennsylvania Dutch area predominately used pottery or earthenware dishes with designs of tulips, birds, and hearts on them, as well as simple, but heavy, cast-iron Dutch ovens, skillets, and casseroles, such dishes and utensils could be displayed around the room. Fruits, especially apples, could add to the decoration.

Other Suggested Foods					
Food	Part of Meal	Preparation Time	Cooking Time	Special Equipment	Review
Lentil Soup	soup	2–3 hr.	1 hr. 5 min.	large kettle	Vegetable Cookery, pp. 160–167 Starch Cookery, pp. 172–174 Meat Cookery, pp. 278–288
Potato Salad	salad	30 min.		saucepan	Vegetable Cookery, pp. 160–167
Potato Pancakes	main dish	10 min.	10 min.	heavy skillet	Flour Mixtures, pp. 177–192
Sour Pot Roast With Dumplings (Sauerbraten)	main dish	2–3 days	2½ hr.	Dutch oven	Meat Cookery, p. 278 Flour Mixtures, pp. 177–192 Egg Cookery, pp. 231–237
Red Cabbage	vegetable	10 min.	10 min.	kettle	Vegetable Cookery, pp. 160–167

MAJOR IDEAS

The following statements give the main ideas within the chapter you have just studied.

1. Neither as sophisticated as French cooking nor as plain as English food, German cookery is essentially food for families.
2. German cookery excels in imaginative treatment of sauerkraut and many varieties of sausages.

QUESTIONS TO STUDY

1. What groups of people brought German cookery to the United States?
2. What is the striking feature of German cookery?
3. What is sauerkraut?

BIBLIOGRAPHY

BEROLZHEIMER, RUTH, *The United States Regional Cookbook.* Chicago, Culinary Arts Institute, 1947.

HUTCHISON, RUTH, *The New Pennsylvania Dutch Cookbook.* New York, Harper and Row, 1958.

SCHULER, ELIZABETH, *German Cookery.* New York, Crown Publishers, 1958.

29 SPANISH AND MEXICAN COOKERY

The first cattle, pigs, horses, goats, cats, grinding stones, hoes, spades, plows, files, and wheels were brought by the Spanish to this country. Therefore it is not surprising to learn that Spanish and Mexican cookery have greatly influenced food habits found in the United States. Traveling through this country is an effective way to document this fact.

When the Spanish conquered Mexico, the native diet was based on corn, beans, and chilies. Corn was the most important; it is essential today, too. No other cuisine is so dependent on this one food as is Spanish cookery. Today, most Mexicans still eat corn in one form or another daily; many have it at every meal. Corn is used in three main forms: fresh, husks, and dried. Fresh corn is used in corn pudding, tamales, and colache, while corn husks are used as wrappers in which to cook tamales. Dried corn in the form of meal is probably the most important, however, because as the basic ingredient of this cookery, masa, or corn dough, is prepared from it. The principal bread, tortillas, and many other dishes are prepared from masa.

"The Market Place" by Thomas Allen, 1879

From the Collection of the Witte Memorial Museum,
San Antonio, Texas

450

MENU .

Enchilada
Flan
Frescas Azucaradas

RECIPES

Enchilada

Enchiladas are tortillas filled with a special filling and then covered with sauce.

Tortillas

1 cup sifted flour
½ cup cornmeal
¼ teaspoon salt

1 egg
1½ cups cold water

Combine all ingredients and beat with rotary beater until smooth. Spoon 3 tablespoons of batter onto a moderately hot, ungreased griddle to make a very thin 6-inch pancake. Turn tortillas when edges begin to look dry, not brown. Bake other side and keep warm in covered pan. *Makes 12 tortillas.*

Equipment: mixing bowl, griddle
Preparation Time: 10 minutes
Cooking Time: 1 hour

Tortilla Filling

2 cups grated sharp yellow cheese
1 cup minced onion
½ teaspoon salt

Mix ingredients thoroughly.

Equipment: large bowl
Preparation Time: 15 minutes

Enchiladas Sauce

2 tablespoons minced onion
2 tablespoons fat (salad oil)
1 tablespoon flour
1 clove garlic, minced

2 teaspoons chili powder
1 teaspoon salt
¼ teaspoon tabasco sauce
1 (no. 2) can tomatoes, drained

Combine all ingredients except tomatoes and tomato juice and brown. Add about ½ cup tomato juice (drained from tomatoes) to make sauce of medium thickness. Add tomatoes. Let simmer till thickened.

Dip tortillas into melted fat, then dip into enchiladas sauce. Place large spoonful of tortilla filling on each and roll up. Arrange in serving dish or baking dish. Cover with remaining reheated sauce, and sprinkle with remaining filling. Serve at once or reheat in moderate oven (375° F.) before serving.

Equipment: kettle
Preparation Time: 10 minutes
Cooking Time: 1 hour

Flan (Custard)

$1\frac{3}{4}$ cups sugar
8 eggs
2 (12–14 ounce) cans evaporated milk
2 teaspoons vanilla extract

Put 1 cup of sugar into a deep pan in which the custard is to be baked and place over moderate heat, stirring constantly until the sugar melts and turns golden. Tip the pan around until it is entirely coated with the caramel; cool while making the custard. Beat eggs, add milk, remaining $\frac{3}{4}$ cup sugar, and vanilla. Mix well. Strain into the caramel-coated pan and place pan in a larger pan containing hot water. Bake custard at 350° F. for about 1 hour, or until a knife inserted in the center comes out clean. Transfer custard to serving

Gommi Associates

platter while still hot. Cool until serving time. Flans are at their best when made several hours before serving and thoroughly chilled. *Serves 8–10.*

Equipment: deep pan, large pan
Preparation Time: 10 minutes
Cooking Time: 1 hour

Frescas Azucaradas

2 packages strawberry flavored gelatin

1 (7-ounce) package finely shredded coconut

2 tablespoons sweetened condensed milk

2 teaspoons vanilla

red coloring — enough to obtain strawberry color

butter frosting

green coloring

Mix 1 package of gelatin and all other ingredients together thoroughly and form into strawberry shapes. Add more condensed milk if the mixture does not hold together. Now roll the cookies in the dry gelatin and chill. To make green leaves and stems, use a butter-base frosting tinted green and apply with a pastry bag. Keep under refrigeration until ready to use. The strawberry garnish freezes well and may therefore be made in large amounts and stored in freezer. *Makes about 2½ dozen strawberries.* These cookies are a wonderful decoration or garnish for cakes, frozen desserts, or fruit salads.

Equipment: mixing bowl, pastry bag
Preparation Time: 20 minutes

Review the cookery principles found on the following pages:		
pp. 177–192	Flour Mixtures	Enchilada
pp. 252–257	Cheese Cookery	
pp. 172–174	Starch Cookery	
pp. 231–237	Egg Cookery	Flan
pp. 203–205	Sugar Cookery	
pp. 247–248	Milk	Frescas Azucaradas

Table Setting

The love of festivals, bull fights and gaiety are all part of Spanish and Mexican life. Bright colors such as hot pink and brilliant golds, red, and turquoise can capture one aspect of the Spanish-Mexican scene. For your table

THE MANAGEMENT OF FOOD RESOURCES

Bernard L. Lewis, Inc.

setting try to create the impression of gaiety with the use of bright colors, per-haps some straw mats, and even a few bright paper napkins and candles.

This may also be a good time to feature a buffet setting rather than indi-vidual table service. Creation of a pinata (paper-constructed animal or bird stuffed with candies) may also add to the gay spirit of this meal. Flatware can be kept to a minimum since many of these foods may be eaten with the fingers.

Other Suggested Foods					
Food	Part of Meal	Preparation Time	Cooking Time	Special Equipment	Review
Antojitos	appetizer	10 min.	10 min.	skillet	Meat Cookery, pp. 278, 282–287
Josefinas	appetizer	10 min.	10 min.	baking sheet	Cheese Cookery, p. 253
Tortillas	main dish	20 min.	20 min.	large bowl griddle	Flour Mixtures, pp. 177–192
Chilaquillas	main dish	10 min.	20 min.	skillet	Cheese Cookery, pp. 253–257 Flour Mixtures, pp. 177–192

Tacos	sandwich	10 min.	10 min.	skillet	Meat Cookery, pp. 278, 282–287
Tamales	main dish	10 min.	20 min.	pan for steaming	Meat Cookery, pp. 278, 282–287 Flour Mixtures, pp. 177–192
Colache	vegetable	45 min.	30–40 min.	heavy pan	Vegetable Cookery, pp. 160–167
Frijoles Refritos	vegetable	1 hr.	20 min.	heavy pan	Vegetable Cookery, pp. 160–167
Sopaipillas	dessert	20 min.	4 min.	deep fat fryer	Cooking with Fat, pp. 307–309 Flour Mixtures, pp. 177–192

MAJOR IDEAS

The following statements give the main ideas within the chapter you have just studied.

1. The Spanish and Mexicans have greatly influenced the cookery of the Southwest.
2. The use of the Tortilla as the basis for many dishes is characteristic of the Spanish and Mexican influence.

QUESTIONS TO STUDY

1. What are Frescas Azucaradas?
2. What are Tortillas?
3. What is Flan? What principles should be considered in the preparation of this food?

BIBLIOGRAPHY

BROWNS, HELEN EVANS, "Southwestern Cook Book." *House and Garden*, August 1963, pp. 131–136.

ZELAYLTA, ELENA, *Elena's Secret of Mexican Cooking.* Englewood Cliffs, N.J., Prentice Hall, 1958.

30 JAPANESE, CHINESE, AND HAWAIIAN COOKERY

This chapter could be called a study in fruits and vegetables since all of these groups of people prepare these foods in an extremely interesting manner. In Japanese cookery, the arrangement, color, and shape of the food are as carefully planned and considered as the flavor. In Chinese cookery meat and vegetables are cooked with very little liquid since the method of stir-frying brings out the natural juices of the food.

Cook Japanese, Kodausha International Ltd.,
Tokyo, Japan

456

Japanese Cookery

Japanese cookery came to the United States during the early days of gold and silver mining. Grilling and baking are common preparation methods and usually courses of small portions are served. Although the main staple is rice, fish is important; one hot dish and one cold platter of fish may be served at each meal. Dried fish is frequently used, and some fish is eaten raw with a typical salad of brined, sliced cucumbers and lettuce. The main dish is sukiyaki, which consists of beef and vegetables. Vegetables such as thinly sliced onions, bamboo shoots, and leeks are browned singly in a little fat, moistened, covered with very thin slices of beef, and simmered a few minutes. The dish is seasoned with shoyu, a sauce made from soybean seeds, wheat, and salt, and it is served with rice. Pork and chicken can be substituted for the beef. Tempura, a batter dipped, deep-fat fried vegetable dish, is another popular dish in Japan.

MENU

Sukiyaki And Rice
Tempura Vegetables
Cucumbers On Lettuce
Mandarin Oranges
Fortune Cookies

RECIPES

Sukiyaki

1 pound sirloin tip
2 tablespoons cooking oil
½ cup shoyu (soy sauce)
⅔ cup water
3 tablespoons sugar
½ teaspoon monosodium glutamate
1 cup of 1-inch pieces of green onion

1 (5-ounce) can bamboo shoots, drained
2 medium size onions, thinly sliced
1 (1-pound) can bean sprouts, drained
1 (5-ounce) can water chestnuts, drained and sliced
1 cup sliced fresh mushrooms

Cut meat into paper-thin slices across the grain, then into strips 1 inch wide. Brown strips in cooking oil in a large skillet, 2 to 3 minutes. Combine soy sauce, water, sugar, and monosodium glutamate. Pour over meat. Push meat

Courtesy Woman's Day Encyclopedia of Cookery,
Copyright 1965, Fawcett Publications, Inc.

Sukiyaki

to one side of skillet. Keeping the ingredients separate, add bamboo shoots, green onions, and onion slices. Cook 5 to 10 minutes, turning vegetables and keeping separate. Push vegetables to one side. Add bean sprouts, water chestnuts, and mushrooms, still keeping ingredients separate. Cook 2 minutes, until hot. Serve with hot rice (which can be prepared by using any of the fast-cooking rices on the market and following the directions on the package). *Serves 4 to 6.*

Equipment: skillet
Preparation Time: 20 minutes
Cooking Time: 15 minutes

Tempura Vegetables

Tempura vegetables are "suteki" (really great). Since the tempura must be served piping hot, it's best done for small groups (not more than 6 to 8 people). Tempura is simple. Batter-dipped pieces of vegetable (or sea food) are deep-fat fried until light brown, with an almost "sheer" crust, and not a trace of greasiness. The vegetables actually steam cook when the ice-cold batter hits the hot fat.

1 cup sifted all-purpose flour	1 egg, slightly beaten
$\frac{1}{2}$ teaspoon sugar	1 cup ice water
$\frac{1}{2}$ teaspoon salt	2 tablespoons salad oil

Combine ingredients, beating together till all dry ingredients are well moistened—a few flour lumps should remain. Prepare batter just before using; keep it cool with an ice cube or two. Vegetables such as carrots, mushrooms, spinach, asparagus, broccoli, onions, and parsley are a few of the vegetables which can be used for tempura cooking. Before placing vegetables in tempura batter, dry them thoroughly so that no water will come in contact with the hot oil. To make sure your vegetables turn out just right:

1. Wash and dry vegetables well. Cut into slices or strips where necessary.
2. Keep sauce and condiments covered and chilled if prepared ahead.
3. Mix batter—not too much at one time—just before using. Don't over-stir. A few lumps help make a crisp, featherlike crust.
4. Keep the batter well chilled while using. A couple of ice cubes do the trick without diluting the batter.
5. Use one set of tongs to dip vegetables into batter; another set to remove them from the hot oil.
6. Use a fresh bland cooking oil for frying. A deep electric skillet will provide good thermostatic control and will maintain the hot oil at an even

Armour & Company, Food Oils Division

temperature of 360° F. to 365° F. Don't cook too much food at one time. Skim off tiny drops of batter that form on the surface of the fat.

7. Drain the Tempura fried foods on racks set on trays. Serve piping hot.

Provide your guests with napkin-lined plates or little baskets and chopsticks, which they will use to dip the drained Tempura fried vegetables in a special Tempura sauce. The sauce is rich in soy and indispensable to Oriental cooking. For condiments, offer grated radishes combined with grated turnips and fresh grated ginger root.

Tempura Condiments and Sauce

fresh grated ginger root
equal parts grated turnip and radish, combined
$1\frac{1}{2}$ tablespoons soy sauce mixed with $\frac{1}{4}$ cup prepared mustard

Cucumber Salad

Cucumbers should be sliced thin and soaked in heavily salted water for a day or two in the refrigerator. They may be served on lettuce.

Mandarin Oranges and Fortune Cookies

These foods may be purchased at a grocery.

Japanese Green Tea

This beverage is the most suitable one for this meal. If this tea is not available, any of the teas on the market will be satisfactory.

Review the cookery principles found on the following pages:		
pp. 278, 282–287	Meat Cookery	Sukiyaki
pp. 160–167	Vegetable Cookery	
pp. 160–167	Vegetable Cookery	Tempura
pp. 309–310	Deep Fat Cookery	
pp. 158–160, 389–391	Vegetable Selection	Cucumber Salad

Table Setting

The Japanese are very artistic in their arrangement of food. Each food is placed on a different dish which enhances its beauty. Cooking is also done at the table by the hostess. It is the custom in Japan to use chopsticks as the only utensil for eating and the drinking of liquids is done with both hands on the cup. It is customary to sit on the floor when eating a Japanese meal.

Since the arrangement of Japanese food is so beautiful, the food can serve as the table decoration. If some kind of decoration is desired, however, a Japanese flower arrangement could be created. Sitting on the floor and using chopsticks could also add to a Japanese atmosphere.

Other Suggested Foods					
Food	Part of Meal	Preparation Time	Cooking Time	Special Equipment	Review
Sukiyaki (to be cooked at table)	main dish	20 min.	15 min.	skillet	Vegetable Cookery, pp. 160–167

MAJOR IDEAS

The following statements give the main ideas within the chapter you have just studied.

1. The Japanese are famous for their methods of preparing vegetables.
2. Since fresh fruits and vegetables are abundant in Japan, they are used extensively in meals.

QUESTIONS TO STUDY

1. Describe Sukiyaki.
2. Name two other traditional dishes of Japan.

BIBLIOGRAPHY

DONOVAN, MARIA, *Far Eastern Epicure.* New York, Doubleday and Company, 1958.

GRIFFIN, STUART, *Japanese Food and Cooking.* Rutland, Vermont, Charles E. Tuttle Company, 1959.

JOHNSTON, MYRNA, "Twelve Great Vegetable Recipes." *Better Homes and Gardens,* May 1965, pp. 77–79.

KEYS, JOHN D., *Japanese Cuisine: A Culinary Tour.* Rutland, Vt., Charles E. Tuttle, 1966.

TADA, TATSUJI, *Japanese Recipes.* Rutland, Vt., Charles E. Tuttle, 1967.

TANAKA, HEIHACHI, and NICHOLAS, BETTY, *Pleasures of Japanese Cooking.* Englewood Cliffs, N. J., Prentice-Hall, 1962.

Chinese Cookery

Good Chinese cooking depends on the relationship between the various ingredients and condiments rather than on the character of the individual elements. An old Chinese proverb tells that if one hopes to become a good match-maker, the flavors of the ingredients must be married and harmonized. Therefore harmony is the central principle of the culinary arts. The art of Chinese cooking lies in the selecting and harmonizing of texture, color, aroma, and taste.

The basic ingredients of Chinese cooking are mushrooms, bamboo shoots, and dried shrimps. During World War II there was an increased interest in Chinese food in America. This interest may have resulted from the meat rationing situation during the war, since Chinese dishes require only about one quarter the amount of meat which a normal American dish may need.

The cooking of most Chinese dishes requires a maximum of preparation and a minimum of fuel and cooking time. Much time will be saved if all the prepared ingredients are assembled in one place—on a large platter, for example—

Madison Devlin

A Chinese grocery store in San Francisco.

before the cooking process is undertaken. The most frequently used methods of Chinese cooking can be classified as (1) stir-frying, (2) shallow frying, (3) deep-fat frying, (4) simmering, (5) braising, (6) steaming, (7) roasting, and (8) barbecuing.

MENU

Egg Rolls
Wonton Soup
Sweet And Sour Pork Cubes
Steamed Sponge Cake

RECIPES

Egg Roll Filling

2 cups finely chopped cooked pork
1 cup finely chopped cooked shrimp
or lobster
2 cups finely chopped celery
1 cup finely chopped green onions
1 cup finely chopped water chestnuts

1 tablespoon monosodium glutamate
1 tablespoon soy sauce
2 teaspoons sugar
1 teaspoon salt
1 small egg
$\frac{1}{4}$ cup melted shortening

Combine first 5 ingredients in a large bowl. Blend in next 6 ingredients and mix thoroughly; refrigerate.

Equipment: large bowl
Preparation Time: 20 minutes

Egg Roll Skins

$1\frac{1}{3}$ cups sifted all-purpose flour
$\frac{2}{3}$ cup cornstarch
$\frac{1}{2}$ teaspoon salt

2 eggs
$1\frac{1}{2}$ cups water
shortening

Sift together flour, cornstarch, and salt. Blend together with a fork the eggs and $\frac{1}{2}$ cup water. Add gradually to dry ingredients and mix with spoon or rotary beater. Gradually add remaining 1 cup water; beat until smooth. Reserve about $\frac{1}{3}$ cup batter for sealing edges of egg rolls. Brush heavy skillet lightly with shortening; place over medium heat. Holding it at a slight angle, pour about 2 tablespoons of batter, all at once, into skillet. Tip quickly in all directions to make a thin 7-inch pancake. Cook until mixture looks dry and begins to curl around edges. Remove from heat. Repeat with remaining batter, stacking egg rolls until all are baked. Place a scant $\frac{1}{4}$ cup filling in center of each egg roll, then fold 2 sides over filling. Brush edges with reserved batter. Beginning at one open end, roll up egg roll, pressing edges gently to seal. Fry immediately or store in refrigerator several hours before frying. Fry in deep, hot fat (360° F.) until crisp and golden brown, about 5–8 minutes; turn only once. Serve hot with apricot sauce, hot mustard, or both. *Makes 24 egg rolls.*

Equipment: large bowl, rotary beater, heavy skillet
Preparation Time: 20 minutes
Cooking Time: 30 minutes

Wonton Soup

$\frac{1}{8}$ pound ground pork
$\frac{1}{8}$ teaspoon salt
$\frac{1}{4}$ teaspoon monosodium
glutamate

12 pieces wonton skin (buy at Chinese grocery)
1 egg, beaten
4 cups chicken broth

Mix pork, salt, and monosodium glutamate. Fold into pieces of wonton and seal with egg. Add wontons to 1 quart boiling water and boil for 5 minutes. Remove wontons and run cold water over them. Heat chicken broth and add wontons.

Equipment: large kettle
Preparation Time: 10 minutes
Cooking Time: 10 minutes

Sweet and Sour Pork Cubes

$\frac{1}{2}$ pound pork tenderloin
3 tablespoons flour
oil for frying
$\frac{1}{4}$ cup sliced green peppers
$\frac{1}{4}$ cup sliced carrots
1 ring pineapple
$\frac{1}{2}$ teaspoon salt
1 clove garlic, crushed

$\frac{1}{2}$ cup water
$\frac{1}{4}$ cup vinegar
$1\frac{1}{2}$ teaspoons soy sauce
5 tablespoons sugar
$\frac{1}{2}$ teaspoon monosodium glutamate
dash of pepper
2 teaspoons cornstarch mixed with
3 tablespoons water

Cut pork into 1-inch squares. Roll in flour. Deep-fry in oil. Pork will float when done. Boil green pepper and carrots for 3 minutes and drain. Slice pineapple in 1-inch pieces. Using a low to medium flame, heat a well-greased skillet and add salt and garlic. Add water, vinegar, soy sauce, sugar, monosodium glutamate, and pepper. Bring this mixture to a boil. Add cornstarch paste and

Bernard L. Lewis, Inc.

Chinese vegetables are usually stir-fried in a wok (a rounded pan) so that the vegetables will remain crisp.

cook and stir for $\frac{1}{2}$ minute. Add green peppers, carrots, pineapple, and pork and cook for $\frac{1}{2}$ minute more.

Equipment: deep fat fryer, saucepan, skillet
Preparation Time: 20 minutes
Cooking Time: 35 minutes

Steamed Sponge Cake

   6 eggs
   $1\frac{1}{2}$ cups granulated or confectioners' sugar
   2 cups flour
   $\frac{1}{2}$ teaspoon baking powder
   $\frac{1}{2}$ teaspoon salt

Separate eggs and beat whites and sugar (add slowly) until stiff (about 15 minutes by hand, 4–6 minutes by electric beater). Add egg yolks and beat for 5 minutes. Sift flour, baking powder, and salt together and mix thoroughly with the eggs and sugar. Put mixture in a lightly greased pan, cover, and steam for 25 minutes. Cut cake into 1- or 2-inch squares and serve hot or cold.

Equipment: large bowl, electric mixer, baking pan, steamer
Preparation Time: 20 minutes
Cooking Time: 25 minutes

Review the cookery principles found on the following pages:

pp. 278, 282–287	Meat Cookery	Egg Rolls
pp. 177–192	Flour Mixtures	
pp. 177–192	Flour Mixtures	Wonton Soup
pp. 278, 282–287	Meat Cookery	Sweet And Sour Pork Cubes
pp. 160–167	Vegetable Cookery	
pp. 172–174	Starch Cookery	
pp. 177–192	Flour Mixtures	Steamed Sponge Cake
pp. 228–231	Functional Properties of Eggs	
pp. 231–237	Egg Cookery	

Table Setting

The unifying principle in all Chinese thought is the concept of harmony. This principle even extends to the art of cooking, where a harmonious relationship between the shapes, sizes, colors, and flavors of foods is desired. Many table customs and practices of etiquette can be traced back over two thousand years to Confucius.

A Chinese table setting usually consists of a pair of chopsticks, a bowl for soup and rice, a saucer for soy sauce, a porcelain spoon, and a tiny tea cup. Soup is usually served first and then the empty soup bowls are filled with rice. Serving spoons are never used in traditional Chinese table settings and all the dishes are placed in the center of the table where everyone can reach them. The Chinese prefer round tables because these make it easier for each person to reach everything on the table. If a long table is used, the food should be divided into two portions and half placed at each end of the table. Dishes are never passed around the table as is the American custom. As in the Japanese meal, the food should provide the decoration.

Other Suggested Foods					
Food	Part of Meal	Preparation Time	Cooking Time	Special Equipment	Review
Chinese Cabbage Soup	soup	20 min.	20 min.	skillet, kettle	Vegetable Cookery, pp. 160–167
Chicken Breasts With Peanuts	main dish	20 min.	20 min.	skillet	Poultry Cookery, p. 291

Bernard L. Lewis, Inc.

A Chinese table setting

MAJOR IDEAS

The following statements give the main ideas within the chapter you have just studied.

1. Harmony of flavor, texture, and color is an important principle of Chinese cookery.
2. Similar to Japanese cookery, Chinese cooking requires a maximum of preparation and a minimum of fuel and cooking time.

QUESTIONS TO STUDY

1. Describe Wonton Soup.
2. What are the basic ingredients of Chinese cookery?

BIBLIOGRAPHY

BENEDICTINE SISTERS OF PEKING, *Art of Chinese Cooking*. Rutland, Vt., Charles E. Tuttle, 1956.

CHAO, BUWEI YANG, *How to Cook and Eat in Chinese*. New York, The John Day Company, 1949.

CHEN, JOYCE, *Joyce Chen Cookbook*. Philadelphia, J. B. Lippincott Company, 1967.

MILLER, Gloria B., *Thousand Recipe Chinese Cookbook*. New York, Atheneum Publishers, 1966.

OLIVER, FRANK, *Chinese Cooking*. New York, Citadel Press, 1955,

OUEI, MIMI, *Art of Chinese Cooking*. New York, Random House, Inc., 1960.

TSUIFENG LIN and HSIANGJU LIN, *Secrets of Chinese Cooking*. Englewood Cliffs, N. J., Prentice-Hall, Inc., 1960.

Hawaiian Cookery

The food of Hawaii represents a combination of Eastern and Western cuisine. Since tropical fruits are so plentiful, extensive use is made of them in the Hawaiian meal.

Since the earliest times, Hawaiians have searched the sea for their food. Day and night, Hawaiians of all ages can be seen exploring the water near the shore for fish. The most exciting kind of fishing is called the hukilau.

Hawaii's red earth also produces two crops of importance: sugar and pineapples.

United Airlines

MENU

Ginger Chicken
Fresh Pineapple
Oriental Peas
Sweet Potatoes
Waikiki Coconut Cream Pie
Hawaiian Punch

RECIPES

Ginger Chicken

1 (1-pound) package frozen chicken thighs	1½ teaspoons ground ginger
1 (8-ounce) package frozen chicken breasts	½ teaspoon monosodium glutamate
1 cup sugar	1 teaspoon onion powder
1 teaspoon salt	dash garlic powder
¼ teaspoon pepper	1 cup flour
	2 tablespoons butter or margarine
	2 tablespoons cooking oil

Defrost chicken. Combine sugar and seasonings. Coat pieces of chicken with sugar mixture. Refrigerate several hours. An hour before cooking, dredge chicken in flour. Brown in the butter and oil over low heat for about 40 minutes, turning occasionally. Cover. Cook chicken about 20 minutes longer or until tender. Remove from skillet. Place chicken in a baking pan lined with paper towels. Bake at 300° F. for 20 minutes. *Serves 4.*

Equipment: skillet, baking pan
Preparation Time: 15 minutes
Cooking Time: 1 hour and 20 minutes

Oriental Peas

1 (10-ounce) package frozen peas
½ cup water chestnuts, sliced
salt and pepper
butter

Place frozen peas and water chestnuts on a square of aluminum foil. Season with salt and pepper and top with several pats of butter. Wrap securely in foil and bake at 350° F. for 1 hour, turning occasionally. The frozen peas will provide water for cooking.

Equipment: aluminum foil
Preparation Time: 5 minutes
Cooking Time: 1 hour

Hawaiian Sweet Potato

4 or 5 large sweet potatoes
1 (9-ounce) can crushed pineapple, undrained
6 tablespoons melted butter
¾ teaspoon salt
dash pepper
½ cup dry bread crumbs
2 tablespoons brown sugar
dash cloves

Boil 4 or 5 large sweet potatoes until tender. Sweet potatoes may be cooked with their skins on, thereby retaining nutritive value. In medium bowl, mash potatoes; stir in pineapple, 2 tablespoons of the butter, salt, and pepper. Turn into a 1-quart ungreased casserole. Combine the remaining butter with bread crumbs, brown sugar, and cloves. Sprinkle over potato mixture; bake 45 minutes in 350° F. oven. *Serves 6.*

Equipment: saucepan, bowl, casserole dish
Preparation Time: 10 minutes
Cooking Time: 1 hour

THE MANAGEMENT OF FOOD RESOURCES

Waikiki Coconut Cream Pie

$\frac{3}{4}$ cups sugar
$\frac{1}{4}$ cup cornstarch
$\frac{1}{8}$ teaspoon salt
$2\frac{1}{2}$ cups milk
4 egg yolks

1 teaspoon vanilla (scant)
baked pie shell
$\frac{3}{4}$ cup whipping cream
1 cup grated coconut

Combine sugar, cornstarch, and salt. Scald milk and add it to the dry ingredients slowly, stirring until a smooth mixture is obtained. Cook for 2 minutes over boiling water, stirring frequently. Cool mixture slightly and combine $\frac{1}{2}$ of it with yolks. Add other half and cook over hot water in double boiler until mixture thickens. Cool, add vanilla, and pour into a baked pie shell. Whip cream and spread over the filling. Sprinkle with grated coconut. *Serves 6 to 8.*

Equipment: double boiler, pie pan
Preparation Time: 30 minutes
Cooking Time: 30 minutes

Hawaiian Fruit Punch

1 cup canned tropical-fruit punch
$2\frac{1}{4}$ cups unsweetened pineapple juice
$2\frac{1}{2}$ cups orange juice

$\frac{1}{2}$ cup lemon juice
confectioners' sugar
1 tablespoon finely chopped mint

In a 2-quart pitcher, combine punch and juices. If desired, add confectioners' sugar to taste. To serve, add fresh mint and pour over cracked ice in tall glasses. *Serves 8.*

Equipment: pitcher
Preparation Time: 20 minutes

Review the cookery principles found on the following pages:		
p. 291	Poultry Cookery	Ginger Chicken
pp. 160–167	Vegetable Cookery	Oriental Peas
pp. 160–167	Vegetable Cookery	Sweet Potatoes
pp. 177–192	Flour Mixtures	Waikiki Coconut Cream Pie
pp. 172–174	Starch Cookery	
pp. 231–237	Egg Cookery	

Table Setting

A Luau, or Hawaiian feast, could be fun for this meal, with girls wearing muu-muus and boys wearing brightly colored shirts. The meal may be served on mats or on a low table arranged on the floor, Hawaiian style, outdoors on a picnic table, or indoors on a dining table. Decorations could consist of fish nets, fruits, and flowers. Hurricane lamps or candles will lend to the romantic atmosphere, and seashells and strips of bamboo will also emphasize this mood. Hawaiian background music could be played.

If guests are invited to the meal, they should be embraced as they arrive and should have a lei put gently around their necks. A lei can be created out of artificial flowers (crepe-paper or tissue paper, or pastel facial tissues) or real flowers. Flowers should be alternately strung with short sections of drinking straws to make a forty-inch necklace.

Other Suggested Foods					
Food	Part of Meal	Preparation Time	Cooking Time	Special Equipment	Review
Polynesian Chicken And Peaches	main dish	10 min.	40 min.	Dutch oven	Poultry Cookery, p. 291 Starch Cookery, pp. 172–174
Bananas Baked In Orange And Lemon Juice	dessert	15 min.	45 min.	baking pan	Fruit Cookery, pp. 160–167

MAJOR IDEAS

The following statements give the main ideas within the chapter you have just studied.

1. Hawaiian cookery represents a combination of eastern and western cuisine.
2. Fish and fruit are basic in Hawaiian meals.

QUESTIONS TO STUDY

1. What is a Luau?
2. Why is Hawaiian (and Japanese and Chinese) cookery a study in fruit and vegetable cookery?

BIBLIOGRAPHY

BAZORE, KATHERINE, *Hawaiian and Pacific Foods.* New York, M. Barrows and Company, 1953.

GARY, LAMORA SAUVINET, *The Pacific Hostess Cookbook.* New York, Coward-McCann, 1956.

31 SCANDINAVIAN COOKERY

To Scandinavians, fine food in lavish quantities is not a luxury, but a necessity of life. The Scandinavian countries—Denmark, Norway, Sweden, Finland, and Iceland—share similar food and food customs. Except for national variations in spelling, even the names of their dishes are the same, thanks to a common historical and geographical inheritance and interdependence. Yet, although these five countries are grouped in a close culinary relationship, each has certain regional specialties and methods of preparation that distinguish the cooking of one from the others. For example, Denmark is noted for pork and dairy products; Norway, for fish and lamb. Sweden boasts superb game and rich, imaginative desserts. Finland specializes in cereals and grows over thirty varieties of mushrooms, while Iceland's fish, particularly the Icelandic cod and tiny sweet shrimp, are world famous.

Norwegian cakes and cookies served to His Royal Highness Crown Prince Harald when he visited the Norwegian-American Museum in Decorah, Iowa, in 1965.

Norwegian-American Museum

474

The excellent Nordic cuisine has its roots not only in the traditional soups and gruels, salted and pickled fish and meat, but also in the extraordinary cookery of the seventeenth and eighteenth century French and German courts. The courts influenced all the European nobility who transmitted these tastes to the middle classes and the peasants who served them. This is especially true of Denmark and Sweden, less so of Norway, a country without a powerful aristocracy. The food of Finland has manifest Russian overtones dating back to the days when Finland was a Grand Duchy of the Czarist Empire. Today Scandinavian food still retains touches of richness and color not found anywhere else in Europe.

Menu

This menu will consist of a smörgasbord which will feature foods from all the Scandinavian countries. The Swedes give as much consideration to the artful arrangement of the smörgasbord as they do to the preparation of each of the dishes. A smörgasbord usually contains several cold herrings, boiled small potatoes, eggs, cheese, shrimp, smoked salmon, sliced cold meat, and one or two hot dishes. The menu will also include smørrebrød which are artistic, delectable openface sandwiches. This particular food is very special with the Danes.

MENU

Smørrebrød
Pickled Herring   Danish Cheese
Norwegian Spinach Soup
Scandinavian Boiled Cod
Danish Meat Balls
Swedish Pickled Beets
Scandinavian Sugar-Browned Potatoes
Swedish Limpa

RECIPES

Smørrebrød

A complete sandwich meal, starting with one sandwich of fish, another of meat, another of salad and one of cheese on rye-crisps can be planned. If it is desired, one open sandwich can be used as an appetizer course. Any food in any combination is good. Left-overs may also be used. It should be remembered, however, that everything should be combined as carefully as an artist arranges the colors on his canvas, though the cook uses food on his

Courtesy Woman's Day Encyclopedia of Cookery,
Copyright 1965, Fawcett Publications, Inc.

Courtesy Woman's Day Encyclopedia of Cookery,
Copyright 1965, Fawcett Publications, Inc.

A garnish can be described as the "finishing touch" to a prepared dish. Garnishing is a way of enhancing a meal's appearance and appeal with a creative, edible decoration.

Since attractive presentation of a dish is of great importance at any meal, garnishes can be used in many ways to stimulate interest in the foods being served. The garnish, however, should complement the food, not overpower or detract from it. Therefore, it is essential to consider color, shape, texture, aroma, and taste factors before deciding which garnishes to use with a particular meal.

Several types of garnishes can be used at one meal, and the garnish itself can serve as one of the main dishes. For example, glazed ham garnished with orange cups containing whipped sweet potatoes would be attractive as well as delicious. Although garnishes usually are edible, a small finger food, such as watercress placed around a jellied salad, could add color and textural appeal.

Raw garnishes may include many fruits and vegetables such as apple wedges, banana slices, grapefruit halves, pineapple slices, grape clusters, cherry halves, whole strawberries, lemon twists, orange slices, melon balls, carrot curls, cucumber circles, radish roses, green pepper strips, scallions, tomato wedges, mushroom slices, and celery curls.

Courtesy Woman's Day Encyclopedia of Cookery,
Copyright 1965, Fawcett Publications, Inc.

The suggestions below will help you create and prepare many types of garnishes.

1. Celery curls—Cut stalks into pieces about 2″ in length. Slit both ends in narrow strips, almost to the center. Place in ice water until strips curl.
2. Celery pinwheels—Stuff 1 celery stalk with well-seasoned cream cheese. Press stalk against two others. Tie together with string. Chill. Slice ½″ thick.
3. Carrot curls—Use large carrots. Scrape raw carrots and slice lengthwise in paper-thin slices. Roll up slices and fasten with toothpicks. Crisp in water until curled.
4. Radish roses—Cut off root end; leave bit of stem. Cut thin petals from stem to root end around radish. Place in ice water until petals open.
5. Onion chrysanthemum—Use a medium-size red onion. Remove outer skin. With point of a very sharp knife, cut from center into about ⅛″ sections about ¾ of the way through. Hold onion under running hot water and spread gently. Drain.
6. Fringed cucumber slices—Cucumbers need not be peeled. Cut off ends. Rake fork firmly down surface lengthwise. Repeat around cucumber. Slice thinly. Chill.

THE MANAGEMENT OF FOOD RESOURCES

"palette," rather than paint. In this way a work of art, perfect in color, form, texture, and flavor will result. Sandwiches should be made as close to serving time as possible since they are at their best when fresh. The following list offers a small sampling of the many sandwich combinations possible (one famous Copenhagen restaurant has a menu boasting 175 different smørrebrød):

1. Smoked salmon, minced dill, lemon slices
2. Roast beef with fried egg and onions
3. Sliced pork loin (Canadian style bacon) with cold pickled beets or warm red cabbage
4. Tiny shrimp piled high and topped with a lemon slice (a whole jar may be put on one slice of bread for the true Danish "shrimp in a crowd")
5. Sliced tomato and onion rings
6. Tuna fish and cucumber salad
7. Any Danish cheese, especially Danish Blue, with a raw egg yolk

Pickled Herring

Purchase at local grocery.

Danish Cheese

Purchase at local grocery.

Norwegian Spinach Soup

2 pounds fresh spinach, chopped or 2 packages chopped frozen spinach	2 tablespoons flour
	1 teaspoon salt
	$\frac{1}{4}$ teaspoon pepper
$1\frac{1}{2}$ quarts hot beef bouillon	$\frac{1}{8}$ teaspoon nutmeg
3 tablespoons butter	2 hard-cooked eggs, sliced

Cook spinach in hot bouillon for 10 minutes. Drain, reserving liquid. Keep spinach hot. Melt butter and stir in flour. When blended and smooth, add hot liquid, a little at a time, stirring until smooth. Cover and simmer for 5 minutes. Add spinach, salt, pepper, and nutmeg and mix thoroughly. Again cover and simmer for 5 minutes. Serve with hard-cooked egg slices floating on top of each bowl of soup. *Serves 4–6.*

Equipment: kettle, saucepan
Preparation Time: 10 minutes
Cooking Time: 25 minutes

Scandinavian Boiled Cod

This makes a very fine dinner when properly prepared, even though American fish do not compare to the Nordic variety in delicacy of flavor and firmness of flesh. In Denmark, Norway, and Iceland, cod is considered a great delicacy.

Scale and eviscerate a 3–4 pound cod (pages 400–401). Rinse it inside and out to remove any trace of blood. The cod may be cooked whole or in slices; for sliced fish, cut off head and reserve, and cut fish into 1½-inch slices (pages 403–404). Place whole fish or fish slices in deep bowl. Cover with ice cubes and set under running water to firm flesh. Drain and pat dry. If using the whole fish, wrap it in a long piece of cheesecloth, leaving long ends for handles. Place fish in kettle in cold water, barely to cover, leaving the ends outside the pan. To each quart of water add 2 tablespoons of salt. Bring to a boil. Lower heat and simmer 6–8 minutes a pound, depending on the size of the fish. Grasp ends of cloth and lift fish out. Drain well.

If using sliced cod, boil water in a large kettle, adding 2 tablespoons of salt for each quart. Put fish slices and head into boiling water. Let water come to a boil, then simmer for 1–3 minutes. Do not overcook.

Meanwhile, peel tiny new potatoes and cook in vegetable steamer over boiling water. To serve, place cod and steamed potatoes on a hot platter. Serve with drawn or creamed butter, chopped hard-cooked egg, grated horse-radish, and chopped parsley. *Serves 4–6.*

Equipment: deep bowl, cheesecloth, large kettle
Preparation Time: 35 minutes
Cooking Time: 18 minutes

Danish Meat Balls

½ pound raw veal	1 egg, beaten lightly
½ pound raw pork	1 onion, grated
2 tablespoons flour	salt and pepper to taste
1½ cups milk	butter

Grind veal and pork together several times until well combined and finely ground. Add flour, milk, beaten egg, onion, salt, and pepper and mix well. Heat butter in skillet, shape meat into small balls and fry slowly until brown. Serve with potatoes and red cabbage or pickled beets.

Equipment: meat grinder, mixing bowl
Preparation Time: 20 minutes
Cooking Time: 40 minutes

Courtesy Woman's Day Encyclopedia of Cookery,
Copyright 1965, Fawcett Publications, Inc.

Swedish Pickled Beets

$\frac{1}{2}$ cup cider or white vinegar
$\frac{1}{2}$ cup water
$\frac{1}{4}$ cup sugar
1 teaspoon salt

$\frac{1}{8}$ teaspoon freshly ground pepper
2 cups (approximately) thinly sliced
cooked and peeled beets

Combine first five ingredients. Bring to a boil and cool. Place beets in a deep bowl and pour dressing over them. Let stand in the refrigerator for at least 12 hours before serving. Serve with fried fish, hot and cold meats, or on the smörgasbord. *Makes about 2 cups.*

Equipment: saucepan, deep bowl
Preparation Time: 1 hour (let stand for 12 hours)

Scandinavian Sugar-Browned Potatoes

2 tablespoons butter
2 tablespoons sugar
10 small boiled potatoes, peeled
$\frac{1}{2}$ teaspoon salt

Melt butter in heavy frying pan. When hot, stir in sugar. Brown the sugar, taking care not to scorch it. Add potatoes, shaking pan constantly to brown on all sides. When potatoes are browned, sprinkle with salt. Serve with meat or poultry. *Serves 4.*

Equipment: heavy skillet
Preparation Time: 5 minutes
Cooking Time: 10 minutes

Swedish Limpa

2 cups water
½ cup brown sugar
2 teaspoons caraway seed
1 teaspoon chopped orange peel or
   1 scant teaspoon anise seed
1 tablespoon shortening

½ cake compressed yeast
3 cups sifted all-purpose flour
   (approximately)
1 teaspoon salt
2 cups rye flour (approximately)

Boil together water, sugar, caraway seed, orange peel (or anise seed), and shortening for 3 minutes. Let mixture become lukewarm. Add yeast, stir thoroughly, and gradually add sufficient wheat flour to make a soft batter. Place batter in a warm place and let it rise for 1½ hours. Then add salt and enough rye flour to make a stiff dough. Let rise again for 2 hours. Knead slightly and shape into loaf. Put into greased loaf pan, 9″ × 5″ × 3″. Let rise again for ½ hour. Bake in moderate oven (350° F.) for 1 hour. *Makes 1 loaf.*

Equipment: mixing bowl, saucepan
Preparation Time: 6 hours or less
Cooking Time: 1 hour

Review the cookery principles found on the following pages:

pp. 172–174	Starch Cookery	Norwegian Spinach Soup
pp. 160–167	Vegetable Cookery	
	Egg Cookery	
pp. 295, 400–401	Fish Cookery	Scandinavian Boiled Cod
pp. 160–167	Vegetable Cookery	
pp. 278, 282–287	Meat Cookery	Danish Meat Balls
pp. 160–167	Vegetable Cookery	Scandinavian Sugar-Browned Potatoes
pp. 177–192	Flour Mixtures	Swedish Limpa

Table Setting

Since a smörgasbord consists of many different foods arranged attractively on a long table, the food itself can serve as the main decoration. Flags of the separate countries, wooden candlestick holders, and carved figures may also be used.

Other Suggested Foods					
Food	Part of Meal	Preparation Time	Cooking Time	Special Equipment	Review
Fruit Soup	soup	15 min.	30 min.	large kettle	Fruit Cookery, pp. 160–167
Sans Rival Torte	dessert	40 min.	20 min.	baking sheet	Egg Cookery, pp. 231–237

MAJOR IDEAS

The following statements give the main ideas within the chapter you have just studied.

1. Scandinavian countries are closely allied in their food habits and customs.
2. Each country, however, has its own particular regional foods. Denmark is noted for pork and dairy products; Norway, for fish and lamb; Sweden, for superb game and rich desserts; Finland, for cereals and mushrooms; Iceland, for fish, especially cod.

QUESTIONS TO STUDY

1. What are Smørrebrød?
2. How does Scandinavian cookery differ from German cookery?
3. What factors influenced Scandinavian cookery?
4. What is a Smörgasbord?

BIBLIOGRAPHY

BROBECK and KJELLBERG, *Scandinavian Cookery for Americans.* Boston, Little, Brown and Company, 1950.

BROWN, B. S., "Deft Swedish Touch." *Good Housekeeping*, Vol. 160, January 1965, p. 142.

"Cooking Danish and Swedish Pancakes." *Sunset*, Vol. 133, November 1964, pp. 175–176.

HAZELTON, MIKA STANDEN, "Scandinavian Cook Book." *House and Garden*, February 1964, p. 139.

"How the Swedes Use Mushrooms." *Sunset*, Vol. 134, February 1965, p. 150.

JENSEN, INGEBORG DAHL, *Wonderful, Wonderful Danish Cooking.* New York, Simon and Schuster, 1965.

SARVIS and O'NEIL, *Cooking Scandinavian.* New York, Doubleday and Company, 1963.

"Two Swedish National Favorites; with Recipes." *Look*, Vol. 29, February 9, 1965, pp. 58–59.

WIDENFELT, SAM, *Swedish Food.* Wezäta Förlag; Gothenburg, Sweden, 1947.

32 FRENCH COOKERY

In probably no other country in the world are the people so devoted to good cooking and eating in the grand manner as they are in France. There is hardly a place in the world where the French cuisine is not known, revered, and imitated. The sauces of France are perhaps a key to the country's superb cuisine. Many of them have royal origins: Béarnaise was created by Henry IV and named for the province of his birth, and Mornay was created by Philippe de Mornay, a prime minister. The French also discovered the art of making bouillon (clear beef soup) which serves as the base of many French sauces. In addition, these people created petits fours—elaborate miniature cakes. Petits fours literally mean "little ovens," for when they were first prepared for Louis XIV they were served piping hot.

The menu presented in this chapter will be more elaborate than a simple family meal in France which usually consists of soup, vegetables, and dessert.

Chez Garin, a French restaurant.

Courtesy Gourmet Magazine, Ronny Jaques photographer

Menu

The French like to begin and end their meal with a lavish array of food. Hors d'oeuvres usually begin the meal and a tray of different cheeses often ends the dinner.

MENU

Hors d'Oeuvres
Onion Soup With Roquefort Cheese
Duck À L'Orange
Asparagus With Hollandaise Sauce
Green Salad
French Bread
Cherries Jubilee

RECIPES

Hors d'Oeuvres

Many hors d'oeuvres require little if any preparation. Others are more elaborate. Below is a list of possible hors d'oeuvres.

Olives. Green olives, plain or stuffed with pimento, anchovies, or almonds. Black olives can be sprinkled with a few drops of olive oil.

Melon. Serve with wedges of lime. Excellent with paper-thin slices of smoked ham.

Radishes. Wash and trim. Serve with salt and butter.

Shrimp. Cook and shell. Cover with mayonnaise combined with lemon juice and paprika.

Stuffed Eggs. Split hard-cooked eggs lengthwise. Combine yolks with mayonnaise and season to taste. Stuff white with yolk mixture. Garnish with pieces of anchovy.

Onion Soup

Onion soup is one French dish which is popular all over the world.

4 tablespoons butter	nutmeg
1½ pounds (5 to 6) onions	12 thin slices of French bread
6 cups water	3 ounces Roquefort cheese
salt and pepper	4 tablespoons grated Gruyère cheese

Heat the butter in a heavy pan and sauté the peeled and finely chopped onions until they are golden. Pour in 6 cups of boiling water and season

Bernard L. Lewis, Inc.

with salt, pepper, and a little freshly grated nutmeg. Boil 5 minutes. Meanwhile, dry the bread in a hot oven and put it in the bottom of a heatproof soup tureen or a deep casserole. Crumble Roquefort cheese over the bread and fill the tureen ¾ full with the soup. Sprinkle with the grated cheese. Bake at 350° F. for 25 minutes. *Serves 6.*

Equipment: heavy pan, heat-proof tureen or casserole
Preparation Time: 15 minutes
Cooking Time: 45 minutes

Duck À L'Orange

This is the family version of the classic duck à l'Orange. It is surprisingly simple to make when compared to the classic one and tastes just as good.

⅓ cup orange marmalade
1 teaspoon soy sauce
1 teaspoon salt
¾ cup orange juice
1 (3½- to 4-pound) duckling, quartered

1 tablespoon butter
1 tablespoon flour
1 tablespoon wine vinegar
1 cup consommé
¼ teaspoon pepper
1 orange, peeled and cut into wedges

In a mixing bowl, combine marmalade, soy sauce, salt, and ½ of the orange juice. Roast duckling at 450° F. for 15 minutes. Then reduce heat to 400° F. and continue roasting for 30 minutes or until meat is tender; brush occasionally

In Europe, duck is prized as one of the greatest of all table delicacies and it is
cooked in various ways, especially in France. The most famous French ducks
are raised in Rouen.

with half of the orange mixture. Meanwhile, heat butter in a small saucepan.
Add flour and cook until flour is browned. Stir in vinegar and consommé.
Bring to boil, stirring constantly. Cover and simmer for 10 minutes. Add re-
maining orange mixture. Cover and simmer for 10 more minutes. Add pepper.

Meanwhile, cook orange wedges in boiling water for 3 minutes. Drain and
keep warm. Remove duckling to heated serving dish, garnish with wedges of
orange, and keep warm. Pour all fat off drippings in the roasting pan. Add
remaining cooking liquid and remaining orange juice to saucepan in which
orange sauce is cooking. Mix. Serve sauce in sauceboat. *Serves 4.*

Equipment: mixing bowl, saucepan, roasting pan with rack
Preparation Time: 15 minutes
Cooking Time: 1 to 1½ hours

Asparagus With Hollandaise Sauce

Cook the asparagus like any green vegetable. Prepare the hollandaise sauce and pour it over the asparagus just before serving.

2 egg yolks
$\frac{1}{4}$ teaspoon salt
dash cayenne pepper
$\frac{1}{2}$ cup melted butter or margarine
1 tablespoon lemon juice

In a small bowl with electric mixer beat 2 egg yolks until thick. Add salt and cayenne pepper, then $\frac{1}{4}$ cup of the melted butter or margarine, about 1 teaspoon at a time, beating constantly. Combine the remaining $\frac{1}{4}$ cup melted butter or margarine and lemon juice; add, about 2 teaspoons at a time, to yolk mixture, beating constantly.

Equipment: saucepan, mixing bowl, electric mixer
Preparation Time: 20 minutes
Cooking Time: 15 minutes

Green Salad

$\frac{1}{4}$ bunch romaine
$\frac{1}{4}$ head lettuce
2 tomatoes
1 cucumber
6 radishes

2 celery hearts
8 pitted olives
6 walnuts, shelled and quartered
Vinaigrette Sauce

Peel or trim the vegetables and cut them into large sections. Cut the olives in half. Put everything into a shallow salad bowl and mix with Vinaigrette Sauce.

Equipment: salad bowl
Preparation Time: 15 minutes

Vinaigrette Sauce

4 tablespoons oil
4 teaspoons vinegar
salt
freshly ground black pepper

Combine ingredients in a small container and shake until the salt has dissolved.

French Bread

Purchase at local grocery.

Cherries Jubilee

Cherries Jubilee is a spectacular dessert invented by the great Escoffier in honor of Queen Victoria's Jubilee. Since then it has remained a festive dessert that, like crêpes Suzette, is a source of attraction and delight. It is surprising that it is not commonly made at home, since the recipe is so simple that the most inexperienced cook cannot but succeed in making it. When it is served, the man of the house can demonstrate his skill and satisfy his dream of glory by being "master of the fire." After a full meal, it is a delicious, light dessert, and is simple to prepare for both expected and unexpected guests for dinner.

1 pound (14-ounce can) dark sweet cherries
2 teaspoons cornstarch
1 tablespoon water
2 tablespoons orange or lemon extract or kirsch
vanilla ice cream

Drain cherries and reserve ¾ cup of the juice. Heat juice to boiling in small saucepan. Add cherries and bring to boil. Mix cornstarch and water and gradually add to hot cherry mixture. Cook, stirring constantly until cherry juice thickens and clears. Lower heat but keep mixture warm. Warm the orange or lemon extract or kirsch. Ignite it, pour on cherry mixture and ladle flaming cherries over scoops of vanilla ice cream. Serve immediately. *Serves 6*.

Equipment: saucepan or chafing dish
Preparation Time: 5 minutes
Cooking Time: 20 minutes

Review the cookery principles found on the following pages:		
pp. 295, 400–407	Fish Cookery	Hors d'Oeuvres
pp. 231–237	Egg Cookery	
pp. 160–167	Vegetable Cookery	Onion Soup With Roquefort Cheese
p. 253	Cheese Cookery	
p. 291	Poultry Cookery	Duck A L'Orange
pp. 172–174	Starch Cookery	
pp. 160–167	Vegetable Cookery	Asparagus With Hollandaise Sauce
pp. 307–309	Fats	
p. 309	Fats	Green Salad
pp. 158–160, 389–391	Vegetable Selection	
pp. 172–174	Starch Cookery	Cherries Jubilee
pp. 160–167	Fruits	

Table Setting

A French setting can be very elaborate or simple, depending on available material, although an elaborate setting is typical of French service. Extra flatware may be needed for this meal. As the setting is created, it should be remembered that cooking is considered an art in France. Therefore, all the dishes should be carefully garnished and beautiful.

Other Suggested Foods					
Food	Part of Meal	Preparation Time	Cooking Time	Special Equipment	Review
Garlic Bread	bread	10 min.	15 min.	baking sheet	Management of Time, pp. 414–415, 422 Flour Mixtures, pp. 177–192
Vichyssoise	soup	20 min.	1 hr.	kettle	Vegetable Cookery, pp. 160–167 Milk Cookery, pp. 247–248
Boeuf À La Mode	main dish	30 min.	3 hr. 30 min.	Dutch oven	Meat Cookery, pp. 278, 282–287
Baked Alaska	dessert	10 min.	8 min.	wooden board	Egg Cookery, pp. 231–237 Flour Mixtures, pp. 177–192
Crêpes Suzette	dessert	40 min.	30 min.	skillet chafing dish	Flour Mixtures, pp. 177–192

MAJOR IDEAS

The following statements give the main ideas within the chapter you have just studied.

1. France has one of the most distinctive cuisines anywhere.
2. One of the characteristic features of French cookery is the extensive use of sauces.

QUESTIONS TO STUDY

1. How is French cookery similar to, yet different from, that of Japanese cookery?

2. What are Hors d'Oeuvres?
3. What is the basic principle for making Hollandaise Sauce?
4. Describe Cherries Jubilee.

BIBLIOGRAPHY

BENET, SULA, *Festival Menus Round the World.* New York, Abelard-Schuman Limited, 1957.

CANNON, POPPY, *Eating European Abroad and at Home.* New York, Doubleday and Company, 1961.

CHILD, JULIA, BECK, SIMONE, and BERTHOLLE, LOUISETTE, *Mastering the Art of French Cooking.* New York, Knopf, 1961.

DIAT, LOUIS, *French Cooking for Americans.* Philadelphia, J. B. Lippincott, 1946.

LUCAS, DIONE, *The Cordon Bleu Cookbook.* Boston, Little, Brown and Company, 1947.

MAPIE, The Countess de Toulouse-Lautrec, *La Cuisine de France.* New York, The Orion Press, 1964.

METZELTHIN, PEARL V., *The New World Wide Cookbook.* New York, Julian Messner, 1951.

MONTAGNE, PROSPER, *Larousse Gastronomique.* New York, Crown Publishers, Inc., 1961.

33 ITALIAN COOKERY

Italian dishes vary from province to province and the food of the north is completely different from the food of the south. In the north, wine, brandies, and butter are used for cooking; in the south, garlic, olive oil, and tomato

Bernard L. Lewis, Inc.

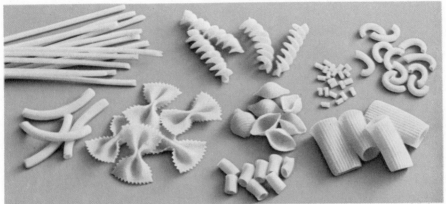

Courtesy Woman's Day Encyclopedia of Cookery,
Copyright 1965, Fawcett Publications, Inc.

sauce are most important. But north or south, most Italians love pasta in its dozen of varieties: spaghetti and macaroni (tubular noodles), lasagne (wide noodles), vermicelli (fine, stringy pasta), stelline (star-shaped noodles), conchigli (sea shells), and tortillini, cappelletti, and ravioli (stuffed pasta).

To the Italian cook, cheese is basic. Some of the famous Italian cheeses are Gorgonzola (blue cheese), Mozzarella (soft, unripened), Provolone (smoked cheese), Parmigiano (sweet, grated for seasonings), Ricotta (a cottage cheese), and Pecorino (a sharp cheese).

MENU

Antipasto
Lasagne Casserole
Green Salad With Anchovies
Italian Garlic Bread
Spumone
Grape Juice

RECIPES

Antipasto

Select a cabbage as the base and anchor relishes to it with toothpicks. The relishes should completely cover the cabbage. Green and ripe olives, pickled artichoke hearts, pickled peppers, celery, carrot sticks, cherry tomatoes, green

Courtesy Woman's Day Encyclopedia of Cookery,
Copyright 1965, Fawcett Publications, Inc.

onions, and lemon cuts can be used as the relishes. Hide the base with salami and red onion rings.

Lasagne Casserole

1 pound Italian sausage
1 clove garlic, minced
1 tablespoon whole basil
1½ teaspoons salt

1 (1-pound) can (2 cups) tomatoes
1 (12-ounce) can (1⅓ cups) tomato paste
10 ounces lasagne

Brown meat slowly; spoon off fat. Add remaining ingredients. Simmer uncovered ½ hour—stir occasionally. Meanwhile, cook lasagne or wide noodles until tender in a large amount of boiling salted water—this may take 15 to 20 minutes. Drain and rinse in cold water.

3 cups fresh Ricotta or creamy cottage cheese
½ cup grated Parmigiano (Parmesan) or Romano cheese
2 tablespoons parsley flakes

2 eggs, beaten
2 teaspoons salt
½ teaspoon pepper
1 pound Mozzarella cheese, sliced very thin

Mix first 6 ingredients. Place half the cooked noodles in a 13″ × 9″ × 2″ baking dish; spread with half of the cheese filling. Cover with half the Mozzarella cheese and half the meat sauce. Repeat layers. Bake in moderate oven (375° F.) for 30 minutes. Before cutting in squares, let stand 10 minutes—filling will set slightly. *Serves 12.*

Equipment: skillet, kettle, casserole dish
Preparation Time: 20 minutes
Cooking Time: 1 hour

Green Salad With Anchovies

1 head romaine lettuce	1 (2-ounce) can anchovies, chopped
1 bunch leaf lettuce	3 tablespoons olive or salad oil
2 tomatoes, cut in wedges	2 tablespoons tarragon vinegar
$\frac{1}{2}$ cup celery slices	2 tablespoons chopped parsley
$\frac{1}{2}$ cup diced green pepper	$\frac{3}{4}$ teaspoon salt
$\frac{1}{2}$ cup radish slices	dash of fresh-ground pepper
$\frac{1}{4}$ cup sliced green onions	$\frac{1}{2}$ teaspoon whole basil

Tear greens into bite-size pieces into a bowl; arrange vegetables and anchovies over lettuce. Sprinkle with remaining ingredients. Toss lightly. *Serves 6-8.*

Equipment: bowl
Preparation Time: 10 minutes

Italian Bread

Italian bread can be purchased at your local store. To make garlic bread, simply make diagonal slits in the long loaf and add garlic butter. Bake at 400° F. until the butter melts.

Spumone

Eggnog Layer:
1 pint French vanilla ice cream
rum flavoring to taste
3 maraschino cherries

Stir ice cream just to soften; stir in rum flavoring to taste. Refreeze only enough to be workable. Spread quickly in a layer over bottom and sides of a quart size chilled bowl. Place cherries in center. Return to freezer and freeze firm.

Pistachio Layer:
1 pint French vanilla ice cream
$\frac{1}{4}$ teaspoon pistachio extract
few drops of food coloring
$\frac{1}{4}$ cup finely chopped unblanched almonds

Stir ice cream just to soften; stir in extract, food coloring, and nuts. Refreeze only enough to be workable. Quickly spread over top and sides of Eggnog Layer. Freeze firm.

Chocolate Layer:
½ cup heavy cream
¼ cup instant cocoa

Combine cream and instant cocoa; whip until mixture holds in peaks. Quickly spread over Pistachio Layer, covering completely. Freeze.

Raspberry Layer:
1 (10-ounce package) red raspberries, thawed
½ cup heavy cream
¼ cup sifted confectioners' sugar
dash of salt

Drain berries (save sirup for a fruit punch); sieve. Combine cream, confectioners' sugar, and a dash of salt. Whip until mixture holds in peaks. Fold in sieved berries (add a few drops of red food coloring if needed). Pile into center of bowl and smooth top; cover with foil. Freeze 4 hours or overnight.

To serve, peel off foil. Invert on chilled serving plate. Rub outside of bowl with towel wrung out with warm water to loosen ice cream. Lift off bowl. Decorate plate with maraschino cherries (stems on). Top spumone with cherries or a sprinkle of chopped almonds or pistachio nuts. Cut in small wedges. *Serves 12.*

Equipment: 1-quart bowl, freezer trays
Preparation Time: 1 hour
Freezing Time: 4 hours or overnight

Review the Cookery Principles found on the following pages:		
pp. 158–160, 382–395	Vegetable Selection	Antipasto
pp. 278, 282–287	Meat Cookery	Lasagne Casserole
p. 253	Cheese Cookery	
pp. 172–174	Starch Cookery	
pp. 158–160, 382–395	Vegetable Selection	Green Salad
pp. 210–211	Frozen Mixtures	Spumone

Table Setting

A red and white checked tablecloth and a candle-dripped wine bottle will be attractive on the table. The lasagne should be served in the dish in which it was baked and a basket should contain the bread. A tray of cheese and grapes would also be decorative as well as tasty.

Other Suggested Foods

Food	Part of Meal	Preparation Time	Cooking Time	Special Equipment	Review
Chicken Cacciatore	main dish	20 min.	1 hr.	skillet	Poultry Cookery, p. 291
Spaghetti And Meat Balls	main dish	30 min.	4 hr.	kettle casserole	Meat Cookery, pp. 278, 282–287 Cheese Cookery, p. 253 Starch Cookery, pp. 172–174
Zucchini Florentine	vegetable	15 min.	55 min.	casserole shallow pan	Vegetable Cookery, pp. 160–167
Tutti-Frutti Tortoni	dessert	20 min.	freeze overnight	baking cups muffin pan	Frozen Mixtures, pp. 210–212
Formaggio E Frutta	dessert	10 min.		large bowl	Fruit Selection, pp. 382–388

MAJOR IDEAS

The following statements give the main ideas within the chapter you have just studied.

1. Italian cookery is influenced by the area from which it is derived. Northern Italians use brandies, wines, and butter in cooking while in the south, garlic, olive oil and tomato sauce are common.
2. Pasta, in various forms and shapes, are an important part of Italian cookery.

QUESTIONS TO STUDY

1. What is the relationship of Antipasto to Hors d'Oeuvres?
2. What is Spumone?
3. Compare Italian cookery with French cookery.

BIBLIOGRAPHY

BONI, ADA, *The Talisman Italian Cook Book.* New York, Crown Publishers, 1958.

"Italian Favorites." *Better Homes and Gardens*, March 1961.

SALTA, ROMEO, *The Pleasures of Italian Cooking.* New York, The Macmillan Company, 1962.

Table 30

NUTRITIONAL VALUE OF FOODS

Ca = Calcium
Cal. = Calories
CHO = Carbohydrate
diam. = diameter

Fe = Iron
Gm. = Gram
" = inches
I.U. = International Unit

Mg. = Milligram
oz. = ounce
H_2O = water
Pro. = Protein

T = Tablespoon
t = teaspoon
Tr. = Trace, or tiny amount
Vit. = vitamin

Adapted from *Composition of Foods—Raw, Processed, Prepared,* Agricultural Research Service, United States Department of Agriculture, Handbook No. 8. Revised 1963; Home and Garden Bulletin No. 72, Revised 1964, U.S.D.A.

Food	Measure	H_2O %	Food Energy Cal.	Pro. Gm.	Fat Gm.	CHO Gm.	Ca Mg.	Fe Mg.	Vit. A I.U.	Thia-mine Mg.	Ribo-flavin Mg.	Nia-cin Mg.	Ascor-bic Acid Mg.
Apples, fresh	1 medium, 3" diam.	85	70	Tr.	Tr.	18	8	.4	50	.04	.05	.1	3
Applesauce, sweetened	1 cup	76	230	1	Tr.	60	10	1.3	100	.05	.03	.1	3
Apricots, fresh	3	85	55	1	Tr.	14	18	.5	2,890	.03	.04	.7	10
Apricots, dried, cooked	1 cup	76	240	5	1	62	63	5.1	8,550	.01	.13	2.8	8
Asparagus, fresh, cooked	1 cup cut spears	94	35	4	Tr.	6	37	1.	1,580	.27	.32	2.4	46
Avocado (alligator pear), fresh	½ pear, 4"	74	185	2	18	6	11	.6	310	.12	.21	1.7	15
Bacon, broiled	2 slices, crisp	8	100	5	8	1	2	.5	0	.08	.05	.8	—
Bananas, fresh	1 medium	76	85	1	Tr.	23	8	.7	190	.05	.06	.7	10
Beans, kidney, canned	1 cup	190	230	14	1	42	72	4.6	Tr.	.12	.1	1.6	—
Beans, baked, canned, pork and sweet sauce	1 cup	71	320	16	7	54	141	4.7	340	.16	.1	1.4	5
Beans, snap, cooked	¾ cup	92	30	2	Tr.	7	62	.8	680	.07	.1	.4	13
Beans, Lima, green, cooked	1 cup	71	180	12	1	32	75	4.0	450	.29	.16	2.0	28
Bean sprouts	1 cup	89	40	6	2	4	46	.7	90	.17	.16	.8	4
Beef, hamburger, lean	3 oz.	60	185	23	10	0	10	3.	20	.08	.20	5.1	—
Beef, roast	3 oz.	40	375	17	34	0	8	2.2	70	.05	.13	3.1	—
Beef, dried, creamed	2 oz.	48	115	19	4	0	11	2.9	—	.04	.18	2.2	—
Beef, steak round, broiled	3 oz.	44	330	20	27	0	9	2.5	50	.05	.16	4.0	—

Beet greens	1 cup, cooked	91	40	3	.4	6	188	3.8	10,200	.14	.30	.6	30
Beets, cooked	1 cup diced	91	50	2	Tr.	12	23	.8	40	.04	.07	.5	11
Biscuits, baking powder	3 biscuits, 2" diam.	29	325	7	9.0	52	68	2.3	Tr.	.27	.22	2.	Tr.
Blackberries, fresh	1 cup	84	85	1	1.	19	46	1.3	290	.05	.06	.5	30
Blueberries, fresh	1 cup	83	85	1	1.	21	21	1.4	140	.04	.08	.6	20
Bologna, all meat	8 slices	56	690	27	62.	2	16	4.1	—	.36	.49	6.0	—
Bouillon cubes	1 cube	4	5	1	Tr.	Tr.	—	—	—	—	—	—	—
Bran flakes, enriched	1 oz.	3	85	3	1.	23	20	1.2	0	.11	.05	1.7	0
Bread, corn, yellow, mix	1 piece, 2" sq.	33	150	3	5	23	50	.8	80	.09	.11	.8	Tr.
Bread, rye	1 slice	36	55	2	Tr.	12	17	.4	0	.04	.02	.3	0
Bread, white, enriched	1 slice	36	60	2	1	12	16	.6	Tr.	.06	.04	.5	Tr.
Bread, whole-wheat	1 slice	36	55	2	Tr.	11	23	.5	Tr.	.06	.03	.7	Tr.
Broccoli, flower stalks, cooked	1 cup, boiled	91	40	5	Tr.	7	132	1.2	3,750	.14	.29	1.2	135
Brussels sprouts, cooked	2 cups	88	45	5	1	8	42	1.4	680	.10	.18	1.1	113
Butter	1 T	16	50	Tr.	6	Tr.	1	0	230	—	—	—	—
Buttermilk	1 cup	90	90	9	Tr.	13	298	.1	10	.09	.44	.2	2
Cabbage, Chinese, raw	1 cup	95	15	1	Tr.	3	43	.6	150	.05	.04	—	25
Cabbage, raw	1 cup, shredded	92	25	1	Tr.	5	49	.4	130	.05	.05	.3	47
Cabbage, cooked	1 cup	94	35	2	Tr.	7	75	.5	220	.07	.07	.5	56
Cake, plain, iced	1 cupcake	24	145	2	6	22	26	.2	70	.01	.03	.1	Tr.
Cake, angel food	2" sector	32	110	3	Tr.	24	4	.1	Tr.	Tr.	.06	.1	0
Cantaloupes	1 half melon	91	60	1	Tr.	14	27	.8	6,540	.08	.06	1.2	63
Carrots, cooked	1 cup, diced	91	45	1	Tr.	10	48	.9	15,220	.08	.07	.7	9
Cauliflower, cooked	1 cup	93	25	3	Tr.	5	25	.8	70	.11	.10	.7	66
Celery, green	2 large outer stalks	94	10	Tr.	Tr.	4	32	.2	200	.02	.02	.7	8
Chard, leaves, stalks	½ cup, cooked	94	20	2	.2	3	73	1.8	5,400	.04	.11	.4	16
Cheese, cheddar, American	1 oz.	37	70	7	5	Tr.	128	.2	220	Tr.	.08	Tr.	0
Cheese, cottage	1 cup	78	240	31	9	7	212	.7	380	.07	.56	.2	0
Cherries, red, canned	1 cup, sirup	76	230	2	1	59	36	.8	1,680	.07	.06	.4	13
Chicken, broiled	3 oz.	71	115	20	3	0	8	1.4	80	.05	.16	7.4	—
Chicken, stewed	3½ oz.	46	369	24	29.5	0	10	1.6	1,190	.04	.21	7.8	—
Chicken, roasted	3½ oz., light meat	71	136	24	3.8	0	9	1.7	90	.05	.19	8.8	—
Chocolate, milk, bar	1 oz.	—	151	3	10.9	14	58	1.8	40	.04	.14	.3	0
Chocolate, bitter	1 oz.	2	145	7	15	8	22	1.9	20	.01	.07	.4	0
Cocoa, beverage	1 cup, 6 oz.	—	174	8	9	20	224	.9	295	.08	.34	.3	2
Coconut, dried, sweet	2 T, shredded	1	80	.5	6	8	2	.3	0	.01	Tr.	.1	—
Cod, steak, baked	4 oz., before cooking	65	170	28.5	5	0	31	1.	180	.08	.11	3.	—

Food	Measure	H₂O %	Food Energy Cal	Pro. Gm.	Fat Gm.	CHO Gm.	Ca Mg.	Fe Mg.	Vit. A I.U.	Thia-mine Mg.	Ribo-flavin Mg.	Nia-cin Mg.	Ascor-bic Acid Mg.
Collards, boiled	½ cup	45	30	2.5	.6	5	145	.55	130	.14	.18	1.2	44
Cookies, astd., commercial	3″ diam., 1 large	3	120	1.5	18	9	1	.2	20	.01	.01	.1	Tr.
Corn, sweet, canned	1 cup, cream style	81	170	5	2	40	10	1.2	690	.06	.12	2	13
Corn bread, yellow	1 piece, 2″ sq.	20	95	3	3	13	34	.5	110	.06	.08	.5	Tr.
Corn flakes, enriched	1 cup	4	110	2	Tr.	24	5	1	0	.14	.1	1.2	0
Corn meal, yellow enriched	1 cup, cooked	5	60	2	1	15	9	.8	0	0	0	0	0
Corn sirup	1 T		23	0	0	5.5	0	0	0	0	0	0	0
Cornstarch	1 T		29	Tr.	0	7	0	0	0	0	0	Tr.	0
Cornstarch blancmange	1 cup	79	290	10	10	42	304	Tr.	420	.08	.42	.1	2
Crab, cooked	3½ oz.		93	17	Tr.	.5	43	.8		.16	.08	2.8	2
Crackers, graham	2 med.	6	50	1.2	1.4	6	.8	.2	0	Tr.	.02	.2	0
Crackers, saltines	2″ square		55	1	1	10	6	.2	0	.01	.03	.2	0
Cranberries, sauce	1 cup	.1	35	1	1	6	4	.2	0	Tr.	Tr.	.1	5
Cream, light	1 cup	62	405	20	1	104	17	.6	40	.03	.03	.1	0
Cream, whipped	1 cup	72	505	7	49	10	245	.1	2,030	.07	.36	.1	Tr.
Cucumber	1 T	57	55	Tr.	6	Tr.	11	Tr.	230	Tr.	.02	Tr.	6
Currants, raw, black	6 slices, ½ med.	96	5	Tr.	Tr.	2	8	.2	Tr.	.02	.02	.1	200
Custard	¾ cup	84	54	.17	.1	13.1	60	1.1	230	.05	.05	.3	Tr.
Dandelion greens	1 cup	154	230	11	12	22	24	.8	700	.08	.38	.2	32
Dates	1 cup, cooked	90	60	4	1	12	252	3.2	21,060	.24	.29	3.9	0
Doughnuts, cake	1 cup	22	490	4	1	130	105	5.3	90	.16	.17	.4	Tr.
Eggs, whole	1 average	24	125	1	6	16	13	.4	30	.05	.05	Tr.	0
Egg, white	1 large	74	80	—	6	Tr.	27	1.1	590	Tr.	.15	Tr.	0
Egg, yolk	1 med.	88	15	4	Tr.	Tr.	3	Tr.	0	.04	.09	Tr.	0
Endive, raw	1 med.	51	60	3	5	Tr.	24	.9	580	.04	.07	.3	6
Farina, cooked	2 oz.	93	10	1	Tr.	2	46	1	1,870	.04	.08	.1	2
Figs, fresh	¾ cup, unenriched	107	50	2	.1	10	5	.2	0	.01	.01	.3	6
Figs, dried	3 small	78	90	1	Tr.	23	40	.7	90	.07	.06	.1	2
Flour, all-purpose	1 large	23	60	1	Tr.	15	26	.6	20	.02	.02	.5	2
Flour, rye	1 cup, sifted	12	400	12	1	84	18	3.2	0	.48	.29	.1	0
Flour, whole-wheat	1 cup, sifted	9	285	8	.8	62	18	.9	0	.12	.06	3.8	0
	1 cup, stirred	12	400	16	2	85	49	4.0	0	.66	.14	5.2	0
Frankfurters, cooked	1	58	155	6	14	.8	3	.8	—	.08	.1	1.3	—

Food	Measure												
Fudge, with nuts	1 oz.	8	115	1	3	21	22	.3	Tr.	.01	.03	.1	Tr.
Gelatin, dry	1 T	13	35	9	Tr.	—	—	—	—	—	—	—	—
Gelatin dessert, plain	1 cup	84	140	4	0	34	—	—	—	—	—	—	—
Gingerale, pale dry	1 cup	92	70	0	0	18	—	—	0	0	0	0	0
Gingerbread	1 piece, 2" x 2"	31	175	2	6	29	37	1.3	50	.06	.06	.5	0
Grapes	1 cup	82	65	1	1	15	15	.4	0	.05	.03	.2	3
Grape juice	1 cup	83	165	1	Tr.	42	28	.8	—	.10	.05	.6	Tr.
Grapefruit, pulp only	½ med.	89	55	1	Tr.	14	22	.6	10	.05	.02	.2	52
Grapefruit juice, fresh red	1 cup, unsweetened	90	95	1	Tr.	23	22	.5	1,080	.09	.04	.4	92
Haddock, fresh	3 oz.	66	140	17	5	5	34	1.0	—	.03	.06	2.7	2
Ham, smoked	3 oz., cooked	54	245	18	19	0	8	2.2	0	.40	.16	3.1	—
Ham, smoked	2 oz., canned	55	165	13	14	1	8	1.2	0	.18	.12	1.6	—
Heart, beef, braised	3 oz.	61	160	27	5	1	5	5	20	.21	1.04	6.5	1
Hominy, cooked, yellow	1 cup, unenriched	174	102	2.4	Tr.	22	2	.2	120	.04	.02	.4	0
Honey	1 T	17	65	Tr.	0	17	—	1.0	1	0	Tr.	.01	0
Honeydew	1 wedge	91	33	.8	.3	7.7	14	.4	40	.04	.03	.6	23
Ice cream, plain	1 slice	62	145	3	9	15	87	.1	370	.03	.13	.1	1
Jelly	1 T	29	55	Tr.	Tr.	14	4	.3	Tr.	Tr.	.01	Tr.	1
Kale, cooked	1 cup	91	30	4	1	4	147	1.3	8,140	.1	.2	1.8	68
Kidney, veal	3 oz.	155	113	16.6	4.6	.1	—	4	—	.1	.04	.4	6
Kohlrabi, cooked	1 cup	138	40	3	.2	8	50	.4	30	.1	.04	.4	64
Lamb, chops, broiled	3 oz., ¾" thick	47	400	25	33	0	10	1.5	—	.14	.25	5.6	—
Lamb, roast, shoulder	3 oz.	50	285	18	23	0	9	1.0	—	.11	.20	4.0	—
Lemon juice, fresh	1 cup	—	60	1	Tr.	20	17	.5	40	.08	.03	.2	113
Lemon juice	1 T	91	5	Tr.	Tr.	1	1	.1	Tr.	Tr.	Tr.	Tr.	7
Lettuce, head, iceberg	1 head, 4¾" diam.	96	60	4	Tr.	13	91	2.3	1,500	.29	.27	1.3	29
Lettuce, leaf	2 large	94	10	1	Tr.	2	34	.7	950	.03	.04	.2	9
Liver, beef, fried	2 oz.	57	130	15	6	3	6	5.0	30,280	.15	2.32	9.4	15
Liver, pork, fried	2 oz.	41	180	22	9	2	11	21.8	11,180	.26	3.3	16.7	17
Lobster, canned	⅔ cup	77	95	18.5	2	.3	65	.8	—	.1	.07	—	—
Loganberries, canned	1 cup	172	110	1.4	1	26	54	1.7	280	.04	.1	.4	34
Macaroni and cheese	1 cup, baked	58	470	18	24	44	398	2	950	.22	.44	2	Tr.
Macaroni, cooked	1 cup, enriched	64	190	6	1	39	14	1.4	0	.23	.13	1.9	0
Mackerel, cooked with butter	3 oz. Atlantic	62	200	19	12	0	5	1.0	450	.13	.23	6.5	—
Marmalade	1 T	29	55	Tr.	Tr.	14	4	.2	Tr.	Tr.	Tr.	Tr.	Tr.
Mayonnaise	1 T	15	110	Tr.	12	Tr.	3	.1	40	Tr.	.01	Tr.	—
Milk, whole, fresh	1 cup	87	160	9	9	12	288	.1	350	.08	.42	.1	2

Food	Measure	H₂O %	Food Energy Cal.	Pro. Gm.	Fat Gm.	CHO Gm.	Ca Mg.	Fe Mg.	Vit. A I.U.	Thiamine Mg.	Riboflavin Mg.	Niacin Mg.	Ascorbic Acid Mg.
Milk, skim	1 cup	90	90	9	Tr.	13	298	.1	10	.10	.44	.2	2
Milk, condensed, sweetened	1 cup	27	980	25	27	166	802	.3	1,090	.23	1.17	.5	3
Milk, evaporated	1 cup	74	345	18	20	24	635	.3	820	.10	.84	.5	3
Milk, malted, dry	1 T	.2	35	1	.7	6	23	.2	80	.03	.04	Tr.	0
Molasses, light	1 T	24	50	—	—	13	33	.9	—	.01	.01	Tr.	—
Muffins, enriched	1 med.	38	140	4	5	20	50	.8	50	.08	.11	.7	Tr.
Mushrooms, canned	1 cup	93	40	5	Tr.	6	15	1.2	Tr.	.04	.60	4.8	4
Mustard greens	1 cup, cooked	93	35	3	1	6	193	2.5	8,120	.11	.19	.9	68
Noodles, cooked	1 cup, enriched	70	200	7	2	37	16	1.4	110	.23	.14	1.8	0
Oatmeal, cooked	1 cup	86	130	5	2	23	21	1.4	0	.19	.05	.3	0
Oil, salad	1 T	91	30	2	.3	6	92	.5	490	.13	.18	.9	.2
Okra, cooked	8 pods, 3" long	0	25	2	Tr.	5	78	.4	420	.11	.15	.8	17
Oleomargarine, fortified	1 T	16	50	Tr.	6	Tr.	1	0	230	—	—	—	0
Olives, green	4 med.	78	15	Tr.	2	Tr.	8	.2	40	Tr.	—	—	—
Olives, ripe	3 small	73	15	Tr.	2	Tr.	9	.1	10	Tr.	Tr.	—	—
Onions, cooked	1 cup	92	60	3	Tr.	14	50	.8	80	.06	.06	.4	14
Onions, raw	1 T	89	40	2	Tr.	10	30	.6	40	.04	.04	.2	11
Onions, green	6 small	88	20	1	Tr.	5	20	.3	Tr.	.02	.02	.2	12
Oranges, raw	1 med.	85	60	2	1	16	49	.5	240	.12	.05	.5	75
Orange juice, fresh	¾ cup	88	115	2	1	26	27	.7	500	.22		.9	122
Oysters, Eastern, raw	1 cup	85	160	20	4	8	226	13.2	740	.33	.43	6.0	—
Oysters, Pacific, raw	1 cup	84	200	11	12	11	269	3.3	640	.13	.41	1.6	—
Parsnips, cooked	1 cup	82	100	2	1	23	70	.9	50	.11	.13	.2	16
Peaches, fresh	1 med., 2" diam.	89	35	1	Tr.	10	9	.5	1,320	.02	.05	1.0	7
Peanut butter	1 T	2	95	4	8	3	9	.3	—	.02	.02	2.2	—
Peanuts, roasted	1 cup	2	840	37	72	27	107	3.0	—	.46	.46	24.7	0
Pears, fresh	1 med., 3" x 2½" diam.	83	100	1	1	25	13	.5	20	.04	.07	.2	7
Peas, green	1 cup, boiled	82	115	9	1	19	37	2.9	860	.44	.17	3.7	33
Peas, canned, drained	1 cup	83	165	9	1	31	50	4.2	1,120	.23	.13	2.2	22
Peas (baby food)	1 oz.	86	15	1	Tr.	3	3	.4	140	.02	.02	.4	3
Pecans	2 T, chopped	6	100	2	10	2	10		20	.12	.02	.2	Tr.
Peppers, green	1 med.	93	15	1	Tr.	3	6	.4	260	.05	.05	.3	79

Food	Measure												
Pie, apple	1 1/6, 9" pie	48	345	3	15	51	11	.4	40	.03	.02	.5	1
Pie, lemon meringue	1 1/6, 9" pie	47	305	4	12	45	17	.6	200	.04	.10	.2	4
Pineapple, fresh	1 cup, no sugar	85	75	1	Tr.	19	24	.7	100	.12	.04	.3	24
Plums, fresh	2 med.	81	25	Tr.	Tr.	7	7	.3	140	.02	.02	.3	3
Popcorn, popped, oil and salt	1 cup	3	65	1	3	8	1	.3	—	—	.01	.2	0
Pork, chops, broiled	1 med. thick	42	260	16	21	0	8	2.2	0	.63	.18	3.8	—
Pork, sausage, cooked	3 links	35	540	21	50	Tr.	8	2.7	0	.89	.39	4.2	—
Potato, white, baked	1 med.	75	90	3	Tr.	21	9	.7	Tr.	.10	.04	1.7	20
Potato, white, boiled, unpeeled	1 med.	80	105	3	Tr.	23	10	.8	Tr.	.13	.05	2.0	22
Potato, white, mashed	1 cup	80	185	4	8	24	47	.8	330	.16	.10	1.9	18
Potato, french fried	10 pieces	45	155	2	7	20	9	.8	Tr.	.07	.04	1.8	12
Potato chips	10 large, 2" diam.	2	115	1	8	10	8	.7	Tr.	.04	.01	1.0	3
Potato, sweet, baked	1 med.	64	155	2	1	36	44	1.0	8,190	.10	.07	.7	24
Prunes, dried, softened	4 med.	28	70	1	Tr.	18	14	1.1	440	.02	.04	.4	1
Prune juice, canned	1 cup	80	200	1	Tr.	49	36	10.5	—	.08	.03	1.1	4
Puffed rice	1 cup	4	50	1	Tr.	13	3	.3	0	.06	.01	.6	0
Puffed wheat	1 cup	3	105	4	1	22	8	1.2	0	.15	.07	2.2	0
Pumpkin, canned	1 cup	90	75	2	Tr.	18	57	.9	14,590	.07	.12	1.3	12
Radishes	4 small	94	5	Tr.	—	1	12	.4	Tr.	.01	.01	.1	10
Raisins, dried	1 cup	18	460	4	1	124	99	5.6	30	.18	.13	.9	2
Raspberries, black	2/3 cup	81	75	2	1	16	30	.9	Tr.	.03	.09	.9	18
Raspberries, red	2/3 cup		70	—	Tr.	17	27	1.1	160	.04	.11	1.1	31
Rhubarb, cooked, with sugar	1 cup	63	385	1	.6	98	212	1.6	220	.06	.15	.7	17
Rice, cooked, brown	1 cup	70	120	2.5	Tr.	26	12	.5	0	.09	.02	1.4	0
Rice, cooked, white	1 cup	73	185	3	.2	41	17	1.5	0	.19	.01	1.6	0
Rutabagas, cooked	1 cup, diced	144	60	1.4	1	14	94	.4	880	.10	.10	1.2	42
Salad dressing, boiled	1 T	68	30	1	2	3	15	.1	80	.10	.03	Tr.	Tr.
Salad dressing, French	1 T	39	60	Tr.	6	3	2	.1	—	.03	—	—	—
Salmon, broiled	1 steak, 3½ oz.	63	180	27	7	0	—	1.2	160	—	.06	9.8	0
Salmon, pink, canned	3 oz.	71	120	17	5	0	167	.7	60	.16	.16	6.8	—
Sardines, Atlantic, in oil	3 oz. can	64	170	20	10	0	20	.5	20	.03	.22	7.3	—
Sardines, Pacific, in oil	3 oz. can	—	—	—	—	—	—	—	—	.11	.3	7.4	—
Sauerkraut, canned	1 cup	93	45	2	Tr.	9	85	1.2	120	.01	.09	.4	33
Sherbet, orange	1 cup	67	260	2	2	59	31	Tr.	110	.07	.06	Tr.	4
Shredded wheat	1 oz.	7	100	3	1	23	18	1.0	0	.02	.03	1.2	0
Shrimp, canned	3 oz., drained	70	100	21	1	1	98	2.6	50	.06	.03	1.5	0
Soup, pea, canned	1 cup, diluted	86	130	6	—	23	44	1.0	340	.05	.05	1.0	7

Food	Measure	H₂O %	Food Energy Cal.	Pro. Gm.	Fat Gm.	CHO Gm.	Ca Mg.	Fe Mg.	Vit. A I.U.	Thia-mine Mg.	Ribo-flavin Mg.	Nia-cin Mg.	Ascor-bic Acid Mg.
Soup, tomato	1 cup	90	90	2	2	16	15	.7	1,000	.06	.05	1.1	12
Soup, vegetable, beef	¾ cup	92	80	3	2	14	20	.8	3,250	.05	.02	1.2	—
Spinach, fresh	1 cup, cooked	92	40	5	1	6	167	4.0	14,580	.13	.25	1.0	50
Squash, winter, yellow	1 cup, baked	81	130	4	1	32	57	1.6	8,610	.10	.27	1.4	27
Strawberries, fresh	1 cup	90	55	1	1	13	31	1.5	90	.04	.10	1.0	88
Sugar, granulated	1 T	Tr.	45	0	0	6.8	0	.1	0	0	0	0	0
Sugar, powdered	1 T	Tr.	30	0	0	8	0	Tr.	0	0	0	0	0
Sugar, brown	1 T	.25	51	0	0	13.1	11.7	1.4	0	0	0	0	0
Swordfish, cooked	1 steak, 3 oz.	65	150	24	5	0	23	1.1	1,750	.03	.04	9.3	0
Tapioca, cream	½ cup	13	535	1	Tr.	131	15	.6	0		0	0	0
Tomato, raw	1 med.	94	35	2	Tr.	7	20	.8	1,350	.10	.06	1.0	34
Tomato juice, canned	1 cup	94	45	2	Tr.	10	17	2.2	1,940	.13	.07	1.8	39
Tongue, beef	3 oz.	61	210	18	14	Tr.	6	1.9	—	.04	.25	3.0	—
Tunafish, canned	3 oz.	61	170	24	7	0	7	1.6	70	.04	.10	10.1	—
Turkey, roasted	3½ oz., light meat	62	175	33	4	0	0	1.2	—	.05	.14	11.1	0
Turnip greens, cooked	1 cup	93	30	3	Tr.	5	267	1.6	9,140	.21	.36	.8	100
Turnips, cooked	1 cup	94	35	1	Tr.	8	54	.6	Tr.	.06	.08	.5	33
Veal, cutlet, broiled	3 oz., cooked	60	185	23	9	—	9	2.7	—	.06	.21	4.6	—
Veal, roast	3 oz.	55	230	23	14	0	10	2.9	—	.11	.26	6.6	—
Waffles, baked	1 waffle, enriched	41	210	7	7	28	85	1.3	250	.13	.19	1.0	—
Walnuts, English	1 T, chopped	4	50	1	5	1	8	.2	Tr.	.03	.01	.1	Tr.
Watercress	10 av. sprigs	9	2	.2	Tr.	.3	815	.2	490	.01	.02	.7	8
Watermelon, 10" x 16" melon	1/16 melon	93	115	2	1	27	30	2.1	2,510	.13	.13	.1	30
White sauce, med.	1 cup	73	430	10	33	23	305	.5	1,220	.12	.44	.6	Tr.
Yeast, compressed	1 oz. cake	71	25	3	Tr.	3	4	1.4	Tr.	.20	.47	3.2	Tr.

Table 31

Adjustment of Calorie Allowances for Adult Individuals of Various Body Weights and Ages*
(At mean environmental temperature of 20° C. (68° F.) assuming average physical activity)

Men					Women				
Desirable Weight		Calorie Allowances†			Desirable Weight		Calorie Allowances†		
Kg.	Lbs.	25 Yrs.(1)	45 Yrs.(2)	65 Yrs.(3)	Kg.	Lbs.	25 Yrs.(4)	45 Yrs.(5)	65 Yrs.(6)
50	110	2,300	2,050	1,750	40	88	1,600	1,450	1,200
55	121	2,450	2,200	1,850	45	99	1,750	1,600	1,300
60	132	2,600	2,350	1,950	50	110	1,900	1,700	1,450
65	143	2,750	2,500	2,100	55	121	2,000	1,800	1,550
70	154	2,900	2,600	2,200	58	128	2,100	1,900	1,600
75	165	3,050	2,750	2,300	60	132	2,150	1,950	1,650
80	176	3,200	2,900	2,450	65	143	2,300	2,050	1,750
85	187	3,350	3,050	2,550	70	154	2,400	2,200	1,850

* This table is reprinted from the 6th Revised Edition, Report of The Food and Nutrition Board, National Academy of Science, National Research Council Pub. No. 1146, Washington, D.C., 1964.

† Adjustment of calorie allowances for individuals of different weights and ages have been calculated from simplified formulas for the age-range periods as follows: (1) 725 + 31W; (2) 650 + 28W; (3) 550 + 23.5W; (4) 525 + 27W; (5) 475 + 24.5W; (6) 400 + 20.5W.

Values have been rounded to the nearest 50 calories. To convert formulas for weight in pounds, divide factor by 2.2.

These formulas were developed on the premise that 25 percent of the energy expenditure is independent of weight and 75 percent is directly proportional to body weight. The factors are derived by dividing by 75 percent of the calorie allowance by the reference weight for each group.

Table 32

FOOD BUYING GUIDES*

Weight, Volume, and Servings per Market Unit of Food Items

Food Item and Form	Market Unit		Serving or Portion		Weight per Cup†	
	Weight	Volume or pieces	Size of serving or specified volume	Approximate number per market unit	Grams	Ounces (approx.)
A. Dairy products						
Butter	1 lb	2 c	2 tsp	48	224	8
Cheese						
Cheddar (natural or processed)	1 lb		2 oz	8		
grated, sieved, or chopped			¼ c	16	113	4
cottage (creamed or uncreamed)	1 lb	2 c	¼ c	8	225	8
cream	8 oz	1 c	2 Tbsp	8	234	8¼
spread	5 oz	½ c	¼ c	2		
Cream						
light (table)		½ pt	2 Tbsp	8	240	8½
heavy (whipping)		½ pt	1 Tbsp	16	236	8⅓
whipped			2 c	1		
sour		½ pt	1 Tbsp	16	245	8⅔
half and half (cream and milk)						
sweet		1 pt	1 Tbsp	32	242	8½
sour		½ pt	1 Tbsp	16	242	8½
Milk						
whole, skimmed, or buttermilk		1 qt	1 c	4	244	8⅔
condensed, sweetened	15 oz	1⅓ c	1⅓ c	1	306	10¾
evaporated, whole or skim	14½ oz	1⅔ c	1⅔ c	1	252	9
reconstituted			1 c	3⅓		
dry, whole	1 lb	3½ c			125	4½
reconstituted			1 c	14		

dry, nonfat						
powder	1 lb	3¼ c			140	5
reconstituted			1 c	17		
crystals	1 lb	6½ c			68	2⅓
reconstituted			1 c	17		
Milk desserts						
ice cream		1 qt	½ c	8	142	5
ice milk		1 qt	½ c	8	187	6⅔
sherbert		1 qt	½ c	8	193	6¾
Yoghurt		½ pt	½ c	2	250	8¾
B. Eggs						
Whole, fresh		1 doz	1 egg	12	243	8½
extra large		1 doz	1 c	3		
large		1 doz	1 c	2⅓		
medium		1 doz	1 c	2		
small		1 doz	1 c	1¾		
frozen	1 lb	2 c	3 Tbsp	10	243	8½
dried, sifted	1 lb	5⅓ c	2½ Tbsp	32	86	3
packed	1 lb	4 c	2 Tbsp	32	114	4
Whites, fresh		1 doz			243	8½
extra large			1 c	2		
large			1 c	1½		
medium			1 c	1⅓		
small			1 c	1¼		
frozen	1 lb	2 c	2 Tbsp	16		
dried						
spray dried, sifted	1 lb	5 c	2 tsp	100	89	3
pan dried, sifted	1 lb	3½ c			132	4⅔
Yolks, fresh		1 doz			243	8½
extra large			1 c	1		
large			1 c	⅞		
medium			1 c	¾		
small			1 c	⅔		

* Handbook of Food Preparation, Copyright 1964, Revised Edition, American Home Economics Association, Washington, D.C.
† Weight per cup is that of food alone without liquid.

Weight, Volume, and Servings per Market Unit of Food Items (cont.)

Food Item and Form	Market Unit		Serving or Portion		Weight per Cup†	
	Weight	Volume or pieces	Size of serving or specified volume	Approximate number per market unit	Grams	Ounces (approx.)
Eggs, yolks (cont.)						
frozen	1 lb	2¼ c	4 tsp	26		
dried						
sifted	1 lb	5⅔ c	2 Tbsp	54	80	2¾
packed	1 lb	4¾			96	3⅓
C. Fats and oils						
Butter (see ***Dairy products***)						
Oils: corn, cottonseed, olive, peanut, and safflower		1 qt			210	7½
Margarine	1 lb	2 c	2 tsp	48	224	8
Hydrogenated fats	1 lb	2½ c			188	6⅔
Lard and rendered fats	1 lb	2 c			220	7¾
Suet, chopped, medium fine	1 lb	3¾ c			120	4¼
D. Fish and shellfish						
Fish, Fresh or frozen						
whole	1 lb		3 oz	1⅓		
drawn	1 lb		3 oz	1⅔		
dressed	1 lb		3 oz	2⅓		
fillets	1 lb		3 oz	3⅓		
steaks	1 lb		3 oz	3		
frozen						
breaded portions	1 lb	4	3¾ oz	4		
sticks	1 lb	16	3	5⅓		
canned						
mackerel	15 oz	1 pt	3 oz	4¼		
salmon	1 lb	1 pt	3 oz	4⅓		
sardines						

Maine	3¼ to 4 oz	½ c	3 oz	1
Pacific, in brine	15 oz	1 pt	3 oz	3¾
tuna	6 to 7 oz	1 c	3 oz	2
Shellfish				
Clams				
live in shell				
hard		12	6	2
soft		12	12	1
fresh or frozen, shucked	1 lb		3 oz	2⅔
frozen, breaded, raw	1 lb		3 oz	3¾
canned, minced	7½ oz	1 c	3 oz	2½
Crabs				
live in shell				
Blue	1 lb		3 oz	¾
Dungeness	1 lb	1	3 oz	1⅓
fresh or frozen				
cooked in shell				
Blue	1 lb		3 oz	¾
Dungeness	1 lb		3 oz	1⅓
meat	1 lb	1 pt	3 oz	5¼
frozen fried cakes	1 lb		3 oz	5
canned, meat	5½ to 7½ oz.	1 c	3 oz	1¾
Lobsters				
fresh or frozen				
cooked in shell	1 lb	1	1	1
meat	1 lb	1 pt	3 oz	4¾
frozen, spiny tails	1 lb	2	4 oz	2
Oysters				
live in shell		12	6	2
fresh or frozen, shucked	1 lb	1 pt	3 oz	2
frozen breaded, raw	1 lb	3 oz	3 oz	4⅔
canned, whole	8 oz	1 c	3 oz	1⅔
Scallops				
fresh or frozen, shucked	1 lb	1 pt	3 oz	3⅓
frozen, breaded, raw	1 lb		3 oz	4⅓

† Weight per cup is that of food alone without liquid.

Weight, Volume, and Servings per Market Unit of Food Items (cont.)

Food Item and Form	Market Unit		Serving or Portion		Weight per Cup†	
	Weight	Volume or pieces	Size of serving or specified volume	Approximate number per market unit	Grams	Ounces (approx.)
Shrimp						
fresh or frozen						
raw in shell	1 lb		3 oz	2⅔		
raw, peeled	1 lb		3 oz	3¼		
cooked, peeled, cleaned	1 lb		3 oz	5⅓		
frozen, breaded, raw	1 lb		3 oz	4¾		
canned	4½ to 6½ oz	½ c	3 oz	1½		
E. Flours, cereals, and related products						
Bread, sliced	1 lb	12 to 16	1 slice	12 to 16		
crumbs, soft			1 c	16¼	28	1
crumbs, dry	10 oz	2½ c			113	4
Cereals						
Bulgur	1 lb	2⅔ c			162	5¾
cooked			½ c	16		
Cornmeal, white or yellow	1 lb	3 c			152	5
cooked			⅔ c	25	238	8½
Farina	1 lb	3 c				
cooked			⅔ c	25		
Hominy, whole	1 lb	2½ c			182	6½
cooked			⅔ c	25		
grits	1 lb	3 c			154	5½
cooked			⅔ c	15		
Oats, rolled	1 lb	5⅔ c			80	2¾
cooked			⅔ c	12	240	8½
Pasta						
macaroni, 1″ pieces, dry	1 lb	4 to 5 c			123	4
cooked			½ c	18	140	5

macaroni, shell	1 lb	4 to 5 c			115	4
cooked			½ c	18		
noodles, 1″ pieces, dry	1 lb	6 to 8 c			73	2⅔
cooked			½ c	16		
spaghetti, 2″ pieces, dry	1 lb	4 to 5 c			94	3⅓
cooked			½ c	18	160	5⅔
Ready-to-eat						
puffed, unsweetened			1 c		12–27	⅓ to 1
puffed, sugar-coated			1 c		29–43	⅔ to 1½
flakes, unsweetened			1 c		23–41	¾ to 1½
flakes, sugar-coated			1 c		43	1½
shredded			1 c		29–62	1 to 2¼
nutrition concentrate	6 oz		½ c		79	2¾
nuggets			½ c		75–109	2¾ to 4
Rice, white polished						
long grain	1 lb	2½ c	⅔ c	12	182	6½
medium grain	1 lb	2⅓ c	⅔ c	12	193	6¾
short grain	1 lb	2¼ c	⅔ c	12	200	7
precooked	8 oz					
Soy, grits, stirred, low-fat	1 lb	3½ c			149	5
Wheat, germ	12 oz	3 c	¼ c	12	113	4
whole	2 lb	4½ c			198	7
Crackers						
Graham	1 lb	66	2	33		
crumbs			1 c	4⅓		
soda	1 lb		2	41		
crumbs			1 c	7		
soda, crumbs, fine	10 oz	4 c			70	2½
saltines	1 lb	130 to 140	4	32 to 35		
Flours						
corn	2 lb	8 c			116	4
gluten	2 lb	6½ c			142	5
rice, sifted	2 lb	6½ c			126	4½
rye, light, sifted	2 lb	10 c			88	3
dark, stirred	2 lb	6⅔ c			127	4½
soy, sifted, full-fat	2 lb	15 c			60	2

† Weight per cup is that of food alone without liquid.

Weight, Volume, and Servings per Market Unit of Food Items (cont.)

Food Item and Form	Market Unit		Serving or Portion		Weight per Cup†	
	Weight	Volume or pieces	Size of serving or specified volume	Approximate number per market unit	Grams	Ounces (approx.)
Flours, soy (cont.)						
low-fat	2 lb	11 c			83	3
wheat						
all-purpose, sifted	2 lb	7 to 9 c			115	4
unsifted	2 lb	6 to 8 c			125	4⅓
instant	2 lb	7 to 7½ c			129	4½
bread, sifted	2 lb	8 c			112	4
cake, sifted	2 lb	9½ c			96	3⅓
pastry, sifted	2 lb	9 c			100	3½
self-rising, sifted	2 lb	8 c			112	4
whole wheat, stirred	2 lb	7½ c			120	4¼
Starch, corn, stirred	1 lb	3½ c			128	4½
potato, stirred	1 lb	3¼ c			142	5
F. Fruits						
Apples						
fresh, whole	1 lb	3 (med)	1 (med)	3		
pared and diced or sliced			½ c	5⅔	122	4⅓
sauce			½ c	3½	252	9
frozen, sliced (sweetened)	20 oz	2¼ c	½ c	5	205	7¼
canned, sliced	20 oz	2⅓ c	½ c	5	204	7¼
juice		46 fl oz	½ c	11½		
sauce	16 to 17 oz	1¾ to 2 c	½ c	4	254	9
dried	1 lb	4⅓ c			104	3¾
cooked			½ c	16	244	8⅔
Apricots, fresh, whole	1 lb	8 to 12	2	4 to 6	115	4
sliced or halved			½ c	5	156	5½
canned, whole (medium)	16 to 17 oz	8 to 14	2 to 3	4		
halved (medium)	16 to 17 oz	12 to 20	3 to 5	4	227	8

dried	1 lb	3¼ c			150	5⅓
cooked			½ c	12	243	8½
Avocado						
fresh (sliced, diced, wedges)	1 lb		½ c	5	142	5
Bananas, fresh, whole	1 lb	3 to 4	1	3 to 4		
sliced			½ c	4	142	5
mashed			½ c	2¾	232	8¼
dried	1 lb	4½ c			100	3½
Blueberries						
fresh	1 lb	1 pt	½ c	4	146	5¼
frozen	10 oz	1¾ c	½ c	4	161	5½
canned	14 oz	1¾ c	½ c	3		
Cherries, red, pitted						
fresh	1 lb		½ c	4¾	154	5½
frozen	20 oz	2⅓ c	½ c	5	242	8½
canned	16 to 17 oz	1¾ to 2 c	½ c	4	227	8
Cranberries						
fresh	1 lb	4 c			114	4
sauce			¼ c	16	216	9½
canned, sauce	1 lb	1⅔ c	¼ c	8	278	9½
juice		1 qt	½ c	8		
Currants, dried	1 lb	3¼ c			140	5
Dates, dried						
whole	1 lb	60	½ c	5		
pitted, cut	1 lb	2½ c	½ c	5	178	6⅓
Figs						
fresh	1 lb	12	3 (med)	4		
canned	16 to 17 oz	12 to 20	3 to 4	4	230	8
dried, whole	1 lb	44	⅓ c	10		
cut fine	1 lb	2⅔ c	⅓ c	7	168	6
Fruit juices						
frozen		6 fl oz	1 fl oz	6		
canned		46 fl oz	½ c	11½	247	8¾
Fruits, mixed						
frozen	12 oz	1⅓ c	⅓ c	4		
canned (cocktail or salad)	17 oz	2 c	½ c	4	229	8

† Weight per cup is that of food alone without liquid.

Weight, Volume, and Servings per Market Unit of Food Items (cont.)

Food Item and Form	Market Unit		Serving or Portion		Weight per Cup†	
	Weight	Volume or pieces	Size of serving or specified volume	Approximate number per market unit	Grams	Ounces (approx.)
Fruits (cont.)						
Grapefruit						
fresh	1 lb	1 (med)	½ c	2	194	6¾
frozen, sections	13½	1½ c	½ c	3	237	8⅓
canned, sections	16 to 17 oz	1¾ to 2 c	½ c	4	241	8½
Grapes, fresh						
seeded	1 lb		½ c	4¼	184	6½
seedless	1 lb		½ c	5	169	6
Lemons						
fresh	3 lb	1 doz				
juice			1 pt	1	247	8¾
frozen, juice		6 fl oz				
canned, juice		8 fl oz			245	8⅔
Oranges						
fresh	6 lb	1 doz	1	12		
diced or sectioned			1 qt	3	214	7½
juice			1 qt	1	247	8¾
canned						
juice		46 fl oz	½ c	11½	247	8¾
Melon, frozen balls	12 oz	1¾ c	½ c	3	231	8¼
Peaches						
fresh	1 lb	4 (med)	1 (med)	4		
sliced			½ c	4	184	6½
frozen, sliced	12 oz	1⅓ c	⅓ c	3 to 4	220	7¾
canned, halves	16 to 17 oz	6 to 10	2	3	224	8
sliced	16 to 17 oz	1¾ to 2 c	½ c	4	244	8½
dried	1 lb	3 c			160	5⅔
cooked			½ c	12	244	8⅔

Food	Amount	Measure	Serving	Servings	Weight per cup† (g)	Cups
Pears						
fresh	1 lb	4 (med)	1 (med)	4		
sliced			½ c	4	158	5½
canned, halves	16 to 17 oz	6 to 10	2	3	227	8
Pineapple						
fresh	2 lb	1 (med)	1 (med)			
cubed		1½ c	½ c	6	136	4½
frozen, chunks	13½		½ c	3	204	7¼
canned, chunks, tidbits	29 oz		½ c	7½	198	7
crushed	29 oz		½ c	7½	260	9¼
sliced	20 oz	10	2	5	208	7⅓
juice		46 fl oz	½ c	11½	185	6½
Plums						
fresh, halved	1 lb	8 to 20	½ c	4	223	7¾
canned, whole	16 to 17 oz	10 to 14	2 to 3	4	196	7
Prunes						
canned	16 to 17 oz	10 to 14	2 to 3	4	165	5¾
dried, whole	1 lb	2½ c			229	8
cooked			½ c	8 to 9	162	5¾
pitted	1 lb	2¼ c			266	9½
cooked			½ c	8 to 9	142	5
Raisins, dried						
seeded, whole	1 lb	3¼ c			182	6½
chopped	1 lb	2½ c			146	5¼
seedless, whole	1 lb	2¾ c			183	6½
cooked			¼ c	11	189	6¾
Rhubarb, fresh, cut	1 lb	2 c		4	122	4⅓
cooked		4 to 8		3	242	8½
Strawberries, fresh, whole						
frozen, sliced	12 oz	1½ c	½ c	8	197	7
fresh, whole	1½ lb	1 qt	½ c	8	144	5
sliced			½ c	4	148	5¼
frozen, whole	16 oz	1½ c	⅓ c	3	204	7¼
sliced or halved	10 oz	1¼ c	⅓ c	4	235	8⅓
canned	16 to 17 oz	1¾ to 2 c	½ c		242	8½

† Weight per cup is that of food alone without liquid.

Weight, Volume, and Servings per Market Unit of Food Items (cont.)

Food Item and Form	Market Unit		Serving or Portion		Weight per Cup†	
	Weight	Volume or pieces	Size of serving or specified volume	Approximate number per market unit	Grams	Ounces (approx.)
G. Leavening agents						
Baking powders						
phosphate	12 oz	1½ c			197	7
SAS-phosphate	14 oz	2 c			173	6
tartrate	6 oz	1 c			182	6½
Baking soda	1 lb	2⅓ c			181	6⅓
Cream of tartar	1¾ oz	5⅓ Tbsp			150	5¼
Yeast						
active dry	0.28 oz	1 Tbsp			120	4½
compressed	0.60 oz	4 tsp			204	7¼
H. Meat						
Fresh or frozen						
Boned or ground meat (flank, clod, beef roll, boneless loin, etc.)	1 lb		3 oz	4 to 5	227	8
cooked, diced					142	5
Meat with minimum amount of bone (steaks, roasts, chuck, ham, chops, etc.)	1 lb			2 to 4		
Meat with large amount of bone (shoulder cuts, short ribs, neck, etc.)	1 lb			1 to 2		
Bacon	1 lb	24	2	12		
Frankfurters	1 lb	8	2	4		
Luncheon meat, sliced	12 oz	8	2	4		
Canned						
corned beef	12 oz		3 oz	4		
ham, smoked	1½ lb		3 oz	6 to 8		
luncheon meat	12 oz		3 oz	4		
sausage, Vienna	4 oz	8 to 10	4 to 5	2		

Food	Amount	Measure	Weight per cup, g†	Serving	Servings	Servings
Dried						
chipped beef	1 lb					6⅔
I. Poultry						
Chicken, ready-to-cook						
broiler	1½ lb			½ bird	2	
fryer	2½ lb			¼ bird	4	
roaster	1 lb			3 oz	2¼	
Rock Cornish hen	less than 2 lb			½ to 1 bird	1⅓	
stewing	1 lb			3 oz	2½	
cooked, boned, diced	5 to 6 oz		136	3 oz		4¾
Chicken, canned, boned	1 lb			3 oz	1½ to 2	
Duck, ready-to-cook	1 lb			3 oz	2½	
Goose, ready-to-cook	1 lb			3 oz	2⅔	
Turkey, ready-to-cook	1 lb				1 to 2	
cooked, diced	5 to 6 oz		133	3 oz		4⅔
Turkey, canned, boned	5 to 6 oz			3 oz	1½ to 2	
J. Sugars and syrups						
Brown, light, packed	1 lb	2¼ c	200	1 c	2	7
dark, packed	1 lb		200	1 c	2	7
granulated	1 lb 4 oz		142			5
Cane or beet, granulated	5 lb	11¼ c	200			7
superfine	2 lb	4⅔ c	196			7
confectioner's, sifted	1 lb	3 to 4 c	128			4½
Corn syrup, light and dark		16 fl oz	328	2 Tbsp	16	11½
Honey	1 lb	1⅓ c	332	2 Tbsp	11	12
Maple syrup		12 fl oz	312	2 Tbsp	12	11
Molasses, cane		12 fl oz	328	2 Tbsp	12	11½
Sorghum	1 lb	1⅓ c	330	2 Tbsp	10	11⅔
K. Vegetables						
Asparagus, spears, fresh	1 lb	16 to 28				
cooked		2 c	181	½ c	4	6½
frozen, spears, cuts and tips	10 oz	2 c	181	½ c	4	6½

† Weight per cup is that of food alone without liquid.

Weight, Volume, and Servings per Market Unit of Food Items (cont.)

Food Item and Form	Market Unit		Serving or Portion		Weight per Cup†	
	Weight	Volume or pieces	Size of serving or specified volume	Approximate number per market unit	Grams	Ounces (approx.)
Vegetables, asparagus (cont.)						
canned, spears	14½ to 16 oz.	16 to 18	4 to 6	3	195	6¾
Beans, green, fresh	1 lb	3 c			114	4
cooked			½ c	5	125	4½
frozen	9 oz	2 c	½ c	4	161	5⅔
canned	16 to 17 oz	1¾ to 2 c	½ c	4	135	4¾
kidney, canned	16 to 17 oz	1¾ to 2 c	½ c	4	187	6⅔
dried	1 lb	2½ c			184	6½
cooked			½ c	11		
Lima, fresh, shelled	1 lb	2 c			155	5½
cooked			⅓ c	5 to 6	166	5¾
frozen	10 oz	1¾ c	½ c	3 to 4	173	6
canned	16 to 17 oz	1¾ to 2 c	¼ c	4	170	6
dried	1 lb	2½ c			180	6½
cooked			½ c	11	186	6½
navy, dried	1 lb	2⅓ c			190	6¾
cooked	1 lb	2¼ c	½ c	11		
soybeans, dried	1 lb	2¼ c			210	7⅓
Beets, fresh, without tops	1 lb	2 c			145	5
cooked			½ c	4	180	6½
canned	16 to 17 oz	1¾ to 2 c	½ c	4	167	5¾
Broccoli, fresh	1 lb					
cooked			½ c	4	164	5¾
frozen, spears, chopped	10 oz	1¾ c	½ c	4	188	6⅔
Brussels sprouts, fresh	1 lb	1 qt			102	3½
cooked			½ c	5	155	5½
frozen	10 oz	19	6	3 to 4		
Cabbage, fresh	1 lb				80	2¾

shredded			½ c	7 to 9	73	2⅔
cooked			½ c	4	146	5¼
Carrots, fresh, without tops	1 lb		½ c	6	130	4½
shredded			½ c	5	112	4
diced					137	4¾
cooked			½ c	4 to 5	160	5⅔
frozen	1 lb					
cooked			½ c	5	165	5¾
canned	16 to 17 oz	1¾ to 2 c	½ c	4	159	5⅔
Cauliflower, fresh	1 lb	1½ c			104	3⅔
cooked			½ c	3	125	4½
frozen	10 oz	2 c			152	5⅓
cooked			½ c	4	179	6⅓
Celery, fresh	1 lb	2 bunches			121	4¼
cooked			½ c	4 to 5	153	5½
Corn, fresh, ears		12 (med)	2	6		5¾
cooked			½ c	5	165	5¾
frozen, cut	10 oz	1¾ c			135	4¾
cooked			½ c	3 to 4	182	6½
canned, cream style	16 to 17 oz	1¾ to 2 c	½ c	4	249	8¾
whole kernel	12 oz	1½ c	½ c	3	169	6
Eggplant, fresh	1 lb					
diced			2½ c	1	99	3½
cooked			½ c	5	213	7½
Greens, fresh	1 lb				77	2¾
cooked			½ c	8 to 12	190	6¾
frozen	10 oz	1⅔ c	½ c	3 to 4	187	6½
Lentils, dried	1 lb	2¼ c			191	6¾
cooked			½ c	10	202	7¼
Mixed vegetables, frozen	10 oz	2 c	½ c	4	182	6⅓
canned	16 to 17 oz	1¾ to 2 c	½ c	4	179	6⅓
Mushrooms, fresh	1 lb	35 to 40	½ c	4 to 6	94	3⅓
canned	4 oz	⅔ c	⅓ c	2	161	5⅔
dried	0.36 oz					
Okra, fresh	1 lb					
cooked			½ c	4½	177	6¼

† Weight per cup is that of food alone without liquid.

Weight, Volume, and Servings per Market Unit of Food Items (cont.)

Food Item and Form	Market Unit		Serving or Portion		Weight per Cup†	
	Weight	Volume or pieces	Size of serving or specified volume	Approximate number per market unit	Grams	Ounces (approx.)
Vegetables, okra (cont.)						
frozen	10 oz	2 c	½ c	4	209	7¼
canned	16 to 17 oz	1¾ to 2 c	½ c	4	171	6
Onions, fresh	1 lb	3 (large)	½ c	4 to 5	135	4¾
cooked					197	7
frozen, chopped	12 oz	3¼ c				
canned	16 to 17 oz	1¾ to 2 c	½ c	4		
Parsnips, fresh	1 lb	4 (med)				
cooked			½ c	4	211	7½
Peas, green, fresh, in pod	1 lb				138	4¾
shelled		1 c			163	5¾
cooked			½ c	2		
frozen	10 oz	2 c			156	5½
cooked			½ c	4	167	
canned	16 to 17 oz	1¾ to 2 c	½ c	4	168	6
dried, split	1 lb	2¼ c			200	7
cooked			½ c	10	194	6¾
Peas, black-eyed, fresh	1 lb				144	5
cooked			½ c	4¾	162	5⅔
frozen	10 oz	2 c	½ c	4	171	6
canned	16 to 17 oz	1¾ to 2 c	½ c	4	205	7¼
dried					200	7
cooked					248	8¾
Potatoes, white, fresh	1 lb	3 (med)		3	164	5¾
cooked			½ c	4½	163	5¾
mashed			½ c	3½	207	7⅓
frozen, French fried, or puffs	9 oz			3 to 4		
canned, whole	16 to 17 oz	8 to 10	2 to 3	4	179	6⅓
dried, flakes	6 to 7 oz	4⅔ c			36	1¼

reconstituted			½ c	21¾	212	7½
granules	1 lb	2¼ c			201	7
reconstituted			½ c	21¼	212	7½
Pumpkin, fresh	1 lb					
cooked, mashed			½ c	2⅓	247	8¾
canned	16 to 17 oz	2 c	½ c	4	244	8½
Rutabaga, fresh, cubed	1 lb	2½ c			139	5
cooked			½ c	4	163	5¾
Sauerkraut, canned	15 to 16 oz	1¾ to 2 c	½ c	4	188	6⅔
Spinach, fresh	1 lb		½ c	8⅓	54	2
cooked			½ c	3	200	7
frozen	10 oz	1½ c	½ c	3	190	6¾
canned	15 to 16 oz	1¾ to 2 c	½ c	4	221	7¾
Squash, winter, fresh	1 lb					
cooked, mashed			½ c	2¼	244	8½
frozen	12 oz	1½ c	½ c	3 to 4	242	8½
canned	15 to 16 oz	1¾ to 2 c	½ c	3⅔		
Squash, summer, fresh	1 lb				136	4¾
cooked, mashed			½ c	3¼	238	8½
frozen, sliced	10 oz	1½ c	½ c	3 to 4	211	7½
canned	1 lb		4 oz	2¾		
Sweet potatoes, fresh	1 lb	3 (med)	1	3		
cooked, sliced					232	8¼
frozen	12 oz			3 to 4	200	7
canned	16 to 17 oz	1¾ to 2 c	½ c	3 to 4	220	7¾
dried, flakes	1 lb				115	4
reconstituted			4 oz	11¾	255	9
Tomatoes, fresh	1 lb	4 (small)		4	162	5¾
cooked			½ c	3		
canned						
whole	16 to 17 oz	1¾ to 2 c	½ c	4	238	8½
sauce	8 oz	1 c			258	9
Turnips, fresh	1 lb	3 (med)			134	4¾
cooked			½ c	4	196	7

† Weight per cup is that of food alone without liquid.

Weight, Volume, and Servings per Market Unit of Food Items (cont.)

Food Item and Form	Market Unit		Serving or Portion		Weight per Cup†	
	Weight	Volume or pieces	Size of serving or specified volume	Approximate number per market unit	Grams	Ounces (approx.)
L. Miscellaneous						
Catsup, tomato	14 oz		2 Tbsp	12	273	9⅔
Cherries, whole, candied	1 lb	2¼ c			198	7
Chocolate, bitter or semi-sweet	8 oz	⅞ c			225	8
prepared drink			1 c	30		
Cocoa	8 oz	2 c			112	4
prepared drink			1 c	50		
instant	8 oz			28		
Coconut, long thread	1 lb	7 c			80	2¼
canned, moist	1 lb	5⅓ c			85	3
Coffee	1 lb	5 c			85	3
brewed			1 c	40 to 50		
instant	2 oz		1 tsp	60		
Gelatin, unflavored, granulated	1 oz	4 Tbsp			150	5⅓
flavored, packaged	3 oz	7 Tbsp	½ c	4	179	7
Infant foods, Regular						
Infant (strained)	4½ to 4¾ oz	9 to 9½ Tbsp	3 to 5 Tbsp	2 to 3		
Junior (chopped)	7½ to 8 oz	15 Tbsp	5 to 7½ Tbsp	2 to 3		
High meat dinners, infant (strained)	4½ to 4¾ oz	9 to 9½ Tbsp	4½ to 9 Tbsp	1 to 2		
Junior (chopped)	4½ oz	9 Tbsp	4½ to 9 Tbsp	1 to 2		
Meats and egg yolks						
Infant (strained)	3¼ to 3½ oz	7 Tbsp	2 to 3½ Tbsp	2 to 3		
Junior (chopped)	3½ oz	7 Tbsp	2 to 3½ Tbsp	2 to 3		

Juices, infant		4 to 4¼ fl oz	¼ to ½ c	1 to 2		
Nuts, shelled						
almonds, blanched	1 lb	3 c	½ c	7	152	5½
filberts, whole	1 lb	3⅓ c	½ c	7	134	4¾
peanuts	1 lb	3¼ c	½ c	6	144	5
pecans, halved	1 lb	4¼ c	½ c	8	108	3¾
chopped	1 lb	3¾ c			118	4¼
pistachio	1 lb	3⅔ c			125	4½
walnuts, Persian, English						
halves	1 lb	4½ c	½ c	7	100	3½
chopped	1 lb	3⅔ c	½ c	7	124	4½
Peanut butter	18 oz	2 c	¼ c	8	259	9
Salt, free running	1 lb	1½ c			288	10¼
Soups, frozen, condensed	10 to 10½ oz	1¼ c	½ c	2 to 3		
ready-to-serve	15 oz	2 c	¾ c	3		
canned, condensed	10½ to 12 oz	1¼ c	¾ c	3		
ready-to-serve	15 oz	2 c	¾ c	3		
Spices, ground	1¼ to 4 oz		1 tsp	12		
Tapioca, quick-cooking	8 oz	1½ c	3 Tbsp	24	152	5½
Tea, leaves	1 lb	6 to 8 c			72	2½
brewed			1 c	300		
instant	1½ oz		½ tsp	64		
Water					237	8⅓

† Weight per cup is that of food alone without liquid.

Index

Italicized entries refer to illustrations.
Tables are indicated by (t).

D

534